GENERAL AND INDUSTRIAL CHEMISTRY SERIES

Edited by H. M. Bunbury, M.SC., F.R.I.C.

HYDROGEN COMPOUNDS OF THE METALLIC ELEMENTS

Other books in Spon's

GENERAL AND INDUSTRIAL CHEMISTRY SERIES

THE CHEMISTRY OF HYDROMETALLURGICAL PROCESSES

by A. R. Burkin, Ph.D., F.R.I.C. *Foreword by R. S. Nyholm, F.R.S.*

PARTICULATE CLOUDS: DUSTS, SMOKES AND MISTS (2nd edition)

by H. L. Green, M.A., F.Inst.P. *and* W. R. Lane, B.Sc., F.Inst.P. *Foreword by Sir Harold Hartley, F.R.S.*

ORGANIC PEROXIDES: THEIR FORMATION AND REACTIONS

by E. G. E. Hawkins, Ph.D., F.R.I.C.

TECHNIQUES FOR THE USE OF RADIOISOTOPES IN ANALYSIS

by D. A. Lambie, B.Sc., F.R.I.C.

SURFACE ACTIVITY (2nd Edition)

by J. L. Moilliet, Ph.D., B. Collie, Ph.D., W. Black, B.Sc.

CHEMICAL CONSTITUTION AND BIOLOGICAL ACTIVITY (3rd Edition)

by W. A. Sexton, Ph.D., F.R.I.C. *Foreword by Lord Todd, F.R.S.*

DISINFECTION AND STERILIZATION (2nd Edition)

by G. Sykes, M.Sc., F.R.I.C. *Foreword by Sir Graham Wilson, F.R.C.P.*

HYDROGEN COMPOUNDS OF THE METALLIC ELEMENTS

K. M. MACKAY
B.SC., PH.D., A.R.I.C.

1966
E. & F. N. SPON LTD
LONDON

First published 1966 by
E. & F. N. Spon, Ltd.,
167 Fleet Street, London E.C.4.

Printed in Great Britain by
Willmer Brothers Limited,
Birkenhead, Cheshire
Catalogue No. 16/1013/63

Contents

Preface *page* vi

1 Introduction 1

1.1 Occurrence of Metal Hydrides 1

1.2 Hydride Types in Relation to the Periodic Table 11

1.3 Experimental Methods and Hazards 13

1.4 Uses of Metal Hydrides 14

2 Ionic Hydrides 18

2.1 The Existence of Ionic Hydrides 18

2.2 The Preparation of the Ionic Hydrides 25

2.3 Properties and Uses of the Ionic Hydrides 29

2.4 Mixed Systems of Ionic Hydrides and Other Salts 33

2.5 Hydrogen Solutions in Liquid Sodium 35

2.6 Borderline Ionic Hydrides 35

3 Transition Metal Hydrides 45

3.1 Theories of Bonding in Transition Metal Hydrides 45

3.2 Non-stoicheiometry in the Metal Hydrides 54

3.3 The Hydrides of the Lanthanide Elements 55

3.4 The Hydrides of the Actinide Elements 64

3.5 The Hydrides of the Transition Elements 71

4 Covalent Hydrides 99

4.1 Introduction 99

4.2 Preparations of the Covalent Hydrides 102

4.3 Beryllium Hydride 105

4.4 Zinc, Cadmium, and Mercury Hydrides 107

4.5 The Hydrides of Aluminium, Gallium, Indium and Thallium 108

4.6 The Hydrides of Silicon, Germanium, Tin, and Lead 116

4.7 Other Volatile Metal Hydrides 126

4.8 Some Remarks on the Reactions of the Covalent Hydrides 127

5 Complex Hydrides of the Transition Elements 138

5.1 Complex Ions Containing Hydrogen Only 138

5.2 The Complex Hydrides Containing other Ligands 141

5.3 Physical Properties of Hydrogen in Complexes 146

6 The Tetrahydroborates, Tetrahydroaluminates, and Related Species 168

6.1 Introduction 168

6.2 Structures and Physical Properties 171

Addendum

Papers appearing up to December 1965 181

Index 183

Preface

The field of metal-hydrogen compounds has undergone rapid expansion in the ten years since the last general review of the subject, and recent progress has clarified much that was formerly obscure, especially in the binary hydrides of the transition elements. At the same time, considerable new areas of great interest have been explored and the time seems ripe for a general review of the subject. By defining the term 'metal' widely, I have tried to avoid any abrupt division between the hydrogen compounds of the metals and non-metals, while at the same time largely omitting the acidic hydrides, and not treating fully the boron and silicon hydrides. The latter two fields have been extensively reviewed recently. Both the binary hydrides, and the hydride complexes, of the transition metals are discussed, as the range and bonding in these two sets of compounds are largely complementary and together show the very wide range of interaction which can exist between hydrogen and a transition metal. The fully ionic hydrides of the active metals and the volatile and polymeric covalent hydrides of the Main Group metals are also treated, and a brief account is given of the tetrahydroboronates and related compounds.

I hope that this book will be of service to senior Honours undergraduates and to postgraduate students. In addition, a considerable amount of tabulated material is provided to make the book a useful introduction and reference source for the research worker in any one of the fields covered by the six Chapters. The literature has been searched up to December 1965: the most recent references are in an Addendum (page 181).

I wish to thank Miss Ann Mills for assistance with the library work on Chapter 3, Mr. Len Nöhre for translation of a Norwegian paper, and my wife for reading the manuscript and supporting me in every phase of the work. I have enjoyed valuable and informative discussions on various aspects of the subject with Professor C. C. Addison and Dr E. A. V. Ebsworth, and I am greatly indebted to Professor H. J. Emeleus who first aroused my interest in hydrides.

K. M. MACKAY

Nottingham, 1966.

CHAPTER 1

Introduction

1.1 Occurrence of Metal Hydrides

The title 'Metal Hydrides' at once involves us in defining our terms as this is indeed a Humpty-Dumpty region of chemistry where 'words mean what I want them to mean'. It is proposed here to define both *metal* and *hydride* in wide senses and to provide sufficient material on borderline topics to allow the reader to link up the main body of this monograph with work in neighbouring fields.

Metals are commonly regarded as giving place to non-metals across a diagonal line drawn across the *p* block of elements of the Periodic Table, and the elements lying about this diagonal are often termed semi-metals or metalloids. Such elements include boron, silicon, germanium, arsenic, antimony, tellurium and polonium. Of these borderline metals, *boron* forms a very wide variety of hydrides with the most extensive range of hydrogen compounds of any element except carbon. This is a fast-growing field which has been the subject of a number of recent books and reviews [1], and it is not discussed in detail here for this reason. However, Table 1.4 summarizes the present state of boron hydride chemistry, some discussion of the bonding in boron hydrides is included in Chapter 4, and the metal borohydrides are included in the final chapter. *Silicon* also forms a variety of hydrides which have been reviewed recently by Ebsworth and by Stone [2]. A number of shorter reviews are also available [3]. Only the more recent developments in the silicon hydride field are discussed here, together with the treatment of hydrogen compounds of germanium, tin and lead. The division between the other metalloids to be included has been made fairly arbitrarily: Group V hydrides have been briefly discussed while the remaining elements are omitted. There is little recent work on these compounds, and the earlier chemistry is included in Hurd's book [4]. Although the chemistry of the hydrides of the remaining Main Group elements is not discussed here, their properties are indicated in Tables 1.2 and 1.3.

A *hydride* may be defined in the most general sense as any compound which contains hydrogen bonded to the metal, including, of course, cases of ionic or metallic bonding. This is the definition which shall be adopted here, as the more restrictive use of the term *hydride* to indicate negatively charged or polarized hydrogen leads to difficulties. These arise, first because it is difficult in a number of cases to determine the polarity of the metal-hydrogen bond, both because of the experimental difficulty of interpreting dipole moments in terms of bond dipoles, and because of the theoretical problems associated with the uncertainty in the electronegativity values to be assigned to a number of elements. The second objection to the use of the term 'hydride' in a narrow sense is that the polarity of the metal-hydrogen bond changes with substitution – compare, Me_3Sn-H with F_3Sn-H to take an extreme case – and also within a group of related compounds (for example, $HMn(CO)_5$ contains positively-polarized, acidic hydrogen while the cyclopentadienyl manganese carbonyl hydride has a negatively-polarized Mn-H bond with hydridic hydrogen). Therefore, 'metal hydride' in the following pages implies only that the compound has hydrogen bonded to a metal.

Table 1.1. *Properties of Hydrogen*

Heat of Dissociation: $\frac{1}{2} H_2 \rightleftharpoons H$	52·089 kcal/mole
$\frac{1}{2} D_2 \rightleftharpoons D$	52·982 kcal/mole
Ionization Potential: $H = H + e$	312 kcal = 13·59 eV
Electron Affinity: $H + e = H^-$	17·37 kcal = 0·752 eV
$D + e = D^-$	17·38 kcal = 0.754 eV
Heat of Hydration of H^+ ion:	260·7 ± 2·5 kcal/mole
Radii of Hydrogen Species:	
normal (Bohr) radius of H atom	0·53Å
covalent radius of H atom	0·28Å (Pauling)
Van der Waals radius of H atom	1·2Å
radius of H^- ion (*a*) free ion	2·08Å (calculated)
(*b*) in ionic hydrides (see Chapter 2)	1·3 to 1·5Å
radius of H^+ ion	10^{-5}Å
Electronegativity of H on Pauling Scale:	2·1
(Most other scales are adjusted to make H = 2·1)	

Thermodynamic and Physical Properties of Hydrogen Species

	Entropy at 25°C (cal/degree-mole)	Heat Capacity at 25°C (cal/degree-mole)
H	27·3927	4·9680
D	29·456	4·9680
H_2	31·211	6·892
D_2	34·602	6·98
T_2	39·394	6·978
HD	34·341	6·98
HT	38·202	6·978

	M.Pt. (°C) (pressure in mm. Hg in brackets)	B.Pt. (°C)	Vapour Pressure (*a*) *A*	*B*	Latent Heats (cal/mole) fusion	evaporation
H_2	−259·20 (54)	−252·77	44·9569	4·66687 (+0·020537T)	28	216
D_2	−254·43 (129)	−249·49	70·044	6·0832 (−0·02111T)	47	293
T_2	−252·89 (157)	−248·24	76·323	5·9444		322
HD	−256·56 (93)	−251·03				

(*a*) *A*, *B* are the constants in the equation, $\log p_{(mm)} = -A/T + B$

The class of metal hydrides may be conveniently divided into two, the *binary hydrides* (sometimes termed *primary hydrides*) containing only the metal and hydrogen, and the remaining compounds which contain a number of different elements. Of this second class, a number of compounds are simply double hydrides, or mixed hydrides, and are conveniently discussed along with the binary hydrides; such compounds include species like $LiBaH_3$ and GeH_3AsH_2. The remainder, of the more complex hydrides, includes transition metal complexes where the hydrogen is present as a ligand attached to the metal, and partially substituted hydrides of various type like $AlHCl_2$ or Me_3PbH. The more complex organometallic hydrides are included in Coates's book and are omitted here [5]. In the following chapters, the transition metal hydride complexes are discussed separately in Chapter 5, and the borohydrides of the metals, (and related species), are treated in Chapter 6. The other three chapters are devoted to the binary hydrides and related compounds.

The binary hydrides may be sub-divided into three broad classes according to the nature of the bonding. These divisions are not, of course, sharp ones and there are a number of borderline cases whose allocation depends on the way in which the different types of bonding are defined. The general divisions are

(*i*) the *ionic* or *saline* hydrides which contain the H^- ion and metal cations,
(*ii*) metal hydrides which show *metallic* bonding,
(*iii*) *covalent* hydrides.

These are treated, in turn, in Chapters 2 to 4.

Some properties of hydrogen are listed in Table 1.1. The element itself is the source of the hydrogen in most metal hydrides, either by direct combination in the case of the more active metals, or indirectly for the less active metals, whose hydrides are commonly prepared by reduction of a suitable compound with an active metal hydride.

The majority of the elements form binary hydrides, and these are listed in Table 1.2. Many solid hydrides are commonly made in non-stoicheiometric proportions, but these are given idealized formulae in Table 1.2 for ease of summarizing. Accurate formulae will be found in the appropriate chapters.

Apart from established compounds which have been prepared on a weighable scale, a number of hydrides have been reported in trace amounts, especially from mass-spectrometric and radioactive tracer work. Such compounds are shown in a separate section in Table 1.2. It will be seen from these two sections of the Table that the heaviest elements of the Main Groups form hydrides which are too unstable to be prepared on a macro scale. It is therefore no surprise that, of the non-actinide heavy elements which exist only in radioactive forms, only polonium is reported to form a hydride, and PoH_2 has been identified only on a tracer scale – attempts to prepare it on a larger scale failed. No reports have appeared of hydrides of astatine, francium, or radium [6]. In some cases, especially that of francium, this may be because the experiment

Table 1.2. *Binary Hydrides*

(A) Hydrides Prepared on a Macro Scale

Non-transition elements

LiH	BeH_2	B_2H_6 etc. (See Table 1.4)	CH_4 etc.	NH_3 N_2H_4	H_2O H_2O_2	HF
NaH	MgH_2	AlH_3	Si_nH_{2n+2} *n* up to 6 $(SiH_x)_n$	PH_3 P_2H_4 $(PH_x)_n$	H_2S H_2S_x (*x* up to 100)	HCl
KH	CaH_2	$(GaH_x)_n$ *x* approx. 3	Ge_nH_{2n+2} *n* up to 5 $(GeH_x)_n$	AsH_3 As_2H_4 $(AsH_x)_n$	H_2Se	HBr
RbH	SrH_2	—	SnH_4 Sn_2H_6	SbH_3	H_2Te	HI
CsH	BaH_2	—	$PbH_{0\cdot19}$	—	—	

Transition elements

ScH_2	TiH_2	VH $VH_{1\cdot6}$	CrH CrH_2?	—	—	—	—	CuH	ZnH_2
YH_2 YH_3	ZrH_2	NbH NbH_2	—	—	—	—	$PdH_{0\cdot7}$	—	CdH_2
LaH_2 LaH_3	HfH_2	TaH	—	—	—	—	—	—	—

Lanthanides: MH_2 by La, Ce, Pr, Nd, Sm, Eu, Gd, Tb, Dy, Ho, Er, Tm, Yb, Lu.
MH_3 by La, Ce, Pr, Nd, Sm, Gd, Tb, Dy, Ho, Er, Tm, Lu: $YbH_{2\cdot5}$ only.

Actinides: AcH_2, ThH_2 and Th_4H_{15}, PaH_3, UH_3, NpH_2 and NpH_3, PuH_2 and PuH_3, AmH_2 and AmH_3?

(B) Hydrides Reported in Trace Amounts

Non-transition elements

BH_3(m)			
AlH_3(m) Al_2H_6(m)	silanes, *n* = 7, 8 (c)	P_3H_5(m)	
	germanes *n* = 6–9 (c)	As_3H_5 (m)	
	PbH_4 (r)(m)	BiH_3 (r)(m)	PoH_2 (r)

Transition elements:

TiH_4 (m)

(m) = mass spectrometer, (c) = gas chromatography,
(r) = radioactive tracer.

has never been attempted, and the negative results for all these elements probably arise because the compound was decomposed by radiation damage as it was formed. It may be that PoH_2 and AtH will never be prepared in normal amounts because of the intrinsic instability of the element-hydrogen bond, and the activity of all the francium isotopes may be too high to allow FrH to be identified. It does, however, seem that it should be possible to prepare radium hydride on a sufficiently large scale to allow its identification.

Brief mention might be made of another class of transient hydrides. These are species, usually of formula MH, and often bearing a charge, which are formed by the majority of elements, including even the rare gases, in flames, electric discharges or by interaction with atomic hydrogen from other sources. These species typically have very short lifetimes and are identified by their spectra. The heats of dissociation are known, as are the bond lengths and stretching frequencies, for most species and such values may give a guide to the properties to be expected for hydride species existing at normal temperatures. These high temperature species will not be further discussed [8].

The hydrides of the non-metals, which are also excluded from further treatment, fall into the class of volatile hydrides. The hydrogen becomes increasingly acidic as the electronegativity of the central element increases. Table 1.3 lists some of their properties, and further references will be found in Hurd's book [4].

The boron hydrides are summarized in more detail in Table 1.4. In addition to the known hydrides, a list of predicted hydrides is also given. This comes from a paper of Lipscomb's [9] in which he extends his topological theory, which has been so successful in accounting for known hydrides [1], to the geometrical prediction of expected species up to B_9. A wide variety of borohydride ions is also found, many of which do not correspond to any of the

Table 1.3. *Properties of Non-metal Hydrides*

(A) Thermodynamic Functions at 25°C

Hydride and Physical State	ΔH_f° (kcal/mole)	ΔG_f° (kcal/mole)	S° (cal/degree/mole)	C_p° (cal/degree/mole)
HF (g)	−64·2	−64·7	41·47	6·95
HCl (g)	−22·063	−22·769	44·617	6·96
HBr (g)	− 8·66	−12·72	47·437	6·96
HI (g)	6·20	0·31	49·314	6·97
H_2O (l)	−68·317	−56·690	16·716	17·996
(g)	−57·798	−54·636	45·106	8·025
D_2O (l)	−70·413	−58·206	18·162	19·70
(g)	−59·563	−56·067	47·379	8·19
HDO (l)	−69·393	−57·926	18·95	18·85
(g)	−58·735	−55·828	47·66	8·06
H_2O_2 (l)	−44·87			21·35
(g)	−32·53	−25·20	55·66	10·31

Table 1.3—*continued*

Hydride and Physical State	ΔH_f° (kcal/mole)	ΔG_f° (kcal/mole)	So (cal/degree/mole)	C_p° (cal/degree/mole)
H_2S (g)	− 4·815	− 7·892	49·15	8·12
H_2S_2 (l)	− 5·5			
H_2S_5 (l)	0·7			
H_2Se (g)	20·5	17·0	52·9	
H_2Te (g)	36·9	33·1	56	
NH_3 (g)	−11·04	− 3·976	46·01	8·523
N_2H_4 (l)	12·00	35·61	29·01	23·62
HN_3 (g)	7·03	78·5	56·74	10·02
PH_3 (g)	2·21	4·36	50·2	
P_2H_4 (l)	6·9	16·0	40	
AsH_3 (g)	41·0	41·6	53·18	9·207
CH_4 (g)	−17·889	−12·140	44·50	8·536
SiH_4 (g)	−14·8	− 9·4	48·7	10·24
B_2H_6 (g)	7·53	19·69	55·60	13·48
B_5H_9 (g)	15·0	38·48	65·95	19
$B_{10}H_{14}$ (c)	26·0	64·66	83·8	52·42

(g) = gas: (l) = liquid: (c) = condensed state

(B) Other Physical Properties

Hydride	M.Pt. (°C)	B.Pt. (°C)	Vapour Pressure A	B	C	Other Properties
HF	− 83·07	19·91	−1316·79	7·3739		Density = 1·0020 − 0·0022625t + 0·000003125t²
DF		18·65	−1261·16	7·2026		
HCl	−114·22	− 85·05	−1158·5	17·080	−3.534	Density = 1·194 at −85·8°C
DCl		− 84·8				
HBr	− 86·82	− 66·73	−1290	17·653	−3·679	Density = 2·16 at −68°C
DBr		− 66·9				
HI	− 50·80	− 35·36	−1456	17·740	−3.764	Density = 2·847 at −4·7°C
DI		− 32·2				
H_2O	0·00	100·00				Densities: At 0°C, 0·9168 (ice) 0·999841 (water) 0·999973 (4°C), 0.997074 (25°C).
D_2O	3·82	101·431	−2286	8·986		Densities: 1·0178 (0° solid) 1·104509 (25°).
H_2O_2	− 2·0	(151)	−3563	29·694	−7·04	Density = 1·442 at 20°C
H_2S	− 85·53	− 60·33	−1377	19·076	−4·177	Density = 0·96 at −60°C:
D_2S	− 86·02					
H_2S_2	− 89·7	70·7	−2077	9·041		
H_2S_3	− 53					
H_2S_4	− 85					
H_2Se	− 65·73	− 41·3	−1067	7·482		Density = 2·12 at −42°C
D_2Se	− 66·92					

Table 1.3—*continued*

Hydride	M.Pt. (°C)	B.Pt. (°C)	Vapour Pressure A	B	C	Other Properties
H_2Te	− 51 (−57)	− 2·3	−1235	7·441		Density = 2·57 at −20°C
NH_3	− 77·70	− 33·38	−1612·500	11·83997		Density = 0·6103 at 20°C
ND_3	− 74·2	− 30·90				
N_2H_4	1·5	113·5	$\log p_{mm} = 7{\cdot}80687 - 1680{\cdot}745/(t + 227{\cdot}74)$			
HN_3	− 80	36	−1578·3	7·8533	0·0567	
PH_3	−133·78	− 87·74	− 797·8	7·180		Density at −90°C = 0·746
P_2H_4	(−99)	51·7				
CH_4	−182·48	−161·49	− 559·6	13·038	−2·514	Density at −164°C = 0·415
SiH_4	−184·7	−112·1	− 645·9	6·881		Density = 0·68 (−185°C): SiD_4, B.Pt. = −112·3
Si_2H_6	−132	− 14·8	−1342	12·918	−2·01	Si_2D_6, B.Pt. = −15·96°C
Si_3H_8	−117	53·0	−1910	16·319	3·02	
Si_4H_{10}	− 84·3	108·4	−2594·5	20·186	−4·02	

A, *B*, *C* are the constants in $\log p_{mm} = A/T + B + CT$

(c) Shapes of the Hydride Molecules

Hydride	H-M Bond Length (Å)	Angle at M (°)
$HF_{(gas)}$	0·9171	
$HF_{(solid)}$	(F–H–F = 2·55)	140 ± 5
$HCl_{(gas)}$	1·2744 (D–Cl = 1·2746, T–Cl = 1·2740)	
$HBr_{(gas)}$	1·408 (D–Br = 1·4144, T–Br = 1·4144)	
$HI_{(gas)}$	1·609 (D–I = 1·6165)	
H_2O	0·9572	104·52
D_2O	0·9575	104·47
H_2O_2	0·97	96·9
H_2S	1·3226	92·1
D_2S	1·345	92·3
H_2Se	1·460	91
NH_3	1·015	106·6
N_2H_4	1·04	HNH = 108, HNN = 112
HN_3	1·021	112·7
PH_3	1·437	93·5
PD_3	1·420	93·1
AsH_3	1·519	91·8
AsD_3	1·5145	91·5
SbH_3	1·707	91·3
SbD_3	1·702	90·9
CH_4	1·093	
SiH_4	1·480	
GeH_4	1·527	
SnH_4	1·701	

uncharged hydrides. The boron hydrides and the ions exhibit a wide variety of structural types, in most of which the boron atoms form a fragment of a regular icosahedron, or sometimes two such fragments are linked as in $B_{10}H_{16}$ or $B_{20}H_{16}$. The ion $B_{12}H_{12}^{2-}$ has the twelve boron atoms in the form of a regular icosahedron, with one terminal hydrogen attached to each. Here the boron atoms are linked directly by delocalized bonding similar to that in a section of a metallic structure, and analogous bonding is postulated in other metal 'clusters' such as $Mo_6Cl_8^{4+}$, $Re_3Cl_{12}^{3-}$, or Bi_9^{5+}. Thus the boron hydrides may be regarded as having bonding which is intermediate between the covalent and metallic types. In most other boron hydrides and boron hydride ions, hydrogen atoms enter into the framework bonding as well as the direct boron-boron bonding, and this form of 'electron-deficient' bonding occurs in other hydrides, such as those of beryllium and aluminium, and is discussed in Chapter 4. In the past two or three years the field of boron hydrides has been considerably extended by the discovery that atoms other than boron can be incorporated into the boron hydride skeletons. The commonest hetero-atom is carbon, giving the *carboranes* or *barenes* [10], but other compounds are starting to appear containing atoms such as silicon [11]. Some examples are included in Table 1.4.

Stock's classical and monumental work on the boron hydrides was so overwhelming that thirty years of relative quiescence followed. After the boron hydrides were brought within the ambit of normal bonding theories, a trickle of new compounds appeared starting about ten years ago. This trickle is now a flood and the field of boron hydrides and related compounds is at present one of the most active in the whole of inorganic chemistry.

Table 1.4. *Boron Hydrides and Related Compounds*

(A) Hydrides Discovered by Stock [12], (pre-1930)

B_2H_6	bpt	−92·5	stable
B_4H_{10}	bpt	18	unstable (decomposition of tetraborane in presence of ethane gave a solid containing both B and C)
B_5H_9	mpt	−46·6	stable
B_5H_{11}	mpt	−128·5	very unstable
B_6H_{10}	mpt	−65·1	fairly stable (on standing gave a yellow solid, M = 320, approx. $B_{26}H_{36}$)
(B_6H_{12})			Claimed and later withdrawn: not obtained free of B_5H_9
$B_{10}H_{14}$	mpt	99·6	stable, sublimes in vacuum (chemistry discussed in reference 13)

In addition, Stock reported a number of involatile hydrides including colourless liquids, two different colourless solids, and yellow solid hydrides. The colourless materials had compositions in the range $BH_{1 \cdot 5}$ to BH_2, while the yellow compounds approximated to BH. These samples probably included some of the recently-discovered higher hydrides.

Table 1.4—*continued*

(B) Other Boron Hydrides

	date and ref.	
B_6H_{12}	1963 [a]	hydrolysis of $Me_4NB_3H_8$; less volatile than Stock's compound and readily separated from B_5H_9
	[b]	discharge with diborane
B_8H_{12}	1964 [c]	discharge with B_2H_6 + B_5H_9, X-ray structure
B_9H_{15}	1957 [d]	first new boron hydride since Stock
	[e]	improved synthesis, mpt 2·6°, X-ray structure (d)
$B_{10}H_{16}$	1949 [f]	proton bombardment of B_5H_9, structure is two B_5H_9 units joined by a B–B bond.
	[g]	pentaborane-9 + H_2 in discharge
n-$B_{18}H_{22}$	1962 [h]	$B_{20}H_{18}^{2-}$ acid hydrolysis
	[i]	X-ray structure, centrosymmetric.
iso-$B_{18}H_{22}$	1963 [j]	non-centrosymmetric, two-fold symmetry axis
$B_{20}H_{16}$	1963 [k]	$B_{10}H_{14}$ in discharge, X-ray structure, mpt 196°
	[l]	$B_{10}H_{14}$ pyrolysis, nmr, infra-red shows no bridging BHB; plus water gives a strong, dibasic acid and no hydrogen
$B_{20}H_{26}$?	1962 [f]	Possible existence of $B_{11}H_{17}$ and $B_{14}H_{22}$?
$B_6H_{12 \text{ or } 14}$ and two heptaboranes	1960 [m]	By mass spectrometry. This may not be the same hexaborane as above, and may be the same as Stock's compound.

(C) Examples of Boron Hydride Ions

Apart from the well-known simpler ions, such as BH_4^- and $B_3H_8^-$, the following are cited as examples of the types discovered in the last few years.

$B_4H_{10}^{2-}$ and $B_5H_{11}^{2-}$	(as amine derivatives only[n])
$B_9H_{14}^-$	1963 [o]
$B_{10}H_{10}^{2-}$ and $B_{10}H_{12}^{2-}$	both occur [p]
$B_{12}H_{12}^{2-}$	(subject of many studies [p, q, r])
$B_{11}H_{14}^-$	1962 [u]
$B_{20}H_{18}^{2-}$ and $B_{20}H_{18}^{4-}$	[s]
$B_{20}H_{19}^-$ and $B_{20}H_{15}^{3-}$	[s, t]

(D) Hydrides Predicted in 1964 by W. N. Lipscomb [9]

B_6H_{10}	C_s	Rearrange to known B_6H_{10}?: C_2 form unlikely.
B_6H_{12}	C_2	Predicted, outer parts like B_4H_{10} } Compare above, refs. [a, m]
B_6H_{12}	C_2	Also predicted } Compare above, refs. [a, m]
B_6H_{12}	C_3	B atoms probably too exposed
B_6H_{14}	C_2	Probable, H atoms somewhat crowded.
B_7H_{13} and B_7H_{15}	C_s	Both predicted (cf. (m)): B_7H_{11} (C_s) unlikely.
B_8H_{12}		(predicted and discovered – [c])
B_8H_{14}	C_2	Probable, slight H atom crowding.
B_9H_{13}	C_s	Predicted.

Table 1.4—*continued*

(E) Some examples of Carboranes [10]

$B_{10}C_2H_{12}$	[10, a, b, c]
$B_{10}Cl_8C_2H_4$	[10 f]
isomeric form – neocarborane	[10 d, e]
$(B_5H_8)_2CH_2$ and $B_5H_8CH_2BCl_2$	[10 g]
$B_4H_6C_2H_2$ and $B_4H_6C_2Me_2$	[10 h] Structures.
$B_9C_2H_{11}$	[10 i] See Chapter 6 for a note on its iron derivative.

The transition element derivatives of BH_3, $(H_3BML_5)^-$, where M = Mn or Re and L=CO, or L_5 = $(CO)_4PPh_3$, are also of interest [14].

Examples of carboranes containing silicon include,

$MeOSi(R)_2CB_{10}H_{10}CSi(R)_2OMe$ [11 a]

$(B_{10}H_{10}CC_2H_2O)_3SiMe$ or $B_{10}H_{10}C_2(CH_2O)_2SiMe_2$ [11 b]

References

[a] D. F. GAINES and R. SCHAEFFER, *Proc. Chem. Soc.*, 1963, 267; *Inorg. Chem.*, 1964, **3**, 438.
[b] C. A. LUTZ, D. A. PHILLIPS, and D. M. RITTER, *Inorg. Chem.*, 1964, **3**, 1191.
[c] R. E. ENRIONE, F. P. BOER, and W. N. LIPSCOMB, *J. Amer. Chem. Soc.*, 1964, **86**, 1451.
[d] R. E. DICKERSON, P. J. WHEATLEY, P. A. HOWELL, and W. N. LIPSCOMB, *J. Chem. Phys.*, 1957, **27**, 200.
[e] A. B. BURG and R. KRATZER, *Inorg. Chem.*, 1962, **1**, 725.
[f] V. V. SUBBANNA, L. H. HALL, and W. S. KOSKI, *J. Amer. Chem. Soc.*, 1964, **86**, 1304; and (L.H.H. and W.S.K.) 1962, **84**, 4205.
[g] R. GRIMES, F. E. WANG, R. LEWIN, and W. N. LIPSCOMB, *Proc. Nat. Acad. Sci.*, (U.S.) 1961, **47**, 996.
[h] A. R. PITOCHELLI and M. F. HAWTHORNE, *J. Amer. Chem. Soc.*, 1962, **84**, 3218.
[i] P. G. SIMPSON and W. N. LIPSCOMB, *J. Chem. Phys.*, 1963, **39**, 26.
[j] P. G. SIMPSON, K. FOLTING, and W. N. LIPSCOMB, *J. Amer. Chem. Soc.*, 1963, **85**, 1897.
[k] L. B. FRIEDMAN, R. D. DOBROTT, and W. N. LIPSCOMB, *J. Amer. Chem. Soc.*, 1963, **85**, 3505; *J. Chem. Phys.*, 1964, **40**, 866.
[l] N. E. MILLER and E. L. MUETTERTIES, *J. Amer. Chem. Soc.*, 1963, **85**, 3506.
[m] S. G. GIBBINS and I. SHAPIRO, *J. Amer. Chem. Soc.*, 1960, **82**, 2968.
[n] N. E. MILLER, H. C. MILLER, and E. L. MUETTERTIES, *Inorg. Chem.*, 1964, **3**, 866.
[o] L. E. BENJAMIN, S. F. STAFIEJ, and E. A. TAKACS, *J. Amer. Chem. Soc.*, 1963, **85**, 2674.
[p] E. L. MUETTERTIES, J. H. BALTHIS, Y. T. CHIA, W. H. KNOTH, and H. C. MILLER, *Inorg. Chem.*, 1964, **3**, 444; 159; 1456.
[q] R. M. ADAMS, A. R. SIEDLE, and J. GRANT, *Inorg. Chem.*, 1964, **3**, 461.
[r] N. N. GREENWOOD and J. H. MORRIS, *Proc. Chem. Soc.*, 1963, 338: I. A. ELLIS, D. F. GAINES, and R. SCHAEFFER, *J. Amer. Chem. Soc.*, 1963, **85**, 3885.
[s] M. F. HAWTHORNE, R. L. PILLING, P. F. STOKELY, and M. GARRETT, *J. Amer. Chem. Soc.*, 1963, **85**, 3704, 3705.
[t] W. N. LIPSCOMB, *Proc. Nat. Acad. Sci.* (U.S.) 1961, **47**, 1791.
[u] V. D. AFTANDILIAN, H. C. MILLER, G. W. PARSHALL, and E. L. MUETTERTIES, *Inorg. Chem.*, 1962, **1**, 734.

Some guidance to the existence of unstable or doubtful hydrides may be gleaned from a report of estimated heats and free energies of formation of simple inorganic molecules, including hydrides [24]. Although the values quoted for known compounds match the experimental ones reasonably well, the calculated values for the less stable hydrides seem somewhat more dubious. For example, ZnH_2 is calculated to lie between HgH_2 and CdH_2 in stability, which is not in accord with observation.

1.2 Hydride Types in Relation to the Periodic Table

The range in type of hydride, from ionic to covalent, follows from the position of the metallic element in the Periodic Table. Bonding becomes more ionic from right to left along a series, and from top to bottom of a Group. Because of its size and electronic structure, hydrogen is unique in the Periodic Table, and all comparisons with other elements must be treated with some reserve. Indeed, this is a topic which always seems to arouse considerable fury when it is debated [15]. However, some comparisons with univalent species are suggestive and serve to correlate hydride chemistry with other fields. As far as the metal hydrides are concerned, two comparisons are of value; first with the halogens and second with the simple carbon radicals like methyl. It might be noted, as an aside, that the oft-quoted comparison with alkali metals – that they and hydrogen give a positive species – is quite misleading as H^+ does not exist in any chemical environment. The loss of the electron from the hydrogen atom leaves the bare proton, with a radius of 10^{-5} of that of any other ion, and an enormous charge density.

Hydrogen resembles the halogens in forming a stable anion, and H^- is approximately the same size as F^-. There are thus crystallographic resemblances between ionic hydrides and ionic fluorides. On the other hand, the electron affinity of hydrogen is so much smaller than those of the halogens (F = 83·5, Cl = 87, Br = 82, and I = 75 kcal/mole) that the tendency for hydrogen to form ionic solids with other elements is much more restricted than that of the halogens. In addition, the hydride ion has two electrons in the field of only a single nuclear charge and is much more polarizable than fluoride, resembling iodide in this respect. The extreme diffuseness of the electron cloud in H^- is reflected in the decrease in radius from 2·08 Å, calculated for free H^-, to the values of 1·3 to 1·5 Å observed in the alkali hydrides. In addition, the hydride ion is much more sensitive to its environment than other ions, and shows considerable variation in radius in its compounds with different cations.

Hydrogen also resembles monovalent carbon, as in an alkyl group such as methyl. Carbon bonded to three hydrogens will be only slightly more electronegative towards a metal than hydrogen, and a strong resemblance exists between M-H and $M\text{-}CH_3$ compounds. For example, the alkali metals form ionic hydrides and also alkyls which are probably ionic; aluminium forms a polymeric hydride, $(AlH_3)_x$ held together by hydrogen bridging and a dimeric alkyl, Al_2Me_6, bonded by bridging methyl groups; cobalt carbonyl gives rise to unstable compounds $HCo(CO)_4$ and $CH_3Co(CO)_4$; and finally, in the volatile, covalent hydrides there is a complete family of compounds MR_x where R = H,CH_3, C_2H_5, etc. of which the hydride clearly behaves as the simplest member and shows parallel reactions to the alkyls. The differences between hydrides and alkyls are slight and can be ascribed to the slight difference in electronegativity (for example, LiH and LiMe are ionic while LiEt and higher alkyls are more covalent) or to size effects (which probably account for the formation of BMe_3 while the hydride is B_2H_6). The one class of compounds where the parallel between hydrogen and carbon compounds is not close is in the metallic hydrides and carbides of the transition metals where both the size and the number of valency electrons differ though, even here, there are some resemblances.

With these ideas in mind, it is easy to see that the distribution of the different types of hydride in the Periodic Table falls into the expected pattern. The *ionic hydrides* are those formed by

(*a*) the alkali metals from Li to Cs,

(*b*) Ca, Sr, Ba, and probably Mg,

(*c*) the MH_2 hydrides of the lanthanides with a stable II state which corresponds to an f^7 or f^{14} configuration (i.e. with no unused *d* electron) – these are EuH_2 and YbH_2,

(*d*) possibly those lanthanides which form an MH_3 compound near the theoretical stoicheiometry.

The *metallic hydrides* are

(*a*) all other hydrides of the lanthanide elements, and ScH_2 and YH_2,

(*b*) the hydrides of the actinide elements,

(*c*) the hydrides of the transition elements (except CuH ?).

The *covalent hydrides* fall into two groups, the volatile compounds and the involatile, polymeric compounds probably with electron deficient bonding. The volatile hydrides are those of

(*a*) the Carbon Group metals,

(*b*) the metals of the succeeding Main Groups,

(*c*) probably the transient MH hydrides are to be included, along with the transient TiH_4.

The polymeric, electron deficient hydrides are those of

(*a*) boron – where the ligher members are volatile,

(*b*) beryllium, aluminium and gallium.

The remaining hydrides are probably intermediate between two or all three of these classes as follows:

(*i*) MgH_2, intermediate between the ionic and the electron deficient polymers but rather more ionic (AlH_3 might also be intermediate but falling more on the covalent side),

(*ii*) ZnH_2, and CuH ?, somewhere between the ionic, the covalent polymer and the metallic (the latter in their hydrogen-deficient forms), (*iii*) the solid, low-valent hydrides of the main group elements such as GeH_2 and AsH_x are probably intermediate between the metallic and the covalent.

The ternary and other mixed hydrides fall into similar classes: thus hydrides like GeH_3AsH_2 are volatile and covalent, the metal borohydrides range from the ionic like $NaBH_4$ to the volatile and electron-deficient like $Be(BH_4)_2$, while mixed metallic hydrides such as ZrAgH are also found. The M-H bond in transition metal complexes ranges from $M^{\delta+}H^{\delta-}$ to $M^{\delta-}H^{\delta+}$, depending on the other substituents. Such complexes, just as complexes of all other ligands, may be discussed equally conveniently in terms of either an ionic, electrostatic model or in terms of a covalent, molecular orbital theory.

The foregoing classification is not intended to imply that a rigid division can be drawn between any of the types of bond mentioned, but within the general bond types, the hydrides divide up in a manner broadly to be expected.

1.3 Experimental Methods and Hazards

The handling of each of the classes of metal hydrides demands its own techniques and it is possible to say only a little in general terms. It is essential that the beginner in any part of the field should become fully acquainted with the appropriate techniques, and references to preparative methods are given in the following chapters. The reactivity of the metal hydrides varies widely, but it is wise to assume that an unknown hydride will react violently with air or water until the converse has been proved. In general terms, the solid hydrides of the alkali metals are somewhat less reactive than the parent elements, the metallic hydrides of the transition elements are at least as reactive as the finely-divided metals, while the covalent hydrides are mainly inflammable in moist air. While many compounds are less reactive than these limits, most hydrides can be persuaded to inflame without much difficulty.

The metal hydrides are generally similar to the elements in toxicity, although organometallic hydrides may well be much more toxic than this. The most dangerous hydrides from this point of view are the volatile hydrides, and PH_3 and AsH_3 must be among the most toxic of all chemical materials. Even SbH_3, although it is of low stability in air, presents a hazard in a confined space and is reported among the electrolytic gases from storage batteries.

Manipulation of the hydrides demands moisture- and oxygen-free conditions, either using vacuum line methods or inert atmosphere glove boxes. For the latter, argon is to be preferred to nitrogen for the alkali and alkaline earth hydrides, and for many of the transition element hydrides, to avoid contamination by metal nitrides – especially if the hydride is to be heated. All solvents should also be rigorously dried, and halogenated or oxygenated solvents should not be regarded as non-reacting until so proven. For example, the formation of chloroform from carbon tetrachloride by transition element hydride complexes is so common as to be regarded as a diagnostic test for the presence of M-H bonds.

Of the techniques used to examine the hydrides, the most common are infra-red and nuclear magnetic resonance spectroscopy and X-ray crystallography. Mass spectroscopy and neutron diffraction are also valuable, if the facilities are available. Structural studies by X-ray diffraction are readily performed on small samples and may be used to find the complete structure for hydrides of light elements. In only special cases, however, can hydrogen be located in the hydrides of average or heavy metals by X-rays, and neutron diffraction is necessary for full structure determination. The number of neutron diffraction studies reported for hydrides is still limited, but structures of members of each of the hydride classes have been found, and a considerable volume of work is at present under way. The day is not far distant when it will be possible to expect both X-ray and neutron diffraction studies to be performed, as a matter of routine, on all important new hydrides. As hydrogen is the lightest element, metal-hydrogen stretching modes usually occur in a region of the infra-red spectrum which is free from other absorptions ($C{\equiv}O$ and $C{\equiv}N$ stretches are the only common interfering modes). In addition, the shift on deuteration by approximately $1/\sqrt{2}$, allows hydrogen modes to be readily identified. Hydrogen bonded to metals shows a very wide range of proton chemical shifts in the nuclear magnetic resonance effect. *Tau* values of 1–10 ppm are observed for hydrogen bonded to Main Group metals, while very high values, of 10–50 ppm, are found for hydrogen in transition metal hydrides. All these methods are non-destructive and, separately or in combination, can give a great deal of information about any hydride in any phase. Mass spectroscopy is of particular value in identifying hydrides of light metals, and in indicating the presence of transient species.

1.4 Uses of Metal Hydrides

Among the applications, and possible applications, of the metal hydrides may be mentioned the following items.

Rocket Fuels. The hydrides of the lightest elements are, in theory, excellent rocket fuels and kerosene and hydrazine have, of course, been widely used. The hydrides of the light metals, especially the boron hydrides and related compounds such as $Al(BH_4)_3$, have also been examined as potential fuels [16]. However, current interest seems to have swung away from these compounds as the loss of energy involved in the condensation of the oxidation products, such as B_2O_3, makes them less attractive than at first thought.

Metal Plating. The decomposition of a volatile hydride on a heated surface provides a method of plating which offers some advantages [17]. The evenness of the coating, especially on highly intricate surfaces, exceeds that produced by conventional electroplating. A specialized adaptation is the possible application to semi-conductor devices by the deposition of silicon or germanium by decomposition of SiH_4 or GeH_4. It is also possible to use solid hydrides, as in the decomposition of titanium or zirconium hydrides on a ceramic surface to provide a base for soldering.

Nuclear Reactors. Hydrides have a number of possible applications in reactor technology. A solid hydride, such as ZrH_2, has a very high hydrogen density at high temperatures and thus has potential uses in slowing neutrons in reactor moderators or shields [18, 25]. The formation of hydrides of titanium, zirconium, or hafnium on the surface of heat transfer vessels has been suggested as a method of protecting these metals from attack by liquid metals used as coolants [19]. The deuterides and tritides of the light elements have potential uses in future thermonuclear reactors.

Metallurgy. In powder metallurgy, the metal hydrides may provide the readiest route to the metal powder. If the lattice parameters of the hydride differ widely from those of the parent metal, hydriding the massive metal will produce the metal hydride in a finely powdered form, as in the case of uranium hydride. The powdered hydride may then be dehydrided by heating to moderately high temperatures leaving the powdered metal. Hafnium powder may be prepared in this way [20]. Such a process may also be used to produce a metal in an activated form, and also as a means of purifying hydrogen. UH_3 or TiH_2 are commonly used for the latter purpose. In a slightly different application, titanium hydride may be added to metal powders to improve fabrication properties and to provide a protective atmosphere.

A number of hydrides are used on a limited scale as reducing agents in metallurgy. For example, calcium hydride, which is relatively easily handled and leaves water-soluble residues, is used in the preparation of metals such as niobium [21]. The much more reactive sodium hydride is used, as a solution in molten sodium hydroxide, as a descaling agent for stainless steel, titanium, and other metals [22].

Hydrogen Sources. The less reactive ionic hydrides, such as lithium hydride, calcium hydride and sodium borohydride, may be used as portable sources of hydrogen for use, for example, in filling radiosonde balloons. The development of fuel cells may open up a further application of such sources. These same hydrides, along with the more reactive sodium hydride and lithium aluminium hydride, may be used as drying agents.

Chemical Syntheses. The alkali and alkaline earth hydrides, borohydrides, and aluminohydrides, especially LiH, NaH, CaH_2, $NaBH_4$, and $LiAlH_4$, are well-known as reducing and condensing agents in organic and inorganic chemistry and find many uses in the pharmaceutical and fine-chemical industries. Their applications in laboratory chemistry are illustrated by the preparations of the covalent and complex hydrides detailed in subsequent chapters. Of these hydrides, $LiAlH_4$, $NaBH_4$, and related compounds such as $NaBH(OR)_3$, are the most versatile and useful reagents in the laboratory, but they are expensive for use on a larger scale and usually replaced by NaH. The recent development of the direct synthesis of lithium aluminium hydride from the elements (see Chapter 6) may lead to a significant reduction in the cost of this reagent.

A further general reaction of metal-hydrogen links is their addition across a double bond. This may be used to lead to a variety of organometallic compounds, and in polymerization catalysis [23].

REFERENCES

[1] W. N. LIPSCOMB, *Boron Hydrides*, W. A. Benjamin, 1963: *Borax to Boranes*, Advances in Chemistry Series, American Chemical Society, 1961: T. ONAK, 'Carboranes and Organo-substituted Boron Hydrides', *Advances in Organometallic Chemistry*, edited by F. G. A. Stone and R. West, Academic Press, 1965, **3**: *Advances in Inorganic Chemistry and Radiochemistry*, edited by H. J. Emeleus and A. G. Sharpe, Interscience, W. N. LIPSCOMB, 'Recent Studies of the Boron Hydrides', 1959, **1**, 118; F. G. A. STONE, 'Chemical Reactivity of the Boron Hydrides and Related Compounds', 1960, **2**, 279: *Progress in Boron Chemistry*, Pergamon Press, 1964, **1**, especially G. W. CAMPBELL 'Structure of Boron Hydrides' p. 167.

[2] E. A. V. EBSWORTH, *Volatile Silicon Compounds*, Pergamon Press, 1963: F. G. A. STONE *Hydrogen Compounds of the Group IV Elements*, Prentice-Hall, 1962.

[3] A. G. MACDIARMID, *Quart Rev.*, 1956, **10**, 208; *Advances in Inorganic Chemistry and Radiochemistry*, 1961, **3**, 207.

[4] D. T. HURD, *An Introduction to the Chemistry of the Hydrides*, Wiley, and Chapman and Hall, 1952.

[5] G. E. COATES, *Organometallic Compounds*, Methuen, Second Edn., 1960.

[6] Polonium, K. W. BAGNALL, *Advances in Inorganic Chemistry and Radiochemistry*, 1962, **4**, 209.
Astatine, A. H. W. ATEN, *Advances in Inorganic Chemistry and Radiochemistry*, 1964, **6**, 216.
Francium, Radium } K. W. BAGNALL, *The Chemistry of the Rare Radioelements*, Butterworth, 1957.

[7] Most of the quantities are from standard sources, especially National Bureau of Standards Circular 500, 'Selected Values of Chemical Thermodynamic Properties' (1952), updated where possible. The heat of hydration of the proton is from H. F. Holliwell and S. C. Nyburg, *Trans. Faraday Soc.*, 1963, **59**, 1126.

[8] See, for example, A. G. GAYDON, *Dissociation Energies and Spectra of Diatomic Molecules*, Chapman and Hall; *Molecular Spectra and Molecular Structure. Infra-red Spectra of Diatomic Molecules*, G. Herzberg, (van Nostrand) 2nd edition, 1950.

[9] W. N. LIPSCOMB, *Inorg. Chem.*, 1964, **3**, 1683.

[10] References to Carboranes.
(*a*) T. L. HEYING *et al.*, *Inorg. Chem.*, 1963, **2**, 1089, 1092, 1097, 1105.
(*b*) L. I. ZAKHARKIN *et al.*, *Izvest. Akad. Nauk. S.S.S.R.*, 1963, 2236, 2069; *Doklady Akad. Nauk. S.S.S.R.*, 1964, **155**, 1119.
(*c*) M. M. FEIN *et al.*, *Inorg. Chem.*, 1963, **2**, 1111, 1115, 1120, 1125.
(*d*) H. SCHROEDER and G. D. VICKER, *ibid*, 1317.
(*e*) D. GRAFSTEIN and J. DVORAK, *ibid*, 1128.
(*f*) J. A. POTENZA and W. N. LIPSCOMB, *J. Amer. Chem. Soc.*, 1964, **86**, 1874.
(*g*) E. R. ALTWICKEN, G. E. RYSCHKEWITSCH, A. B. GARRETT, and H. H. SISLER, *Inorg. Chem.*, 1964, **3**, 454.

(*h*) F. P. BOER, W. E. STREIB and W. N. LIPSCOMB, *ibid.*, 1666.

(*i*) F. TEBBE, P. M. GARRETT, and M. F. HAWTHORNE, *J. Amer. Chem. Soc.*, 1964, **86**, 4222.

[11] (*a*) S. PAPETTI, B. B. SCHAEFFER, H. J. TROSCIANIEC, and T. L. HEYING, *Inorg. Chem.* 1964, **3**, 1444, 1448.

(*b*) N. N. SCHWARTZ, E. O'BRIEN, S. KARLAN, and M. M. FEIN, *Inorg. Chem.*, 1965, **4**, 661.

[12] A. STOCK, *Hydrides of Boron and Silicon*, Cornell University Press, 1933.

[13] M. F. HAWTHORNE, *Decaborane*-14 *and its Derivatives, Advances in Inorganic Chemistry and Radiochemistry*, 1963, **5**, 308.

[14] G. W. PARSHALL, *J. Amer. Chem. Soc.*, 1964, **86**, 361.

[15] H. M. DASH, *Nature*, 1964, **202**, 1001: L. L. HAWES, *ibid*, 1965, **206**, 188: H. M. DASH, *ibid*, 188.

[16] N. BOWMAN and W. PROELL, *J. Space Flight*, 1950, **2**, 1; 6.

[17] H. G. BELITZ and O. F. DAVIS, U.S. Pat., 2,631,948 (1953): M. V. SULLIVAN and J. H. EIGLEN, *J. Electrochem. Soc.*, 1956, **103**, 218.

[18] H. M. MCCULLOUGH and B. KAPELMAN, *Nucleonics*, 1956, **14**, 146.

[19] D. H. GURINSKY, O. F. KAMMERER, J. SADOFSKY, and J. R. WEEKS, U.S. Pat. 2,864,731 (1958).

[20] H. B. MICHEALSON, *Materials and Methods*, 1955, **14**, 92 (general review): R. N. HONEYMAN and C. T. WALC, U.S. At. En. Comm., KAPL–1929 (Krolls Atomic Power Lab. Rept.) (Hafnium powder.)

[21] P. P. ALEXANDER, 'Hydrimet Process', U.S. Pat. 2,702,234 (1955); and 2,606,100 (1952).

[22] W. J. BARTH and A. L. FIELD, Jr., *Metal Progress*, 1955, **61**, 114: N. L. EVANS, *Corrosion Techn.* 1956, **3**, 47; W. F. S. TAYLOR, *Metal Treatment and Drop Forging*, 1956, **23**, 465; U.S. Pat., 2,796,336 (1957).

[23] W. MARCONI, A. MAZZEI, M. ARALDI, and M. DE MALDE, *J. Polymer Sci. A.*, 1965, **3**, 735.

[24] D. E. WILCOX and L. A. BROMLEY, *Ind. Eng. Chem.*, 1963, **55**, 32.

[25] G. G. LIBOWITZ, *J. Nuclear Materials*, 1960, **2**, 1.

CHAPTER 2

Ionic Hydrides

2.1 The Existence of Ionic Hydrides

If a standard Born cycle is evaluated for the formation of an ionic compound, MX, from alkali metals and halogen or hydrogen molecules:

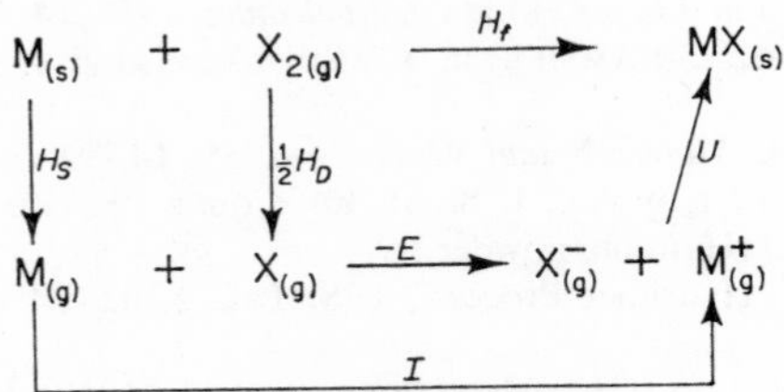

where H_f is the heat of formation from the elements in their standard states at 25°C,

H_S is the heat of sublimation of the metal,

$\frac{1}{2}H_D$ is half the heat of dissociation of the X_2 molecule,

E is the electron affinity of the X atom,

I is the ionization potential of the metal,

and U is the lattice energy of the ionic solid M^+X^-,

it may be calculated from the hydrogen parameters given in Table 1.1, that the hydrogen contribution to the endothermic terms in the heat of formation is $(\frac{1}{2}H_D - E) = 34{\cdot}7$ kcal/mole, while the corresponding halogen contributions are *exothermic*, F = 46, Cl = 30, Br = 37, and $I = 40$ kcal/mole. Thus the heat of formation of an alkali metal ionic hydride averages about 70 kcal/mole less than that of the ionic alkali halides, assuming that the lattice energies of the hydrides and halides are similar. As the observed heats of formation of the alkali halides are of the order of -100 kcal/mole (for example, sodium chloride $= -98{\cdot}2$ kcal/mole), this implies that the alkali hydrides should still have exothermic heats of formation as ionic solids. Less information is available for the alkaline earth hydrides, but a similar calculation indicates that the formation of ionic hydrides should be exothermic, provided again that the lattic energies of the hydrides and halides are similar.

It is thus seen that, although the formation of ionic hydrides is much less favourable, energetically, than that of ionic halides, there is good reason to expect that the more electropositive elements, with low ionization potentials, should form ionic hydrides exothermically.

However, these calculations only indicate that ionic hydrides may be formed, and are not proof of the ionic nature of the alkali hydrides. Some further confirmation may be derived from lattice energy data, as there is reasonable agreement between the experimental values of the lattice energies derived from the Born cycle and those calculated on the basis of an ionic model: Table 2.1. The value under (*a*) is from an exact calculation while those under

Table 2.1. *Lattice Energies of the Alkali Hydrides* [18]

	Experimental Value (kcal/mole)	Calculated Values (*a*)	(*b*)	(*c*)
LiH	216·5	218·2	234·0	222
NaH	193·8	—	202·0	191
KH	170·7	—	177·2	169
RbH	164·4	—	168·6	161
CsH	156·1	—	162·0	155

(For comparison, the lattice energies of the alkali halides [18] range from 241·2 kcal/mole for LiF to 140·3 kcal/mole for CsI (cycle values), and calculated values generally agree to within a kilocalorie except for LiI.)

(*b*) were calculated [18] by a simple method which did not allow for the compressibility of H^-. The values under (*c*) were calculated [32] from the Born-Landé equation. This agreement is therefore satisfactory and provides support for the formulation of the alkali hydrides as ionic.

There is also experimental evidence from conductivity measurements for the ionic formulation. The only hydride which melts before decomposition is lithium hydride. This melt is conducting to the extent expected for an ionic system, and electrolysis produces hydrogen at the anode. The other alkali hydrides decompose below their melting points, but they are soluble in fused salts, such as the LiCl-KCl eutectic above 352°C, or in fused alkali hydroxides. They are ionized in solution and evolve hydrogen at the anode on electrolysis [11]. Such solutions in hydroxides are used for cleaning metal surfaces and are quite stable, solutions of low hydride concentration being stable above 600°C [60].

It is important to be certain of the ionic nature of the alkali hydrides as these then provide a standard against which other solid hydrides may be compared. The case of LiH has been the most thoroughly examined as it is amenable to calculation as well as to experimental measurement. As the Li-H distance (Table 2.3) is approximately equal to the calculated radius of the free hydrogen ion, H^-, it had been suggested that extensive charge separation could not occur in lithium hydride. However, an X-ray and neutron diffraction study [52], has confirmed that a marked contraction in the H^- radius occurs in the solid. The results correspond to the transfer of 0·8 to 1·0 of an electron charge from lithium to hydrogen in crystalline lithium hydride. A similar order of charge transfer is observed from infra-red reflectivity and dielectric constant measurements and also agrees well with calculated values. Electron diffraction studies of solid lithium hydride [54] lead to similar conclusions.

As lithium hydride would be the least ionic of the alkali metal hydrides, because of the strong polarizing effects of the small Li^+ ion, these results mean that, *a fortiori*, the other alkali hydrides are essentially ionic.

There is much less experimental evidence available for the alkaline earth hydrides. Calcium, strontium, and barium hydrides are insoluble in ordinary organic solvents but are soluble in alkali halide melts. Electrolysis of these solutions gives hydrogen at the anode. Lattice energy calculations also support the ionic formulation. The experimental values are given in Table 2.6 and agree closely with the calculated values of 600 for CaH_2, 542 for SrH_2, and 522 for BaH_2 [32], which best fit the redetermined M-H distances in these compounds (see note (*c*) to the Table). These results indicate that the alkaline earth hydrides may also reasonably be formulated as ionic.

Of the other hydrides, ionic formulations are conceivable for MgH_2, for hydrides of the lanthanide elements of formula LnH_3, for hydrides LnH_2 of

Table 2.2. *Thermodynamic Functions of the Alkali Hydrides as Solids at 25°C*

(References in square brackets)

Hydride	ΔH_f° (kcal/mole)	Method (*b*)	ΔG_f° (kcal/mole)	S° (cal/degree/mole)
LiH	−21·666 ± ·026	A [1]	−16·72 [3]	5·9 [3]
	−21·34 ± ·015	A [2]		
LiD	−21·784 ± ·021	A [1]		
NaH	−13·487 ± ·020	A [1]	− 9·0 [7]	7·1 [8]
	−13·60 ± ·24	A [2]		
	−13·94	B [5, 6]		
NaD	−13·339 ± ·007	A [1]		
KH	−13·819 ± ·011	A [1]	− 8·9 [7]	10·2 [8]
	−15·16 ± ·16 (*a*)	A [2]		
KD	−13·238 ± ·011	A [1]		
RbH	−11·3	[8]	− 7·3 [7]	17·0 [8]
	−12·98 ± ·19	B [6]		
RbD	Early results give RbD as 0·7 kcal/mole less stable than RbH at 320°C [10].			
CsH	−11·92	C [9]	− 7·3 [7]	20·8 [8]
	−10·1	[8]		
	−13·48 ± ·20	B [6]		
CsD	Early results give CsD as 2·9 kcal/mole less stable than CsH at 235°C [10]			

Notes (*a*) Earlier values for KH by method B give results in the range −13·6 to −14·2 kcal/mole: thus the value −13·819 kcal/mole is to be preferred.

(*b*) Method A is a calorimetric comparison of the heats of reaction of M and of MH with water.
Method B is from the temperature variation of the dissociation of MH.
Method C is similar to A but reacting with HCl.

Table 2.3. *Properties of Solid Alkali Hydrides*

Hydride	Decomposition Pressure (*a*)				Structure			
	A	B	Temperature Range (°C)	Ref.	Unit cell length (Å)	M-H or M-D dist. (Å)	H^- or D^- radius (Å)	Ref.
LiH	9520	11·28	Around melting point	[3]	4·093			[16]
	9600	11·227	500–650	[22]	4·083	2·043	1·37	[15, 19]
	8224	9·926	700–800	[23]				
LiD					4·073			[16]
					4·069	2·035	1·35	[15, 19]
NaH	6100	11·66	100–325	[5]	4·879	2·445	1·46	[15, 16]
			280–415	[6]				
	5958	10·47	500–600	[20]				
NaD					4·867	2·433	1·45	[15]
KH	6175	11·69	289–415	[6]	5·708	2·856	1·52	[15]
	5850	11·2	310–480	[21] (*b*)				
	6300	11·86	350–415	[8]				
KD					5·696	2·848	1·51	[15]
RbH	4534	9·20		[10]	6·037	3·025	1·54	[16]
	4930	9·51	400–450	[8]				
	5680	11·80	246–350	[6]				
CsH	4410	9·25	340–440	[8]	6·376	3·195	1·52	[16]
	5900	11·79	245–378	[6]				

Notes (*a*) The constants are given for the equation $\log p_{(mm)} = -A/T + B$.

(*b*) The values from reference [21] are earlier results of Hérold and are partly superseded by the results of reference [6]. They are given here as they cover a higher temperature range.

the lanthanide elements with a II state, and possibly for beryllium hydride, aluminium hydride, and for the hydrides of the d^{10} elements, i.e. CuH and the zinc Group dihydrides. All these cases are discussed in the later sections of this chapter.

Some physical properties of the ionic hydrides are given in Tables 2.2 to 2.6. Also included are some data on the gaseous molecules MH and related species, Table 2.7

A few comments on the physical data may be made at once. It is seen that the heats of formation are indeed in the range expected, with the values for the alkaline earth hydrides about twice those of the alkali hydrides, a result similar to those for the corresponding halides. The deuterides differ from the hydrides by small, but probably significant, amounts in the heats of formation and the lattice parameters. There is also some evidence, Table 2.4, for small differences in lattice energies. Similar changes are observed on isotopic substitution in the hydrides of the transition elements and some of the latter differences are rather more significant and are discussed in the next chapter. The isotopic differences in the ionic hydrides may be ascribed to differences in

Table 2.4. *Further Properties of the Alkali Hydrides*

	LiH	NaH	KH	RbH	CsH
X-ray Density of solid (g/cc) (values differing by less than 1% have been averaged)	0·772 [16, 19]	1·363 [15] 1·396 [11]	1·430 [15]	2·595 [16]	3·410 [16]
	LiD	NaD	KD		
	0·881 [16, 19]	1·440 [15]	1·477 [15]		
Lattice Energies [15] (differing from those in Table 2·1) (kcal/mole)	LiH = 217·76 LiD = 218·76	NaH = 192·74 NaD = 193·47 KH = 170·12 KD = 170·42			
Melting Point (°C)	LiH [12] 690·8 ± 0·2 (Experimental value for 99·6–99·9% pure samples of LiH) 692 ± 2 (Value extrapolated to 100% purity and zero rate of heat change) LiD [3] 686 ± 5				
Heat of Fusion	LiH = 5·210 kcal/mole [12] 5·095 kcal/mole [13]				
Heat Capacity	LiH = 8·3 calories per degree per mole [3]				
Activation Energies:	the reaction $NaH = Na + \frac{1}{2}H_2$ At 100–140°C the activation energy of the forward reaction is 24·9 kcal/mole, and of the back reaction is 11·0 kcal/mole [5] At 150–200°C the activation energy of the forward reaction is 16·5 kcal/mole [28]. For the reaction $LiH \rightarrow Li + \frac{1}{2}H_2$ At 25–250°C, the activation energy is given as 6·3 ± 2·5 kcal/mole [57].				

Table 2.5. *Thermodynamic Properties of the Alkaline Earth Hydrides as Solids at 25°C*

Hydride	ΔH_f° (kcal/mole	ΔG_f° (kcal/mole)	S° (cal/degree/mole)
CaH_2	−41·65 [47]	−32·61 [47]	30·4 [47] (*a*)
	−45·1 [3]	−35·8 [3]	10 [3]
SrH_2	−42·3 [3]	−33·1 [7]	13 (*b*)
BaH_2	−40·9 [3]	−36·6 [3]	16 (*b*)

Notes (*a*) The recent values from reference [47] are to be preferred as the metal was probably of higher purity. The older values are also given as they compare more directly with those for SrH_2 and BaH_2

(*b*) These values are calculated.

Table 2.6. *Structural Properties of the Alkaline Earth Hydrides*

Hydride	Density (g/cm^3)	Decomposition Pressures (*a*) *A*	*B*	Temperature range °C	Structure: Unit Cell (Å)	Structure: M–H distance (Å)	Lattice Energy (kcal/mole) (32)
CaH_2	1·902 [16]	9,610 8,890 9,840 (for 25 to 95% CaH_2)	7·346 6·660 10·7	600–780 } [47] 780–900 } 710–940 [29]	$a = 6{\cdot}851$ } [16] $b = 5{\cdot}948$ } (*e*) $c = 3{\cdot}607$ }	Seven Ca-H of 2·32 and two of 2·85 [25]	580 (*b*)
					Transforms to a second (β) form at 780° C (48) (*c*) Enthalpy of the α-β transformation is approximately 1·60 kcal/mole		
SrH_2	3·269 [16]	10,400 (92·3% SrH_2)	11·10 [3]		$a = 7{\cdot}358$ } [16] $b = 6{\cdot}377$ } (*e*) $c = 3{\cdot}882$ }	Seven Sr-H of 2·49 and two of 3·06 (*d*)	540 (*b*)
					Transforms to a β form at 855°C [49]		
BaH_2	4·21 [11] 4·156 [16]	4,000 (97% BaH_2)	6·86	500–1000 [3	$a = 7{\cdot}845$ } [16] $b = 6{\cdot}801$ } (*e*) $c = 4{\cdot}175$ }	Seven Ba-H of 2·67 and two of 3·28 (*d*)	518
					Transforms to β form at 598°C [50] (This has been tentatively indexed as a fcc unit cell with a lattice constant of 9·465Å)		

Notes (*a*) The constants are given for the equation, $\log p_{(mm)} = -A/T + B$.

(*b*) Calculated from reference [32] Table XVI using the values for heats of formation given above in Table 2.5.

(*c*) The dissociation pressure equation of reference [29] does not take account of this.

(*d*) The X-ray determination [16] of the metal atom positions continues to be accepted but these authors chose the wrong H atom positions, which were corrected in the neutron diffraction study [25] on CaH_2. The M-H distances in SrH_2 and BaH_2 are calculated on the assumption of similar hydrogen positions in these hydrides as in CaH_2, and that the M-H distances bear the same ratio to the Ca-H ones as do the lattice constants of the respective unit cells.

(*e*) The low temperature (α) form is orthorhombic P_{nam} structure similar to $CaCl_2$.

Table 2.7. *Properties of Gaseous Diatomic Hydrides of the Elements of the Lithium and Sodium Groups*

	Gaseous Molecules at 25°			Bond Length	Electronic Binding Energies	
	ΔH_f° (kcal/mole)	ΔG_f° (kcal/mole)	S° (cal/°/mole)	[17] (Å)	Calculated [30] (kcal/mole)	Found [17] (kcal/mole)
LiH	30·7	25·2	40·77	1·5954	165·4	167
NaH	29·88	27·78	44·93	1·8873	141·6	150
KH	30·0	25·1	47·3	2·244	121·3	127
RbH	33·0			2·367	117·0	119
CsH	29·0			2·494	112·7	114
BeH	78·1	71·3	40·84	1·3431		
MgH	41	34	47·61	1·7306		
CaH	58·7	51·9 (calc)	48·18	2·002		
SrH	52·4	45·8	49·43	2·1455		
BaH	52	46	52·97	2·2318		

The bond lengths of MD are also known for M = Li, Na, K, Be, Mg, Ca, and Sr and are all 0·001Å, or less, longer than the MH distances. In the ions, the bond lengths, Be-H in BeH^+ = 1·3122 and Mg-H in MgH^+ = 1·649, are reported. All these values are given in reference [17] and reported in references [3] and [31]. Some approaches to the calculation of such values are given in references [55] and [56].

zero point energies arising from H^- or D^- vibrations in the lattice. Substitution of D for H should decrease the vibration leading to slightly smaller M-D distances and slightly larger lattice energies for the deuterides. The heats of formation of the deuterides change from being slightly greater for LiD to being (apparently) increasingly less for the heavier metal deuterides, than for the hydrides. Although the data are obviously of varying quality, this trend could result from the combined effect of the greater dissociation energy of D_2 compared with H_2, and the change in lattice energy between the hydride and deuteride, which gets smaller from the lithium to the cesium compounds. More detailed comment must await more accurate experimental data, especially for the heavy element deuterides.

As Table 2.7 shows, the formation of the gaseous hydrides is endothermic, and the binding energies observed agree well with the calculated values. This calculation [30] allows for the polarization of each ion in the other's electrostatic field, but otherwise treats the MH species as an ion pair. Similar good agreement is found for gaseous halides, MX, treated in the same way while HX and alkaline earth gaseous oxides, MO, show only poor agreement between experimental and calculated values. These results help to indicate the similarities between the hydrides and the halides already noted. They also add support to the postulate of ionic bonding in the solid, as the calculation succeeds on the basis of ions pairs in the gas and ionic solids are even more likely because of the lattice energy effect. The infra-red spectrum of gaseous LiH has been recorded; the band centre is at 1406 cm^{-1} [84].

2.2 The Preparation of the Ionic Hydrides

All the ionic hydrides are prepared by direct combination with hydrogen. The methods are discussed in detail by Gibb [32] and by Messer [33]. The preparation of sodium hydride is described in Inorganic Syntheses [34].

As these hydrides, on heating, dissociate reversibly into the metal and hydrogen, and as the metal can dissolve some hydrogen and the hydride phase can be hydrogen-deficient, the composition of any metal-metal hydride system varies with the pressure of hydrogen in contact with it as shown in the schematic diagram in Figure 1. The mutual solubility varies with the temperature as

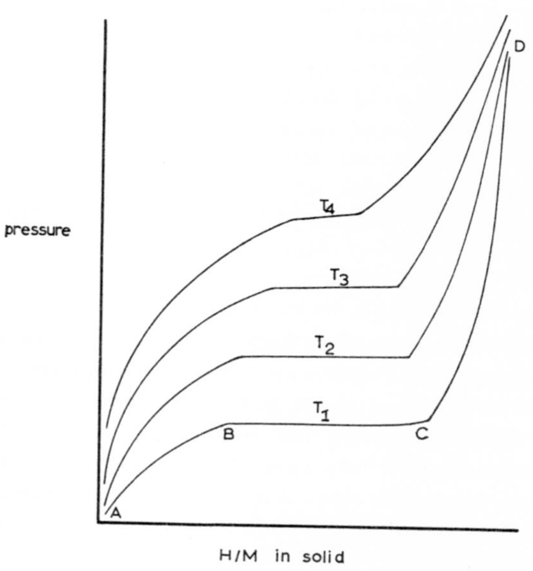

Figure 1. Representation of a typical family of pressure-composition isotherms for the formation of a metal hydride. The temperatures increase in the order, $T_1 < T_2 < T_3 < T_4$.

shown by the different isotherms in the Figure, and the solubilities and compositions also vary from metal to metal. In the case of some of the transition metal hydrides, more than one hydride phase may exist and the diagram may be more complicated.

In any one of the isotherms in Figure 1, the first, steeply-rising portion AB corresponds to solution of hydrogen in the metal. When saturation is reached, at B, the hydride phase forms and, as this is coexisting with the metal phase, the system becomes invariant and the 'plateau' region appears for compositions BC. At C, the metal phase has completely reacted and hydrogen-deficient hydride phase remains which requires a rapid increase in hydrogen pressure to approach stoicheiometry. At higher temperatures, the plateau region shortens and higher hydrogen pressures are required to approach stoicheiometry. The variation of pressure with temperature usually approximates to the well-known formula

$$\log p = -A/T + B$$

where A and B are constants. This holds for the plateau pressures, which are the ones usually determined, and for the 100% hydride pressures, as far as the latter have been reported. Tables 2.3 and 2.6 include some of the more recent values for A and B over various temperature ranges.

The problem in preparing a particular hydride involves finding a suitable compromise between working at as low a temperature as possible and having the reaction going at a reasonable rate. In some cases, fully stoicheiometric hydrides can be formed only by using hydrogen pressures greater than atmospheric. A further problem arising in the case of most ionic hydrides is that the hydride layer on the surface of the metal is strongly coherent and becomes impervious to the penetration of further hydrogen so that the reaction becomes very slow. This problem occurs only for the ionic hydrides as these are denser than the parent metal and have shorter M-M distances in the hydride than in the metal structure. (The metallic hydrides are less dense than the metal and the hydride skin on the surface fissures allowing reaction to continue.) In some cases, the addition of surface active agents is sufficient to prevent film formation, or else the film is broken by mechanical agitation.

The preparation of hydrides of high purity demands the use of very pure metal and hydrogen, and suitable methods of handling the compounds in an inert atmosphere. In recent years, techniques have improved considerably, especially on the handling side, both by the accumulation of experience and the advent of efficient glove boxes and of pure argon (or helium in the United States) for inert atmosphere work. For this reason, more recent experimental results in the hydride field are generally to be preferred to earlier work where the two are in conflict. The modern tyro is probably able to work under better conditions than the pre-war master.

Pure hydrogen may be obtained by diffusion through palladium but a convenient, and increasingly-used source, is the thermal decomposition of a suitable hydride, usually UH_3 or TiH_2. Many of the metals can now be bought in a high state of purity, otherwise vacuum distillation in a stainless steel still is usually used. In the case of relatively large-scale work with sodium, an apparatus for purification by continuous filtration of the liquid metal has been described [35]. For less critical work, the metal may be cleaned by cutting off the oxide film in a glove box, or purified by melting under an inert high boiling organic liquid with rapid stirring to form a suspension of finely-divided metal which can be filtered from the oxide scum. Although argon is the preferred inert atmosphere gas, carbon dioxide can be used for less critical work with some metals such as lithium. Nitrogen cannot be used with lithium and it is not satisfactory for use with the other metals when they are heated.

In a typical preparation, aimed at producing a sample of better than 99% purity, the metal is purified and weighed out into a boat in an argon-filled glove box. The boat is placed inside a stainless steel bomb tube, fitted with a needle valve and thermocouple well, which is closed and evacuated. The bomb is then placed in a tube furnace and the sample is heated at a moderate temperature, under vacuum, to outgas the sample and apparatus. Hydrogen in known quantity is then admitted to the sample and the temperature is raised to a suitable point, as indicated in the isotherm diagrams for the metal. The hydriding reaction typically may take from an hour to a day for a metal sample of a few grams, and further hydrogen may be admitted to the reaction vessel from time to time as the reaction proceeds. When the rate of hydrogen uptake becomes negligibly small, the sample is allowed to cool very slowly in an atmosphere of hydrogen. This is the stage where the final uptake of hydrogen by the defect hydride phase occurs, so slow cooling is essential to allow the closest possible approach to stoicheiometry, in the CD portion of the isotherm, as the temperature falls and the system passes from one isotherm to the next. It is necessary to find the best balance between the approach to stoicheiometry corresponding to the temperature and pressure used, and the rate of the reaction. The sample is finally unloaded in the glovebox. A pure sample of the hydride will be white and crystalline.

Typical conditions for the preparation of LiH and CaH_2 are

	Reaction Temperature	Reaction Time	H_2 Pressure	Annealing Temperature	Product Purity
LiH	725°C	10 hr for 4g Li	>100 mm	Slow cooling to 680° (mpt)	99·6–99·8%
CaH_2	380°C } with stirring	4 hr for 5g Ca	few mm	380°C	99·1%
	500°C } with stirring			380°C	99·9%

In these cases, surface effects are not serious. The temperature and time of the reaction vary with the purity of the metal, impure samples requiring a longer reaction time and, sometimes, substantially higher temperatures to initiate the reaction. Strontium and barium hydrides have been less extensively studied but can be made by the method described above at the appropriate temperatures. Although glass or quartz suffer rapid attack by lithium, the reaction of other metals with these is slower and they can sometimes be used in place of stainless steel.

The synthesis of sodium hydride by the straightforward method above fails because of the formation of a protective surface layer of hydride on the metal. This problem is most commonly overcome by using small amounts of a surface active agent. Typical compounds include fatty acids or their salts, from a C_8 chain length upwards, anthracene, and a number of other aromatic condensed hydrocarbons, all in quantities from 0·1 to 1·0%. The organic compound may be removed from the hydride afterwards by extraction with hexane or a similar solvent. With such reagents, formation of sodium hydride proceeds rapidly at one atmosphere hydrogen pressure and a temperature of 250–400°C. An alternative method involves rapidly stirring molten sodium under a suitable paraffin oil to form a finely divided dispersion and then bubbling hydrogen through this, as in the procedure described in *Inorganic Syntheses* [34]. The reaction takes place at 280–300°C and the sodium hydride is again recovered by washing with hexane. A further suitable method for small amounts of hydride (and this is equally applicable to all the other metals) is to pass a stream of hydrogen over or through molten sodium at 400°C, when the reaction takes place in the vapour phase and the hydride is deposited on colder parts of the reaction vessel. The reaction is relatively slow and suitable for amounts of metal of the order of a gram. Higher temperatures speed the reaction at the expense of the purity of the product. A simple apparatus is described by Addison, Pulham, and Roy [5] in which hydrogen is passed over and through sodium at 375–400°C and the gas stream is carried down a tube along which the temperature drops to 300°C. By appropriate adjustment of the temperature gradient and the gas flow, conditions were readily obtained where pure hydride condensed out in the region of this tube nearest the reaction vessel, while unreacted sodium vapour condensed in a separate zone towards the cooler end. The hydride was obtained as completely colourless needles.

The hydrides of potassium and the other alkali metals are similar to sodium hydride and may be made by similar methods involving surface active agents, dispersions, or gas phase reactions at the appropriate temperatures. For these very reactive metals the reported temperatures of reaction vary considerably, probably reflecting the purity of the metal. Reported ranges are 3–400°C for KH, and above 600°C for rubidium and cesium in the direct reaction at ordinary pressures (giving 90 to 50% conversion). A dispersion of either metal in sand or clay in a rotating vessel reacts with hydrogen in the presence of a surface agent at 385°C, while complete reaction of the metal at about 300°C and in the absence of any catalyst, occurs if the pressure is raised to 50 atmospheres [6]. Similarly, Mikheeva [36] reports that while 98% KH in 18% yield results at an optimum temperature of 400°C at one atmosphere pressure, increasing the pressure to 3–4 atmospheres reduces the reaction temperature to 200–250°C.

It is suggested that potassium hydride is prepared more readily than sodium hydride as a result of the lower coefficient of thermal expansion in the former case [36, 53]. The values are 39×10^{-6} for KH and 64×10^{-6} for NaH in the temperature range 20–400°C. As the values for the metals are 84×10^{-6} for K and 72×10^{-6} for Na, it is probable that the surface hydride layer is much less coherent in the potassium reaction.

The methods discussed above are necessary if products of high purity are required. In many applications of the hydrides, especially for syntheses, pure products are not required and the hydride may be formed *in situ* and used without isolation. In such cases, the reaction of hydrogen with a metal dispersion in an oil is probably the most convenient method. Gibb [37] has shown that heating a mixture, or solution, of an alkali metal in one of its halides in hydrogen gives a product which is a solid solution of the metal hydride in the metal halide. This is recommended as a convenient way of handling the hydrides for reductions, particularly on a large scale, as there is less hazard and the hydride solution is more stable to air and water. Concentrations of 0·01 to 0·1 mole percent are attainable. Alexander [38] proposes making calcium, strontium, or barium hydrides by the reaction of sodium hydride on the metal chlorides at 400°C (most conveniently by heating sodium, the dichloride, and hydrogen together). The product may be freed from sodium hydride and sodium chloride by dissolving these out with liquid ammonia.

All the ionic hydrides are white or colourless crystals when pure. Impure products are variously described as pale grey to black. Presence of excess metal is shown by a blue colour due to the presence of F centres (compare the alkali halides with excess alkali [39]). All the ionic hydrides are denser than the parent metal, to the extent of 25 to 45% in the case of the alkali hydrides and 5% to 10% in the case of the alkaline earth compounds.

2.3 Properties and Uses of the Ionic Hydrides

The alkali hydrides have the sodium chloride structure and the structural parameters are shown in Table 2.3. Neutron diffraction results [40] have confirmed the hydrogen positions in sodium hydride and lithium hydride. The simplicity of the structure allows the metal-hydrogen distance to be reliably determined, and the results show a marked increase in the radius of H^- from the lithium to the cesium compound. This change reflects the ease of compressing the very diffuse charge cloud of the hydride ion, where two electrons are held in the field of a single nuclear charge. It is noteworthy that the free H^- ion has been calculated to have a radius of 2·08Å.

The hydrides of calcium, strontium and barium have an orthorhombic structure, as determined by the X-ray study of Zintl and Harder [16]. In this, the metal atoms are in hexagonal close packed positions and the structure is similar to that of calcium chloride. Zintl and Harder assumed that the hydride ions were in two types of position, half in octahedral sites and half in distorted, five-coordinated, sites in the centre of the common base of two tetrahedra, giving a very distorted lead chloride structure, and leading to the values for the metal-hydrogen distances generally quoted in structure reviews. However, a recent neutron diffraction study on CaH_2 and CaD_2 [25] has shown that these positions for the hydride ions give poor agreement with the observed diffraction. The best agreement was found for a slightly distorted lead chloride structure where each calcium was surrounded by seven hydrogens at a distance of 2·32Å, with two others farther away at 2.85Å. A regular $PbCl_2$ structure (in which the cation has six anions at the corners of a trigonal prism and three more beyond the three rectangular faces) gave a better fit to the diffraction curve than the Zintl and Harder structure, but a poorer fit than the structure above. Clearly, as the neutron diffraction experiment gives more direct information about the hydrogen positions, these results are to be preferred to those deduced from the X-ray structure, and it follows that the reported metal-hydrogen parameters in strontium and barium hydrides, which depend on the same X-ray work, are probably incorrect also. The seven shorter metal-hydrogen distances in the new structure are approximately equal to the average metal-hydrogen distances derived from the Zintl and Harder results, so that the discrepancies are not too great. The Zintl and Harder values were 2.35Å, 2·53Å, and 2·71Å for the different types of hydrogen. The shorter metal-hydrogen distances, in the corrected structure, correspond to hydride ion radii in the range 1·4 to 1·5Å, and there is some indication of a contraction in the hydride ion radius between the barium and calcium hydrides. The alkaline earth hydrides thus show similar radius effects to those observed in the alkali metal hydrides. At higher temperatures, the alkaline earth hydrides undergo a transformation to a second, β phase, which may be cubic. This might correspond to a change to the calcium fluoride structure, from the low-temperature form which is like that of calcium chloride.

The hydrides become less stable and more reactive as the atomic weight of the metal increases: for example, the dissociation pressure of hydrogen above the hydride reaches one atmosphere at about 850°C for LiH, 425° for NaH, and at 390° for CsH. The ionic hydrides are all stable in an inert atmosphere at room temperature in ordinary light, but ultra-violet light causes dissociation.

Chemical reactivity increases from lithium to cesium, and from calcium to barium, with calcium hydride rather less reactive than lithium hydride. Generalizations are difficult as the reactivity depends on the state of the sample (compare magnesium hydride for an extreme example) and the hydrides of rubidium, cesium, strontium and barium have not been much studied. The reactivities with water are described as 'mild' for calcium hydride, 'vigorous' for strontium hydride, barium hydride and lithium hydride, 'more violent than that of sodium' for sodium hydride, with enough heat generated to ignite the hydrogen, and then as increasingly violent for the hydrides of potassium, rubidium, and cesium. The hydrides of the lighter elements do not react too quickly with dry air but rubidium and cesium hydrides ignite in air. All react with moist air, even lithium hydride igniting when finely divided. A similar reactivity is observed towards the halogens; thus sodium hydride will not react with bromine in the cold – as long as the hydride is not finely divided – while rubidium and cesium hydrides do so react. Calcium hydride is stable to chlorine at room temperature, as is strontium hydride although the latter reacts on slight heating.

The important reactions of these hydrides are in the preparative field, as reducing agents in the formation of metals and hydrides, and as condensing agents in organic chemistry. As these hydrides are formed by direct reaction, they provide the route by which hydrogen is introduced into the compounds of many of the less reactive metals and of the non-metals, either directly or via the formation of complex hydride ions such as $LiAlH_4$ or $NaBH_4$ which act as the direct agents. For these reactions, lithium, sodium, and calcium hydrides are by far the most important, although potassium hydride may be useful because of its greater reactivity. Thus [41] an alkyl arene reacts with a KH/BuLi mixture to metallate the sidechain which then reacts with an olefin with ring formation, whereas the corresponding sodium system gives mainly an extended side-chain with only a slight amount of ring closure.

Calcium Hydride. Calcium hydride is the least reactive of these hydrides and is therefore the most easily handled. It is the preferred reagent for reductions on an industrial scale and it has been used to prepare boron, titanium, vanadium, niobium and tantalum, among others. The advantage over other reduction methods is that the product calcium oxide, and unreacted calcium hydride, can simply be washed out from the reduced metal leaving it in a suitable powdered form for powder metallurgical processes. Calcium hydride is also used as a desiccant and as a hydrogen source, and its relatively easy handling properties are important here. One industrial application as a desiccant is in the drying of transformer oils, while it finds a valuable laboratory use as an analytical reagent for determining small amounts of water in organic solvents and for determining the water content of hydrated compounds. Among reports of its use in laboratory preparations are the formation of $Ca(BF_4)_2$ by its reaction with boron trifluoride [42], and the formation of diborane by its reaction with boron trichloride. All these reductions by calcium hydride require elevated temperatures. For example, the diborane reaction goes at 250°C, while the metal reductions are usually conducted at 600–1000°C. Calcium hydride may also be used, as is calcium metal, in the preparation of the alkali metals from their halides. The reaction is carried out at a temperature at which the alkali metal distills out of the reaction vessel. Reactions with metallic rubidium or cesium commonly use the metal generated, in the apparatus, in this way. Calcium hydride is also used as a condensing reagent in organic reactions in the same way as the alkali hydrides. It is much less useful, however, as an organic reducing agent than is sodium or lithium hydride.

Lithium Hydride. Lithium hydride, although it is the most expensive of these three hydrides, is important as a reducing agent because it is very slightly soluble in ethers [51] and similar organic solvents whereas the other ionic hydrides are quite insoluble in organic solvents. Thus lithium hydride, as with the lithium alkyls, is more covalent than the other alkali hydrides.

Lithium hydride may be used for both organic and inorganic reduction reactions, and it may also be used as a condensing agent in organic reactions, though here sodium hydride is equally effective and less expensive. The main use is in reactions of the type

$$n\ \mathrm{LiH} + \mathrm{MX}_n = \mathrm{MH}_n + n\ \mathrm{LiX}$$

between halides, and similar compounds of the elements, and lithium hydride. The reaction, with hydrolysable halides, is commonly carried out in dry ether at room temperature and provides an effective reduction system under mild conditions. The success of lithium hydride in this reaction, as compared with sodium hydride, for example, which is much less effective, results from its slight solubility in ether. Lithium hydride may be used for organic reductions under similar conditions.

Although these reactions of lithium hydride are important, they have been largely superseded by the use of lithium aluminium hydride which is a more effective reagent, mainly because its solubility in ethers is higher. Thus, an important use of lithium hydride is in the preparation of lithium aluminium hydride,

$$4\ \mathrm{LiH} + \mathrm{AlCl_3} = \mathrm{LiAlH_4} + 3\ \mathrm{LiCl}.$$

Examples of the use of $LiAlH_4$ are given in the following chapters, and many of the reactions given there can also be carried out with lithium hydride, though usually with lower yields.

Lithium hydride, in common with most of the other ionic hydrides, has been found to act as a catalyst or co-catalyst in a variety of polymerization reactions, especially those producing regular or crystalline polymers from olefins; see for example [43].

Sodium Hydride. Sodium hydride may be used for similar reduction reactions to those outlined above, but its particular application is as a condensing agent in organic chemistry. It is cheaper than lithium hydride, and a more moderate reagent than metallic sodium, (for example, it does not reduce double bonds at low temperatures), and so finds wide application. Out of many examples, its use in the acetoacetic ester synthesis illustrates some of its merits. Sodium hydride may be used instead of any particular sodium alcoholate in this synthesis so it has the advantage of being a universal reagent and it avoids the problem of preparing the alcoholate in a sufficiently pure form. In addition, sodium hydride reacts with the alcohol formed in the reaction and so drives the reaction to completion, avoiding the necessity for the final distillation.

As a reducing agent sodium hydride is also valuable, particularly at slightly higher temperatures. Thus, at temperatures in the region of 150°C, sodium hydride reduces a variety of esters and carbonyls to alcohols,

$$(\mathrm{C_6H_5})_2\mathrm{CO} + \mathrm{NaH} = (\mathrm{C_6H_5})_2\mathrm{CHOH}$$

Sodium hydride acts as a reducing agent in inorganic chemistry, but requires more vigorous conditions and is usually less useful. One successful example is the reduction of silicon tetrachloride to silane in 95% yield using a zinc compound as catalyst [44]. This reaction may well proceed by way of a zinc hydride intermediate.

In a different type of application, the use of a solution of sodium hydride in molten sodium hydroxide as a descaling agent has already been mentioned (Chapter 1). It has also been used in polymerization reactions (for example, [45]), and for the removal of sulphur from organic compounds [46].

2.4 Mixed Systems of Ionic Hydrides and Other Salts

There are a number of studies of mixed hydride-halide or hydride-oxide systems involving the alkali hydrides. These confirm the ionic nature of these hydrides. The most-studied hydride is LiH, and the systems LiH-LiF [61], LiH-Li_2O [13], LiH-LiCl [58, 62] and LiH-LiBr [62], have been studied. (Mixed metal dihydride-lithium hydride systems are discussed in section 2.6.)

As the cell constants of lithium fluoride and lithium hydride are very similar, 4·027Å and 4·083Å respectively, these two salts should be mutually soluble, by analogy with the alkali halides which are soluble in all proportions when the cell sizes are within five per cent of each other. Melting-point data for 0–100% lithium hydride in lithium fluoride show solid solutions in all proportions. There is a minimum in the melting point curve at 13·0 moles per cent LiF, and a temperature of 628°C, only seven degrees below the melting point of lithium hydride. X-ray studies on the solids, measured over a temperature range above 25°C, show the presence of two phases from 25° to 321°C. The lithium fluoride-rich phase contains appreciable amounts of lithium hydride, but the lithium hydride-rich phase holds only small amounts of the fluoride. These are the expected results as the lattice energy of lithium fluoride is higher than that of lithium hydride. This system differs from mixed alkali halide systems in this separation into two phases, probably as a result of the ready polarizability of the hydride ion introducing an extra energy term into the lattice energy. (It may be remarked that the largest difference between experimental and calculated lattice energies found among the alkali halides is that for LiI: this illustrates the analogy between iodide and hydride in their ease of polarizability.) The LiH-LiF system is rather similar to the AgCl-NaCl one, where there is a corresponding similarity in the lattice parameters but the room temperature mutual solubility is also low.

The LiH-Li_2O system shows similar effects, and is comparable with the LiF-Li_2O system. The eutectic is at 654·3°C and 9·2 moles per cent Li_2O. At the eutectic temperature, the solubility of Li_2O in solid LiH is slight (0·7 moles %). As the Li-O distance is very similar to the Li-H and Li-F ones while the lattice energy is higher, these are the expected results.

In the LiCl-LiH and LiBr-LiH systems, no solutions are formed in the solid state at all, although there is complete solubility in the liquid state for both systems. This effect is not unexpected and can be ascribed to the differences in sizes. In both systems, an eutectic is formed. The lithium chloride one is reported as giving an eutectic of 34·0 mole per cent lithium hydride melting at 495·6°C [58], or of 32·0 mole per cent lithium hydride melting at 450°C [62]. There is no obvious reason for this discrepancy although the former authors do report difficulty in defining the correct solid-liquid temperature on the lithium chloride-rich side of the composition range until they had modified their apparatus. The eutectic in the lithium bromide system contained 29 mole per cent lithium hydride and melted at 400°C. In the lithium chloride system the experimental data show a positive deviation from ideality which can be explained very well, on the lithium hydride-rich side, by postulating that the dimeric species Li_2Cl_2 exists in solution.

A quite different experiment [59] is interesting in the light it throws on the interaction between hydrogens in an ionic lattice. A small amount of hydrogen was incorporated in calcium fluoride by heating the salt to 900°C, in an atmosphere of hydrogen. The sample was then treated with X-rays for four hours and its electron spin resonance spectrum measured. By heating the sample at 88°C, it was found that the esr response decayed linearly and the kinetics corresponded to the annihilation of two bodies. Further irradiation restored the esr signal to its former intensity, and this signal was stable indefinitely at room temperature. The esr signal is typical of atomic hydrogen, and it is suggested that the resonating–non-resonating transition involves, not atom migration, but a change in electronic state. The resonating state has two (unpaired) 1*s* electrons which form a hydrogen molecule-like singlet state by interaction between two H atoms in neighbouring sites in the F sublattice of the crystal. Hydrogen atom migration is provisionally excluded because of the long-term stability at room temperature. This relatively long-range spin-spin interaction is reasonably accounted for by the high dielectric constant of CaF_2. In related experiments at the other limit of hydrogen content, electron nuclear double resonance of lithium or sodium hydrides containing small amounts of metal shows interaction between the nuclear spins of the 'metallic' and 'ionic' metal atoms [64]. This type of experiment is important as it is capable of giving an insight into the interactions in the hydrides, and an extension of such studies is likely.

In the alkaline earth mixed hydride-halide systems, new compounds MHX, are formed for M = Ca, Sr, Ba and X = Cl, Br, I [80]. For example, the phase diagram of the calcium hydride-calcium bromide system shows a simple two-eutectic system with CaHBr corresponding to a melting point at 690°C. All the mixed compounds have a tetragonal structure of the PbFCl type, and the crystals range from colourless to red-brown and black as the masses of the metal and halogen increase. Some properties are listed below (page 35). The compounds decompose in vacuum between 25 and 120 degrees below the melting point.

Although more work in the field of mixed hydride–other phase systems is to be expected, the work to date supports the analogy between hydride and the halide ions.

Compound	Crystal Structure (Å)		Density	H^- radius	Mpt. (°C)
	a	c	(g/cc)	(Å)	
CaHCl	3·843	6·847	3·53	1·23	700
SrHCl	4·092	6·947	3·52	1·41	840
BaHCl	4·399	7·188	4·15	1·40	850
CaHBr	3·850	7·859	3·41	1·29	690
SrHBr	4·246	7·276	4·24	1·35	835
BaHBr	4·555	7·403	4·69	1·33	860
CaHI	4·063	8·923	3·76	1·56	685
SrHI	4·362	8·433	4·43	1·70	710
BaHI	4·818	7·851	4·80	1·54	770

2.5 Hydrogen Solutions in Liquid Sodium

Interest is being shown in alkali metal/hydrogen systems of very low hydrogen content, at temperatures where the metal is liquid. These systems correspond in composition to the region AB at the extreme left of the typical isotherm of Figure 1, where no hydride phase exists and the hydrogen gas is in equilibrium with a solution of hydrogen in the metal. Although studies focused on this type of system are just beginning, some results are available for hydrogen solutions in liquid sodium [65]. The solubility of hydrogen is extremely low, but it rapidly increases with rising temperature:

Temperature (°C)	250	300	315	330	450
Wt. % hydrogen in solution	0·00042	0·0022	0·0052	0·0104	0·02

This direction of change is the opposite to that shown by gases dissolving in molecular liquids. Among the properties reported for these systems is the fact that oxygen and hydrogen can both dissolve in liquid sodium.

There is no evidence at present as to the nature of the species present in such hydrogen solutions, although the presence of H_2 or H^+ is held to be unlikely in view of the large excess of electrons present. The more likely species are H atoms, or H^-, though there is no necessity that the hydrogen should be associated with an integral number of electrons. These systems resemble those found for the transition metal-hydrogen systems in regions of low hydrogen content, where the hydrogen in the α phase is regarded as being in solution in the metal. The fact that the alkali metal systems can be studied as liquids, means that work on the two types of system should be complementary. The transition metal 'solutions' occur over a wider range of hydrogen content, up to twenty or thirty moles per cent for the vanadium Group metals and palladium.

2.6 Borderline Ionic Hydrides

(*a*) *Lanthanide II Dihydrides.* Of all the borderline cases, the hydrides EuH_2 and YbH_2 are the most nearly ionic. As will be discussed in the next chapter, the lanthanide elements form hydrides of type MH_2, which are typical metallic hydrides when the lanthanide shows only a III state in its normal chemistry. In these cases, the third valency electron contributes metal-metal bonding to the structure. However, europium and ytterbium have fairly stable II states where the third valency electron is used to fill the f shell giving the f^7 or f^{14} configurations respectively. Because of the large exchange energy in these half-filled or filled f shell configurations, the lower oxidation state is stabilized, and Eu II and Yb II behave similarly to the alkaline earth metal cations. Their dihydrides differ from all the other lanthanide dihydrides in showing no metallic properties, and they also have a quite different structure. The normal LnH_2 has a cubic fluorite structure while EuH_2 and YbH_2 have the same orthorhombic P_{nma} structure as the alkaline earth hydrides. In addition, the other lanthanides easily form hydrides with higher hydrogen content than MH_2, the heavier ones reaching MH_3. Europium will not form any hydride with a higher H content than EuH_2, while ytterbium, while it will form a higher hydride, does so less easily than the other heavy lanthanides. Structural parameters for EuH_2 and YbH_2 are given in Table 2.8.

Table 2.8. *Properties of Europium and Ytterbium Dihydrides*

	Structural Parameters P_{nma} cell constants in Å			M-H distance (A)	Volume Contraction compared with metal
EuH_2 [66]	$a = 6{\cdot}26_2$,	$b = 3{\cdot}79_9$,	$c = 7{\cdot}21_3$	2·45	
$EuD_{1\cdot95}$ [27]	$a = 6{\cdot}21$,	$b = 3{\cdot}77$,	$c = 7{\cdot}16$	2·43 (*a*)	12·5%
$YbD_{1\cdot93}$ [27]	$a = 5{\cdot}871$,	$b = 3{\cdot}561$,	$c = 6{\cdot}763$	2·30 (*a*)	13·5%

Note (*a*) The authors of [27] assumed the Zintl and Harder [16] structure of CaH_2. These M-H values have been recalculated on the basis of the corrected [25] hydrogen positions: compare Table 2·6, note (*c*).

These two hydrides further resemble the alkaline earth hydrides and differ from all other dihydrides of the lanthanides, and from the transition metal dihydrides, in being soluble in molten lithium hydride. Europium dihydride, like strontium and barium dihydrides which have similar sized unit cells, forms a new phase of inverse perovskite structure. Ytterbium dihydride and calcium dihydride, which are of smaller, and similar, cell size do not form the inverse perovskite phase but all form eutectics with marked depression of the lithium hydride freezing point. The properties of these MH_2/LiH systems are shown in Table 2.9, together with the results of other dihydrides tested.

It is noteworthy that samarium, which is the other lanthanide element to exhibit a II state, forms a dihydride with the fluorite structure and this does not dissolve in lithium hydride. These perovskite structures show very short Li-H distances compared with lithium hydride, where Li-H equals 2·04Å. This is a further effect of the deformable hydride ion which can fit the structure over a wider range than expected. It is noteworthy that inverse perovskite formation occurs in the LiF/BaF_2 system but not in the LiF/SrF_2 case. Here, the fluoride ion is less deformable than the hydride ion and enters a narrower range of structures. In all the perovskite phases, the metal-hydrogen distance in $LiMH_3$ is increased over that in MH_2 (compare Tables 2.6 and 8) reflecting the change in coordination number from seven in the simple hydride to twelve in the mixed hydride. These larger M-H distances in the strontium and barium perovskites are less than the distances to the two more distant hydrogens in the simple hydrides.

Table 2.9. *Systems of Lithium Hydride-Metal Dihydride*

Dihydride	Eutectic Temp (°C)	Eutectic % MH_2 (mole)	Depression of LiH F.Pt. (°)	Inverse Perovskite Phase ($LiMH_3$) Unit cell parameter, a_0	Li-H (*a*) Distances (Å)	M-H Distances (Å)	Density (g/cc)
BaH_2 [67] [12]	670·8	5·0	20·0	4·023	2·01	2·84	3·756
SrH_2 [67] [12]	644·6	11·2	46·2 (b)	3·833	1·92	2·71	2·877
EuH_2 [66] [12]	664·1	6·8	26·7	3·796	1·90	2·68	3·378
CaH_2 [13]	614·0	18·3	76·8	not formed		(*c*)	
YbH_2 [66] [12]	668·7	6·8	22·1	not formed		(*c*)	

$ScH_{2\cdot0}$, $LaH_{2\cdot2}$, $SmH_{2\cdot2}$ in 2–4 mole % had no effect (less than 0·7°) on the LiH freezing point [12]

TiH_x [13] x in ranges 0·89–0·94 or 1·6–1·75: no effect on freezing point
x in range 1·0–1·6: possible marginal effect with 2·4 ± 0·5° change, which might be due to reaction with residual oxygen

ZrH_x [13] x in range 1·80–1·90: no effect on freezing point.

Notes (*a*) The structure of the probable inverse perovskite phase $LiMH_3$ rests on X-ray data alone, and the Li and H positions are calculated from the metal atom ones. Neutron diffraction would be needed to determine these directly.
(*b*) $LiSrH_3$ has a congruent mpt of 745°C. Those of the other $LiMH_3$ phases were beyond the range of the apparatus.
(*c*) The M-H distances in the dihydrides are Ca-H = 2·32Å, Yb-H = 2·30Å.

While it is possible that these solubility effects may be a result of lattice energy differences (those calculated for TiH_2 and ZrH_2 are about 150, and that for LaH_2 about 60, kcal/mole higher than the alkaline earth dihydride values), Messer points out [12] that Li_2O also has a lattice energy about 140 kcal/mole above the dihydrides of calcium, strontium, and barium, and Li_2O is soluble in LiH ([13] and section 2.4). It is possible to give coherence to these results on the basis of the theory of residual metal-metal bonding in the transition metal hydrides, to be discussed in the next chapter. The process of solution in lithium hydride would involve the loss of this bond energy in the cases of TiH_2, ZrH_2, ScH_2 and the other LnH_2. It is therefore proposed by Messer [12], that solubility in molten lithium hydride provides a means of distinguishing ionic hydrides from those in which there is significant metal-metal bonding. This criterion certainly seems to hold for the dihydrides of europium and ytterbium, which are also distinguished from the other lanthanide dihydrides by their crystal structures and by their unwillingness to form any phase higher in hydrogen content than the dihydride. There is little other experimental evidence available for these two compounds, but, on present evidence, it is certainly justifiable to group EuH_2 and YbH_2 with the alkaline earth hydrides as saline compounds. The magnetic properties of EuH_2 have been measured down to 4·2°K [83]. Above 25°K, the hydride follows the Curie-Weiss law with a moment of 8·4 Bohr magnetons per europium, corresponding to the seven unpaired electrons of the Eu^{2+} ion. However, there is a Curie point at 24°K, below which the hydride is ferromagnetic. This ordering is ascribed to the ability of the *f* orbitals to interact, aided by the lattice contraction in the hydride compared with the metal. Thus, the hydride does show residual metallic properties, but only at a very low temperature – much lower than the temperature at which ordering effects take place in the metal. A similar effect is not observed in the lanthanide trihydrides which have been examined, such as GdH_3, TbH_3, and HoH_3. In these cases, all the metallic electrons are used up in forming H^- ions, but here the hydride is less dense than the metal and the longer metal-metal distance is presumed to be too great to permit interaction between metal *f* orbitals.

(*b*) *Lanthanide Trihydrides, LnH_3*. The lanthanide elements in the trivalent state form compounds, with the halogens for example, which are basically ionic. The trihydrides might also be expected to be ionic, with no electrons left to contribute any metallic bonding. However, it is not easy to form hydrides of composition LnH_3, and a continuous range of compositions between MH_2 and MH_3 is usually observed (see next chapter). Extreme conditions are needed to attain high hydrogen contents; for example, at 700°C and twenty atmospheres pressure, the lanthanum hydride reaches only the composition $LaH_{2\cdot5}$. It is thus found that information on the stoicheiometric, or near-stoicheiometric, MH_3, phases is slight. It appears that the hydrides become more ionic at higher hydrogen content, but metallic or at least semi-conductor and magnetic ordering properties, remain. The heavier lanthanides show a change in structure at high hydrogen contents (above 2·85H/M for gadolinium for example) from the cubic form of the MH_2 hydride to a hexagonal structure. In addition, the magnetic and conduction properties change: thus $LaH_{2\cdot7}$ is diamagnetic and has temperature dependent conductivity.

The lanthanide hydrides thus lose their metallic properties as the hydrogen content increases, but the changes are gradual, come at different compositions for different metals, and are difficult to observe as the formation of hydride phases with high hydrogen content demands work at high hydrogen pressures. The lanthanide trihydrides thus represent the limiting property range of the metallic type of hydride, and can be regarded as borderline between the ionic and metallic types.

The hydrides of the actinide elements all show metallic properties and are discussed, along with the lower lanthanide hydrides, in the next chapter.

(*c*) *Magnesium Hydride, MgH_2.* Magnesium hydride represents a different borderline, that between ionic and covalent bonding. In its general chemistry, magnesium forms ionic compounds with halogens, oxygen, nitrogen and similar elements, but, as there is a considerable charge density on the relatively small Mg^{2+} ion, polarization effects are important. In the related cases of beryllium and aluminium, neighbours to magnesium in the Periodic Table, the charge densities are even higher and these two elements form much more covalent type compounds. Thus, as the hydride ion is readily polarized, magnesium hydride is expected to be a borderline case, though probably on the more ionic side. It may be remarked here that the covalent hydrides in this region of the Periodic Table, have a strong tendency to form polymeric structures using electron-deficient hydrogen-bridged bonding. This clearly happens in the case of boron hydrides, and in $Be(BH_4)_2$, and is probably the case in BeH_2 and AlH_3 as we shall see. Thus, any covalent character in magnesium hydride would be reflected in the formation of bonding of this type.

Magnesium hydride has been prepared by three different routes:

$$(1)\ Et_2Mg \text{ or } EtMgI \xrightarrow{175-280°C} MgH_2 + C_2H_4 + \text{other products}$$

$$(2)\ 2\ LiAlH_4 + MgMe_2 \xrightarrow{\text{ether}} MgH_2$$

$$(3)\ Mg + H_2 \xrightarrow[\text{and temperature}]{\text{high pressure}} MgH_2$$

The pyrolysis of the Grignard reagent was the method used in the original report of magnesium hydride in 1912 [68], and this reaction and the pyrolysis of a dialkylmagnesium have been investigated by later workers [69, 70]. This method gives a very reactive form of the hydride which may inflame in air and reacts vigorously with water. The reaction begins at 175°C but is not complete below the temperature at which the hydride begins to decompose, and so does not yield a pure product.

The metathesis with lithium aluminium hydride [71] is a general route to hydrides, including lithium hydride for example, and gives a product which is relatively reactive and free from contaminants other than the ether used in the reaction. It is, however, impossible to remove the last ten per cent or so of this ether without decomposing the sample.

In contrast to the first two reactions, the third route leads to a product which is much less reactive. It is reported to be stable to laboratory air and reacts only slowly with water. Hydrolysis had proceeded to only about fifty per cent in twenty-four hours. A variety of conditions have been suggested: a pressure of 200 atmospheres at 570°C with MgI_2 as catalyst [72]; pressures up to 70 atmospheres and temperatures up to 450°C with no catalyst [24]; at 380–450°C and 100–200 atmospheres with iodine as catalyst and continuous grinding [74]. Other catalysts such as carbon tetrachloride and copper have also been tried. The best products reported from this type of reaction contained over 98% hydride, with magnesium metal and magnesium oxide as the usual impurities.

The product is 'very light grey' [24] as contrasted with the black products resulting from the pyrolysis preparations. The function of the catalysts is, in part, at least, to bring magnesium metal into reaction when it is protected by the surface hydride layer, and the formation of the subiodide, MgI, is suggested [74] as one possibility.

Some properties of magnesium hydride are collected in Table 2.10. The structure is the rutile one, as in the magnesium halides.

Table 2.10. *Properties of Magnesium Hydride*

ΔH_f° (kcal/mole)	Density g/cc	Unit Cell (Å)	Mg-H Distance (Å)	Lattice Energy (kcal/mole)	Decomposition Pressures (*b*) *A*	*B*	
$-17{\cdot}7 \pm 0{\cdot}7$ [75]	1·45	$a = 4{\cdot}517$ [24]	1·95 [24]	647 (*a*)	3857	9·78	[75]
$-17{\cdot}790$ [76]		$c = 3{\cdot}020_5$			3790	9·74	[24]
$-21{\cdot}71$ [77] (*c*)					(337–415°)		
$\Delta G_f^\circ = -8{\cdot}170$ kcal/mole: $\Delta S^\circ = -32{\cdot}3$ cal/degree/mole [76]							
For MgD_2 (cont. 10%H)							
$-17{\cdot}48$ [76]		$a = 4{\cdot}5026$ [26]	1·95 [26]				
		$c = 3{\cdot}0123$	(*d*)				
$\Delta G_f^\circ = -7{\cdot}800$ kcal/mole: $\Delta S_0 = -32{\cdot}5$ cal/degree/mole [76]							

Notes (*a*) Calculated from [32] with the average of the heats of formation given above.
(*b*) Constants for the equation, $\log p_{(mm)} = -A/T + B$.
(*c*) Measured from the heat of combustion of MgH_2 (made by method of [74] in O_2: other results calculated from the decomposition pressures.
(*d*) The MgD_2 structure was determined by both X-ray and neutron diffraction: the MgH_2 by X-ray diffraction only. [70] reports that the pyrophoric MgH_2 from the pyrolysis preparation (1) has the same rutile structure.

Values of the heat of formation are in disagreement, and earlier values were lower, which may reflect the difficulty of obtaining pure samples of the hydride: indeed, all the determinations were performed on acknowledgedly impure samples. It would seem that the dissociation pressure measurements are more seriously in doubt as the effect on the hydrogen pressure of the oxygen in the sample is unknown. The combustion analysis [77] probably suffers from less uncertainty as far as the reactions of impurities are concerned, and the supporting data on the heat of formation of MgO and H_2O are well-established [4, 79]. The heat of formation of MgH_2 is only about half that of any of the alkaline earth hydrides, and is similar to that of lithium hydride.

The structure of MgH_2 is clearly shown to be rutile from both X-ray and neutron diffraction determinations. The Mg-H distance corresponds to a hydride ion radius of 1·31Å, compared with 1·37Å in LiH and 1·23Å as the smallest value so far reported, that in $LiSrH_3$. The closest H-H distance in the crystal is one of 2·47Å and the others are all 2·76Å (compare 2·72Å in LiH). One very short, non-bonded, distance is a feature of the rutile structure. The lattice energy, which is an experimental one, is less than the calculated values of 667 or 672 kcal/mole [32].

The structural evidence thus does not exclude an ionic formulation for magnesium hydride, although the Mg-H distance is rather short and there is some uncertainty in the lattice energy figures. As the reactivity of magnesium hydride varies so startlingly with the physical form produced in the different preparations, no conclusion can really be drawn from the general chemistry. The massive hydride formed by direct combination seems to be rather less reactive than the alkaline earth hydrides, while the finely-divided material from the pyrolyses is more reactive than lithium hydride. A study of the general chemistry of magnesium hydride with a variety of reagents is reported [78], and seems to be largely as expected. Magnesium hydride in the inert form from the direct combination reacts rapidly with acids and strong oxidizing agents but more slowly with milder reagents like hydrogen peroxide or iodine. As chromic acid reacts rapidly with MgH_2 and not at all with metallic magnesium due to passivation, this is proposed as a useful reagent for determining the hydride content of hydrided magnesium.

One infra-red study of magnesium hydride in a KBr disc is reported [81]. A very broad band stretching from 900–1600 cm^{-1}, centred at 1160 cm^{-1}, was found which is reminiscent of the band in BeH_2 centred at 1758 cm^{-1} with a half-width of over three hundred wave numbers (see Chapter 4). Compare the absorption in a thin film of LiH which is centred around 600 cm^{-1} [73]. This band was ascribed to incipient bridge bonding in the hydride

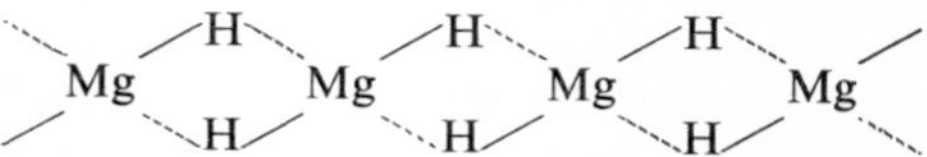

Equally well, such bridge bonding could be added to an ionic hydride formulation. It is noteworthy that magnesium hydride is much more stable than the hydrides of beryllium and aluminium which do seem to be bridge-bonded but, from the conditions of preparation at very high pressures, it is clearly less stable than the alkaline earth hydrides.

The compound HMgX, which may be regarded as the hydrogen parent Grignard reagent, has been prepared by the reaction of diborane on a Grignard solution, such as EtMgX, at −25°C [82]. The compounds HMgCl.2THF, $HMgCl.2Et_2O$, $HMgBr.2Et_2O$ or $HMgI.2Et_2O$ were isolated as colourless needles by appropriate choice of solvent and Grignard reagent. These compounds appear to be very similar in properties to the simple Grignard reagents and probably have related structures involving Mg-H bonds and perhaps Mg . . . H . . . Mg bridge bonding. Mixed alkyl hydrides, RMgH, are also known.

(*d*) *Other Possible Ionic Hydrides*. It is conceivable that CuH, ZnH_2, CdH_2, and AlH_3 could be ionic as these elements do form some ionic compounds.

However, the properties of these compounds place them well on the opposite side of the borderline. Aluminium hydride, like beryllium hydride, shows its closest resemblance to the hydrides of boron and appears to be a hydrogen-bridge polymer. The zinc and cadmium hydrides are also basically similar to these compounds and show no ionic properties. They, with CuH, are best regarded as borderline metallic-covalent hydrides. All these compounds are therefore discussed elsewhere; AlH_3, BeH_2, ZnH_2, and CdH_2 in Chapter 4, and CuH in Chapter 3.

Two other elements which commonly form ionic compounds are thallium and lead, in the I and II states respectively. The only reports of hydrides of these compounds are of extremely unstable species corresponding to the higher oxidation states, and of $PbH_{0\cdot19}$. It is possible that TlH or PbH_2 might be formed under appropriate conditions: for example, by hydriding a dispersion or solution of the metal in an alkali or alkaline earth hydride respectively.

REFERENCES

[1] S. R. GUNN and L. G. GREEN, *J. Amer. Chem. Soc.*, 1958, **80**, 4782.

[2] C. E. MESSER, L. G. FASOLINO, and C. E. THALMAYER, *J. Amer. Chem. Soc.*, 1955, **77**, 4526.

[3] *Some Physical Properties of the Hydrides*, Compiled by R. E. Elson, H. C. Hornig, W. L. Jolly, J. W. Kury, W. J. Ramsey and A. Zalkin, University of California, UCRL–4519 (Revised) 1956. (Based mainly on [4]).

[4] National Bureau of Standards Circular 500. *Selected Values of Chemical Thermodynamic Properties*. Washington, D.C., 1952.

[5] C. C. ADDISON, R. J. PULHAM, and R. J. ROY, *J. Chem. Soc.*, 1964, 4895.

[6] A. HÉROLD, *Comptes rendus*. 1949, **228**, 686; *Ann. chim.*, 1951, **6**, 536.

[7] W. M. LATIMER, *The Oxidation States of the Elements and their Potentials in Aqueous Solution*, Prentice-Hall, (2nd. Edition) 1952.

[8] C. E. MESSER, H. HOMONOFF, R. F. NICKERSON, and T. R. P. GIBBS, Jr., NYO–3955, 1953 (TIS, Oak Ridge): Quoted in [3].

[9] M. B. SMITH and G. E. BASS, Jr., *J. Chem. and Eng. Data*, 1963, **8**, 342.

[10] L. HACKSPILL and A. BOROCCO, *Bull. Soc. chim. France*, 1939, **6**, 91.

[11] D. T. HURD, *An Introduction to the Chemistry of the Hydrides*, John Wiley, N.Y., Chapman and Hall, London, 1952.

[12] C. E. MESSER and I. S. LEVY, *Inorg. Chem.*, 1964, **4**, 543.

[13] C. E. MESSER, J. MELLOR, J. A. KROL, and I. S. LEVY, *J. Chem. and Eng. Data*, 1961, **6**, 328.

[14] C. E. JOHNSON, S. E. WOOD, and C. E. CROUTHAMEL, *Inorg. Chem.*, 1964, **3**, 1487.

[15] A. ZALKIN and V. SILVEIRA, Unpublished Observations, Quoted in [1].

[16] E. ZINTL and A. HARDER, *Zeit. phys. Chem.*, 1931, **B14**, 265; 1935, **B28**, 478; *Zeit. Elektrochem.*, 1935, **41**, 33.

[17] G. HERZBERG, *Molecular Spectra and Molecular Structure. Diatomic Molecules*. van Nostrand 2nd edition, 1950.

[18] T. C. WADDINGTON, *Lattice Energies* in *Advances in Inorganic Chemistry and Radiochemistry*. Edited by H. J. Emeleus and A. G. Sharpe (Academic Press) 1959, **1**, 157.

[19] E. STARITSKY and D. J. WALKER, *Anal. Chem.*, 1955, **28**, 1055.

[20] M. D. BANUS, J. J. MCSHARRY, and E. A. SULLIVAN, *J. Amer. Chem, Soc.*, 1955, **77**, 2007.

[21] A. HÉROLD, *Comptes rendus*, 1947, **224**, 1826; **225**, 249.
[22] C. B. HURD and G. A. MOORE, *J. Amer. Chem.* Soc., 1935, **57**, 332.
[23] F. K. HEUMANN and N. C. SALMON, *The Lithium Hydride, Deuteride, and Tritide systems*, KAPL–1667, 1956; *Nucl. Sci. Abstr.*, 1957, **11**, 4811.
[24] F. H. ELLINGER, C. R. HOLLEY, Jr., B. B. MCINTEER, D. PAVONE, R. M. POTTER, E. STARITZSKY, and W. H. ZACHARIASEN, *J. Amer. Chem. Soc.*, 1955, **77** 2647.
[25] J. BERGSMA and B. O. LOOPSTRA, *Acta Cryst.*, 1962, **15**, 92.
[26] W. H. ZACHARIASEN, C. E. HOLLEY, and J. F. STAMPFER, *Acta. Cryst.*, 1963, **16**, 352.
[27] W. L. KORST and J. C. WARF, *Acta Cryst.*, 1956, **9**, 453.
[28] G. NAUD, J. SANNIER, and P. VALLET, *Comptes rendus*, 1963, **257**, 1276.
[29] W. D. TREADWELL and J. STITCHER, *Helv. Chim. Acta.* 1953, **36**, 1820.
[30] W. A. KLEMPERER and J. L. MARGRAVE, *J. Chem. Phys.*, 1952, **20**, 527.
[31] Tables of Interatomic Distances and Configurations in Molecules and Ions, Chemical Society Special Publication 11, 1958.
[32] T. R. P. GIBB, Jr., *Primary Solid Hydrides* in *Progress in Inorganic Chemistry*. Edited by F. A. Cotton, Interscience 1962, **3**, 315.
[33] C. E. MESSER, *Saline Hydrides* in *Preparative Inorganic Reactions*, Edited by W. L. Jolly, Interscience, 1964, **1**, 203.
[34] *Inorganic Syntheses*, Volume **5**, Edited by T. Moeller, G. W. Mattson and T. P. Whaley, 1957, 10.
[35] See C. C. ADDISON, R. J. PULHAM, and M. G. BARKER, *J. Chem. Soc.*, 1965, in press.
[36] V. I. MIKHEEVA and M. M. SHRABKINA, *Zhur. neorg. Khim.*, 1962, **7**, 463–8.
[37] T. R. P. GIBB, Jr., U.S. Pats. 2,702,281, 1955.
[38] P. P. ALEXANDER, U.S. Pats. 2,702,234 and 2,702,740, 1955.
[39] M. C. R. SYMONS, *Quarterly Review*, 1960, **14**, 62.
[40] C. G. SHULL, E. O. WOLLAN, G. A. MORTON, and W. L. DAVIDSON, *Phys. Rev.*, 1948, **73**, 842.
[41] G. G. EBERHARDT, *J. Org. Chem.*, 1964, **29**, 643.
[42] R. DE PAPE, *Ann. Chim.* (*France*), 1963, **8**, 185.
[43] Brit. Pat. 921,806, (1963): Fr. Pat. 1,322,041 (1963): E. F. COX and F. HOSTETTLER, U.S. Pat. 3,021,309 and 3,021,317 (1962).
[44] E. I. DU PONT DE NEMOURS, Brit. Pat. 909,950 (1962).
[45] H. W. COONER and N. H. SHEARER, U.S. Pat., 3,058,969 (1962).
[46] K. ACHENBACH, K. OSTERLOH, and W. ROETHE, Ger. Pat. 1.148,679 (1962).
[47] R. W. CURTIS and P. CHIOTTI, *J. Chem. Phys.*, 1963, **67**, 1061.
[48] D. T. PETERSON and V. G. FATTORE, *J. Phys. Chem.*, 1961, **65**, 2062.
[49] D. T. PETERSON and R. P. COLBURN, *USAEC Report IS*–613 (1963); *Nucl. Sci. Abstr.*, 1963, **17**, 40771.
[50] D. T. PETERSON and M. INDIG, *J. Amer. Chem. Soc.*, 1960, **82**, 5645.
[51] D. A. BRANDRETH and M. C. MOLSTAND, *J. Chem. and Eng. Data*, 1962, **7**, 449.
[52] R. S. CALDER, W. COCHRAN, D. GRIFFITHS, and R. D. LOWDE, *J. Phys. and Chem. Solids*, 1962, **23**, 621.
[53] V. G. KUZNETSOV and M. M. SHKRABKINA, *Zhur. Strukt. Khim.*, 1962, **3**, 553.
[54] Z. G. PINSKEV and R. N. KURDYUMOVA, *Kristallografiya*, 1958, **3**, 501.
[55] F. JENČ, *Coll. Czech. Chem. Comm.*, 1963, **28**, 2052: R. R. GETTY and J. C. POLANYI, *Trans. Faraday Soc.*, 1961, **57**, 2099: D. C. JAIN and P. SAH, *J. Chem. Phys.*, 1963, **38**, 1553.
[56] R. V. R. WIEDERKEHN, *J. Chem. Phys.*, 1962, **37**, 1192; 2238: I. G. CSIZMADAI, B. T. SUTCLIFFE, and M. P. BARNETT, *Canad. J. Chem.*, 1964, **42**, 1645.
[57] E. E. SWAIN and F. K. HEUMANN, KAPL–1067, (1954), *Nucl. Sci. Abstr.*, 1955, **9**, 5598. (Quoted in [33]).
[58] C. E. JOHNSON, S. E. WOOD and C. E. CROUTHAMEL, *Inorg. Chem.*, 1964, **3**, 1487.

[59] H. A. ATWATER, *J. Chem. Phys.*, 1964, **40**, 606: also J. L. HALL and R. T. SCHUMACHER, *Phys., Rev.*, 1962, **127**, 1892.
[60] V. I. MIKHEEVA and M. M. SHKRABKINA, *Doklady Akad. Nauk. SSSR.*, 1962, **143**, 1362.
[61] C. E. MESSER and J. MELLOR, *J. Phys. Chem.*, 1960, **64**, 503.
[62] P. EHRLICH and W. DEISSMAN, *Naturwiss.*, 1964, **51**, 135.
[63] R. T. SCHUMACHER and J. L. HALL, *Phys., Rev.*, 1962, **125**, 428. (Cf. 59 above).
[64] C. RYTER, *Phys. Letters*, 1963, **4**, 69: W. T. DOYLE and W. L. WILLIAMS, *Phys. Review Letters*, 1961, **6**, 537.
[65] C. C. ADDISON, R. J. PULHAM, and R. J. ROY, *J. Chem. Soc.*, 1965, 116: D. D. WILLIAMS, J. A. GRAND, and R. R. MILLER, *J. Chem. Phys.*, 1957, **61**, 379: see also reference [28] above: D. W. MCCLURE, *Diss. Abstracts*, 1964, **24**, 4426.
[66] C. E. MESSER and K. HARDCASTLE, *Inorg. Chem.*, 1964, **3**, 1327.
[67] C. E. MESSER, J. C. EASTMAN, R. G. MERS, and A. J. MAELAND, *Inorg. Chem.*, 1964, **3**, 776.
[68] P. JOLIBOIS, *Comptes rendus*, 1912, **155**, 353.
[69] E. WIBERG and R. BAUER, *Zeit. Naturf.*, 1950, **5b**, 396; *Angew. Chem.*, 1950, **62**, 448.
[70] W. FREUNDLICH and B. CLAUDEL, *Bull. Soc. chim. France*, 1956, 967.
[71] G. D. BARBARAS, C. DILLARD, A. E. FINHOLT, T. WARTIK, K. E. WILZBACH, and H. I. SCHLESINGER, *J. Amer. Chem. Soc.*, 1951, **73**, 4585.
[72] E. WIBERG, H. GOELTZER, and R. BAUER, *Zeit. Naturf.*, 1951, **6b**, 394.
[73] D. J. MONTGOMERY and K. F. YEUNG, *J. Chem. Phys.*, 1962, **37**, 1059.
[74] T. N. DYMOVA, Z. K. STERLYADKINA, and V. G. SAFRONOV, *Russian J. Inorg. Chem.*, 1961, **6**, 389 (corresponding to *Zhur. neorg. Khim.*, 1961, 763).
[76] J. E. STAMPFER, C. E. HOLLEY, and F. J. SUTTLE, *J. Amer. Chem. Soc.*, 1960, **82**, 3504.
[77] V. I. PEPEKIN, T. N. DYMOVA, YU. A. LEBEDEV and A. YA. APIN, *Russ. J. Phys. Chem.*, (*Zhur. phys. Khim*) 1964, **38**, 562.
[78] T. N. DYMOVA, Z. K. STERLYADKINA, and N. G. ELISEEVA, *Russ. J. Inorg. Chem.*, 1961, **6**, 392. (corresponding to *Zhur. neorg. Khim.*, 1961, 768).
[79] I.U.P.A.C. Symposium on Thermodynamics and Thermochemistry, Lund, 1963, Butterworth, London, 1964. Lecture of H. A. Skinner.
[80] P. EHRLICH and H. GÖRTZ, *Zeit. an Chem.*, 1956, **288**, 148: P. EHRLICH and H. KULKE, *ibid*, 156: P. EHRLICH, B. ALT, and L. GENTSCH, *ibid*, 1956, **283**, 58.
[82] E. WIBERG and P. STREVEL, *Annalen*, 1957, **607**, 9.
[83] R. ZANOWICK and W. E. WALLACE, *Phys. Rev.*, 1962, **126**, 537: see also J. CALLOWAY, *Nuova Cimento*, 1962, **26**, 626.
[84] T. C. JAMES, W. G. NORRIS, and W. KLEMPERER, *J. Chem. Phys.*, 1960, **32**, 728.

CHAPTER 3

Transition Metal Hydrides

3.1 Theories of Bonding in Transition Metal Hydrides

In this chapter the hydrides of the transition and inner transition elements – the actinides and lanthanides – will be discussed. It is in this region of the Periodic Table that the nature of the bonding in the metal hydrides is most uncertain. The hydrides of the alkali and alkaline earth metals are ionic to a good degree of approximation, and the covalent nature of the hydrides of the *p* elements of the Main Groups is equally clear, but the nature of the transition element hydrides is not yet clear, and a number of theoretical descriptions are to be found. The situation is further confused as the transition metals are capable of adsorbing considerable quantities of hydrogen and, as a result, a number of hydrides have been reported which are spurious.

The transition metal hydrides have metallic properties and are commonly obtained as powders or as brittle solids which are dark and metallic in appearance, and have conductivities and magnetic properties typical of metals. In addition, most preparations give hydrides which are non-stoicheiometric, and the ease and reproducibility of the hydride preparation depends sensitively on the purity of the metal. When it is recollected that many of the transition, lanthanide and actinide elements were mere chemical curiosities before the war, and that many of the earlier preparations were carried out with impure samples, it is no surprise that the early results were difficult to interpret. The first tentative theory of the transition metal hydrides is implied in their classification, along with carbides, nitrides, borides, and other compounds of small atoms, as 'interstitial'. It was thought that the small atoms formed interstitial compounds by entering, as single atoms, the interstices in the metal lattice: the small hydrogen would be expected to enter the tetrahedral sites while the other, larger, interstitial atoms were to be found in the octahedral sites in the (usually) close-packed metal structure. This theory seemed to imply, in its simplest form at least, that there was no particular bonding interaction between the interstitial atoms and the metal. Most older papers are written in these terms.

This approach, in its simple form, soon became untenable. Clearly the description of the bonding was unsatisfactory, but the most important evidence which undermined it arose from structural investigations. It soon became apparent that most hydrides did not have their metal atoms in the same positions as in the parent metal (although a number of hydride structures had metal atom positions corresponding to a high temperature form of the metal). The position is summarized in Table 3.1. Although some expansion of the metal lattice was explicable on the 'interstitial compound' theory, a change of structure was not. Arguments that a high temperature structure, formed during vigorous preparation conditions, was frozen in at lower temperatures were confuted as it became clear that most hydrides could be prepared under mild conditions if the metal and hydrogen were in a sufficiently high state of purity. The idea of hydrogen atoms in the metal lattice may be developed on a more rigorous basis and used to account for the 'solution' or α regions of the metal-hydrogen composition diagrams, where the hydrogen is present in the lattice of the metal. The approach seems less satisfactory for the discussion of the distinct hydride phases.

Table 3.1. *Structures of the Metals and their Hydrides*

Metals		Hydrides (idealized formulae)			
Sc	hcp	ScH_2	ccp		
Y	hcp	YH_2	ccp	YH_3	hcp
La	hcp with double c axis (ccp)	LaH_2	ccp	LaH_2	ccp
Ce	ccp (hcp)	CeH_2	ccp	CeH_3	ccp
Pr, Nd	hcp with double c axis	MH_2	ccp	MH_3	ccp
Sm	rhombohedral	SmH_2	ccp	SmH_3	hcp
Eu	bcc	EuH_2	orthorhombic		
Gd, Tb, Dy, Ho, Er, Tm, Lu	hcp	MH_2	ccp	MH_3	hcp
Yb	ccp	YbH_2	orthorhombic	YbH_3	ccp
Ac	ccp	AcH_2	ccp		
Th	ccp (bcc)	ThH_2	ccp	Th_4H_{15}	bcc
Pa	bct	PaH_3	β-W		
U	complex	UH_3	β-W		
Np, Pu		MH_2	ccp	MH_3	hcp
Ti, Zr, Hf	hcp (bcc)	MH_2	ccp		
V, Nb, Ta	bcc	MH	bcc		
Cr	bcc	CrH	hcp	CrH_2	bcc
Pd	ccp	PdH	ccp		

hcp = hexagonal close packed, ccp = cubic close packed, bcc = body-centred cubic, bct = body-centred tetragonal. These designations apply to the positions of the metal atoms in the hydrides; the actual structures may be somewhat expanded from the close packed form.

At present, two quite different theories are used to discuss the metal hydrides. In one, the hydrogen is regarded as losing its electron to the conduction band of the metal structure and as being present in the lattice as H^+. This theory describes the transition metal hydrides as *metallic* or as *alloys*. The alternative theory considers that the hydrogen atom acquires an electron from the conduction band and is present as H^-. The depleted conduction band remains to give residual metallic bonding in the hydride, and to account for the metallic properties. This theory describes the hydrides as *ionic* or *hydridic*. It is possible that covalent bonding could be introduced into either theory, although few attempts have been made to do so.

The metallic theory of hydrogen in hydrides has been formulated by Ubbelohde [1] and Isenberg [2] and has been used in the interpretation of a number of recent studies, particularly in nuclear magnetic resonance investigations. The theory obviously explains the overt metallic properties of the hydrides, and a number of additional items of experimental evidence are adduced in its favour and discussed below. It is not, of course, implied that the bare proton, with its enormous positive charge density, exists in the metallic lattice (except as an excited state) but that the hydrogens on the average donate electrons and acquire a fractional positive charge or, in other words, there is a shift of electron density towards the metal. It is worth remarking at this stage that the theory was first formulated to deal with palladium hydride.

The specific experimental results quoted in favour of the metallic hydrogen theory are listed:

(*i*) In a number of hydrides, the hydrogen is very mobile, and has only a small activation energy for diffusion. This mobility is ascribed to the small size of H^+, which allows it to move freely within the metal lattice and means that it crosses the lowest potential barriers between two metal ions (compare reference 3).

(*ii*) The magnetic susceptibility of palladium falls as hydrogen is added, and the system becomes diamagnetic at a composition of about $PdH_{0\cdot 6}$. This is ascribed to the filling of the palladium conduction band, with ultimate pairing of all the valency electrons.

(*iii*) If a potential is applied across a filament of hydrided metal, such as palladium, titanium, or tantalum, the hydrogen migrates towards the cathode. Further studies showed this to be a genuine bulk effect and not a surface phenomenon [4].

The main arguments in favour of the ionic theory, with anionic hydrogen, have been put by Gibb in a recent review [5], and later work is said not to have altered the main conclusions [6]. This review gives a very clear and thorough account of the solid hydrides and treats the bonding theories in considerable detail. It is possible here only to summarize the main points and the interested reader must be referred to [5] for a more detailed account. See also [186] and Libowitz' review [187].

The ionic theory accounts for the metallic properties of the hydrides as due to residual metallic bonding by those valency electrons which remain after the hydrogen has ionized. In a hydride MH_n, formed by a metal with V valency electrons (V is usually taken as the Group number of the metal in the Periodic Table), there will be $(V - n)$ metallic electrons and nH^- ions. Thus, the ionic hydrides are simply those where $V = n$, and the theory gives a natural explanation for the gradual disappearance of metallic properties where metals such as the lanthanides are hydrided towards the composition MH_V.

The indications of the presence of H^+ listed above are accounted for in the following way [5], as an alternative to postulating H^+.

(*i*) The mobility of the hydrogen. The experimental evidence shows that hydrogen is very mobile in palladium hydride, in hydrides of the vanadium Group of elements with hydrogen contents up to about $MH_{0\cdot5}$, and in other hydrides of low hydrogen content. The evidence derives partly from nuclear magnetic resonance experiments. For example, [7] tantalum hydrides of compositions TaH_x ($x = 0{\cdot}669, 0{\cdot}408, 0{\cdot}245$, and $0{\cdot}11$) had a very narrow proton resonance line width, of less than one gauss, corresponding to rapid internal motion of the hydrogen. In contrast, wide lines were observed for ionic hydrides where the hydrogen is immobile (line widths of 6·3 gauss for NaH and 9·9 gauss for CaH_2 under the same experimental conditions). However, titanium hydride samples TiH_x ($x = 1{\cdot}57, 0{\cdot}72$, or $0{\cdot}38$) also showed wide lines, of the order of twelve gauss. Thus the two metallic hydrides showed quite different properties at room temperature, and free motion of the proton does not occur in some, at least, of the metallic hydrides. Later studies [8] showed that there was a sharp decrease in line width at about 50°C in the titanium hydrides, and calculations [3], based on the assumption that the migrating species was the proton, gave good agreement with the experimental value for the activation energy for movement and its variation with temperature and hydrogen content. The first point is therefore that all the transition metal hydrides are not alike in the mobility of the hydrogen, and the 'proton content' may vary with temperature–assuming, as these authors do [3], that a hydrogen atom with a negative charge, or partial charge, is excluded by its size from being the mobile species.

While these results fit very well with the theory that the proton is present in the metal hydrides, Gibb has pointed out [5] that this need not mean that the proton is the major or only form of the hydrogen. The H^+ species is an excited state, both of H and of H^-, and its unique properties of small size and mobility lead to its dominating the observations, even if it were present in only minute amount in the 'tail' of a Boltzmann distribution of excited forms of H^-. The decrease in radius by a factor of 10^5, or even the decrease in size of a partially positively charged hydrogen ion, make the proton so vastly different from all other chemical species that very small proportions would suffice to provide unusual properties.

(*ii*) The magnetic properties of hydrided palladium are misleading as later experiments showed that, if hydrogen is carefully removed from hydrided palladium at low temperatures, an expanded lattice of palladium remains which is diamagnetic. Thus the diamagnetism is a result of the increased metal-metal distance in the hydride and gives no information on the population of the conduction bands.

(*iii*) The migration of hydrogen in a hydride under a potential field, although a genuine phenomenon, does not admit of simple interpretation in terms of the hydrogen charge, as conduction and migration mechanisms in a defect solid are by no means simple or due only to one cause. The migration of hydrogen towards the cathode, and towards the anode, has been observed in different solid hydrides, and a similar phenomenon is observed in metal alloys. Indeed, in LiCu, both metals migrate to the cathode. The current transport depends not only on the mobility of the carriers but also on their interaction with the conduction electrons. In addition, especially in the non-stoicheiometric hydrides, the migration of a particular species may simply be a result of the migration of vacancies in the opposite direction in an electron-deficient conduction mechanism. Thus, although the phenomenon is clear, the interpretation is not.

In addition, even if the hydrogen moves as H^+, the same argument applies as in the case of hydrogen diffusion. Because of the unique nature of the proton, a small proportion of hydrogen in an excited state may suffice to explain the transport under an applied field.

In summary, there is a certain amount of evidence in favour of the existence of H^+ in metal hydrides, but the interpretation of much of it is difficult. The much more substantial agreement between calculations on mobility which assume the presence of H^+ and the experimental results confirms the usefulness of the 'alloy' theory but need not imply the existence of H^+ as a major constituent in the solid.

Among the evidence in favour of the alternative, ionic, theory with H^- and residual metal-metal bonding may be listed the following points:

(*i*) Calculations of metal-hydrogen distances show that the distance calculated from the cation radius and the radius of the H^- ion (Table 3.2) with

Table 3.2. *Metal–Hydrogen Distances in Hydrides*

Hydride	Calculated Distances (Å) from reference [9]			Experimental Distances (Å) from reference [9]
ScH_2	Sc^{3+}	1·98	(8:4)	—
YH_2	Y^{3+}	2·18	(8:4)	—
TiH	Ti^{2+}	2·20	6:6	2·20
TiH_2	Ti^{4+}	1·90	8:4	1·92
ZrH	Zr^{2+}	2·32	6:6	2·39
ZrH_2	Zr^{4+}	2·07	ca8:ca4	2·07
$VH_{<1}$	V^{5+}	1·70	ca4:ca4	1·68
$NbH_{<1}$	Nb^{5+}	1·78	ca4:ca4	1·72
CrH	Cr^{6+}	1·63	4:4	1·67
CuH	Cu^{2+}	1·72	4:4	1·73
LaH_2	La^{3+}	2·41	8:4	2·45
ThH_2	Th^{3+}	2·38	8:4	2·41
UH_3	U^{4+}	2·34	12:4	2·32
MgH_2	Mg^{2+}	2·05	6:3	1·95
CaH_2	Ca^{2+}	2·34		2·35 (mean)

Calculated values from sum of octahedral radii (for cations shown) with corrections for other co-ordination numbers.

suitable correction for co-ordination number agrees well with the measured distances for both the ionic hydrides and the metal hydrides. It should be noted that these calculations use a value of 1·3 Å for the radius of the hydride ion, H^-, similar to the values found for the alkali hydrides. A number of earlier authors have used the calculated value for the free hydride ion, 2·08 Å, and concluded that H^- was sterically incompatible with measured M-H distances. The marked compressibility of the hydride ion has already been noted, and use of the free ion value is quite misleading. Clearly, this type of result does not prove anything about the bonding (for example, the sum of the tabulated *covalent* radii give an equally good fit to the experimental data for many hydrides) but it does show that the postulate of ionic hydrides is not incompatible with the data.

(*ii*) In a rather similar fashion, calculations of the lattice energies of the metal hydrides by Gibb show a strong correlation with experimental results, and provide similar evidence that the theory is compatible with the observations. Gibb [5, 31] calculates the lattice energy, on the basis of an ionic solid, adds an additional energy term for the residual metal-metal bonding, and corrections for crystal field stabilization energy where appropriate (although here a value of the crystal field constant, $10Dq$, similar to that of fluoride was used, while results on hydride complexes suggest that a value similar to that of cyanide may be more appropriate, see Chapter 5) and this value is compared with the sum of the endothermic terms of the Born cycle (compare section 2.1). The calculation of the metal-metal bonding contribution allows for the use of n of the V valency electrons to form hydride anions, in the hydride MH_n, and calculates the bonding due to the remaining $(V - n)$ electrons at the increased metal-metal distance in the hydride. The results of the calculation are tabulated overleaf; the hydride is predicted to exist if the various bonding contributions exceed the endothermic terms.

It will be seen that the predictions are borne out remarkably well, and many of the exceptions can be explained. Thus, the metallic bonding contribution would just stabilize monohydrides of the alkaline earths but these are not observed because of the greater heat of formation of the dihydrides (Waddington [32] has calculated that the alkaline earth monohalides would form exothermically). The existence of non-stoicheiometric hydrides, like $PdH_{0\cdot 6}$, is not considered in these calculations, and configurational entropy may be an important factor in their stabilization as discussed in the next section.

These calculations were carried out on a simple basis and are not claimed [5] to be anything other than general estimates, although attempts to refine them were not successful. However, their success in qualitative prediction of the existence of metal hydrides is high enough to show, again, that the ionic theory is not incompatible with the facts.

(*iii*) Further support for the anionic hydrogen formulation comes from the close similarity between the hydrides and the halides in structure, and the fact that the hydride structures can be predicted satisfactorily from the radius ratio rules. Furthermore, the ionic formulation with residual metal-metal bonding has been applied successfully to a number of lower halides and oxides of the transition elements (see [10] for a recent example).

(*iv*) In a number of cases, hydrogen and oxygen co-exist in metallic hydrides [11]–though not in palladium hydride. This would seem unlikely if the hydrogen was protonic or atomic, but is reasonable for H^- and O^{2-}, or for species with fractional negative charges.

In summary, there is not, at present, any generally accepted theoretical description of the metallic hydrides. The two theories outlined above, with protonic or hydridic hydrogen, are both in current use, and both have been successfully applied to explain and predict various experimental results. It seems likely that this situation may well continue for some time. Furthermore, the two descriptions are not as dissimilar as would appear at first sight. As was seen in the last chapter even in the alkali hydrides a full negative charge is not transferred to the hydrogen, so that the metallic hydrides would have only a fractional negative charge on hydrogen on the ionic model. Equally, on the metallic model, the bare proton would not exist in the metallic lattice, except as a transient, excited state, and the description reduces to having the hydrogen with a fractional positive charge. To some extent, the two theories are reconciled by Gibb's postulate that H^+ occurs as an excited state of H^-, in sufficient amount to account for the mobility of the hydrogen in the hydrides, while the overall structural features of the hydrides are governed by the size and thermodynamic properties of H^-. This version of the anionic description is particularly useful as it accounts neatly for the gradual transition from metallic to ionic (or at least, semi-metallic) properties observed to the left of the transition elements. In particular, the lanthanide hydrides in the composition range between LnH_2 and LnH_3 show a steady decrease in metallic properties. Conductivities fall by a factor of 10^5–10^6 (from values similar to those of metals to values typical of semi-conductors), and at the same time the magnetic susceptibility decreases and the hydrides become diamagnetic, at some point in the composition range $LnH_{2 \cdot 5}$ to $LnH_{3 \cdot 0}$. All these changes are predicted by the ionic theory since the electrons forming the metallic conduction bands become used up by H^- formation as the hydrogen content increases.

Calculations based on the ionic theory give endothermic heats of formation for hydrides towards the middle of the transition series. The theory thus accounts for the disappearance of metallic hydrides to the right of the transition series (except for palladium). As the heats of formation of hydrides of molybdenum and the Group VIII elements are approximately zero, this might be used to explain their adsorbing power for hydrogen and their catalytic function in hydrogenations.

The theories discussed so far have taken no account of covalent interactions in the hydrides. These undoubtedly come into play for the hydrides of the *p* block metals, and are important in copper hydride and the zinc Group hydrides. Samsonov [12] argues that covalent character would appear quite early in the transition block, possibly in Group V and certainly for molybdenum and

Table 3.3. *Prediction of the Existence of Metal Hydrides from Lattice Energy Calculations*

(All the predictions are taken from reference [5]).

Monohydrides, MH			Dihydrides, MH_2			Trihydrides, MH_3		
	Prediction	Found		Prediction	Found		Prediction	Found
LiH	formed	stable	BeH_2	not	unstable	AlH_3	formed	stable?
NaH	formed	stable	MgH_2	formed	stable	YH_3	formed	stable
KH	formed	stable	CaH_2	formed	stable	LaH_3	formed	stable
RbH	formed	stable	SrH_2	formed	stable	ScH_3	formed?	
CsH	formed	stable	BaH_2	formed	stable			
BeH, MgH	not	no	LiH_2 to CsH_2	not	no			
CaH, SrH, BaH	just stable by metal bonding contribution	no	RaH_2	formed	no study reported			
ScH	borderline	no?	ScH_2	formed	stable			
YH	not	no	YH_2	formed	stable			
LaH	not	no	LaH_2	formed	stable			
TiH	borderline		TiH_2	formed	stable			
VH	not		VH_2	formed?	$VH_{1 \cdot 6}$ prepared at high pressures			
CrH	borderline		CrH_2	borderline	?			
MnH, FeH, CoH, NiH, ZnH	not NiH??	no	MnH_2, FeH_2, NiH_2, CuH_2	not	no			
CuH	not	formed but decomposes irreversibly	CoH_2	borderline	no			
			ZnH_2	no	unstable			
GaH	formed	no?	GaH_2	not	no			
GeH	not	(a)	GeH_2	formed	(a)			
ZrH	not	no?	ZrH_2	formed	stable			

NbH	not	$NbH_{<1}$	NbH_2	formed?	formed under high pressure
MoH, TcH, RhH, RuH, PdH, AgH	not	not but $PdH_{0\cdot6}$ is	MoH_2, TcH_2, RhH_2, RuH_2, PdH_2, AgH_2	not	no
CdH	not	no	CdH_2	not	v. unstable
InH	formed	no?	InH_2	not	no
SnH	not	no	SnH_2	formed	no
HfH	formed	no?	HfH_2	formed	stable
TaH	not	$TaH_{<1}$	TaH_2	not	no
WH, ReH, OsH, IrH, PtH, AuH	not	no	WH_2, ReH_2, OsH_2, IrH_2, PtH_2, AuH_2	not	no
HgH	not	no	HgH_2	not	not above – 120°C
TlH	not	no	TlH_2	not	no
PbH	not?	no	PbH_2	formed	no ($PbH_{0\cdot2}$ exists)

Notes *Stable* in these columns is used only to imply that the hydride exists at about room temperature in a hydrogen atmosphere: *unstable* is used for hydrides which decompose below room temperature.

(a) The composition of the lower hydride of germanium is in doubt.

tungsten. The non-existence of the hydrides of these elements then reflects the greater strength of the H-H bond compared with the H-M bond.

A number of other theories have also been proposed to deal with the metal hydrides, many of them related to those given above. These are discussed by Gibb in his review [5].

From a purely pragmatic point of view, the author chooses to discuss the transition metal hydrides in terms of the 'ionic' theory, that is, in terms of hydride anions and metal cations with the remaining metal valency electrons in conduction bands providing metal-metal bonding. The hydrides to the right of the transition block are then regarded as intermediate between covalent and ionic-metallic hydrides, providing a bridge to the covalent hydrides of the *p* block. This theory is preferred largely because it provides a more pictorial account of the compounds and one more in accord with a chemist's concepts, whereas the 'alloy' or metallic theory with protonic hydrogen demands the use of metal theory which tends to be less familiar to most chemists.

3.2 Non-stoicheiometry in the Metal Hydrides [186]

The transition metal hydrides are commonly found in non-stoicheiometric forms and, in cases such as the palladium hydride system, the stoicheiometric formula, PdH, is unstable at room temperature. Anderson [13] has pointed out that, while most crystals have only a small proportion of defects present at thermal equilibrium at ordinary temperatures, there are some compounds where the equilibrium concentration of defects is abnormally high, even in the stoicheiometric crystal. In the latter case, which includes many transition element hydrides, the interaction between defects becomes important and entropy changes make significant contributions to the free energies.

In a non-stoicheiometric hydride there will be a configurational entropy arising from the random distribution of the hydrogen in the sites of one particular type: a common example is where the hydrogen is entering tetrahedral sites in a cubic structure of metal atoms. In this case, either sections of the structure will fill and become ordered, eventually separating out as a new phase, or there may be random fillings of the available sites over a wide range of composition. Thus, in the lanthanon hydrides, a cubic hydride phase occurs for all compositions up to LnH_2 with the tetrahedral sites filling at random until all available sites are occupied at the stoicheiometric composition. (In some cases, as noted later, a small proportion of sites are never occupied giving a limiting composition such as $MH_{1\cdot95}$.) In the intermediate, non-stoicheiometric, compositions an entropy contribution to the free energy arises from the number of alternative configurations possible. Calculations of such configurational entropies show that they are large enough for the $T\Delta S$ term to make a significant contribution to the free energy of formation of the hydride at temperatures around room temperature.

One particular case, that of the body-centred cubic metal lattice, has been the subject of more detailed calculations by Gibb [14]. This is the structure of palladium hydride, and of the vanadium Group hydrides, which are the most common non-stoicheiometric examples. Gibb shows that simple calculations of the number of arrangements, W, assuming all sites are occupied at random, give entropy values which do not accord with the experimental results. However, if it is assumed that the occupation of certain sites excludes occupation of others in their neighbourhood, satisfactory values result. The assumptions made were that, among the octahedral sites, of which there are six in the body-centred cube unit cell, occupation of an edge centre site excluded occupation of the neighbouring face-centred sites, while occupation of a tetrahedral site, of which there are twelve in the unit cell, excluded occupation of the three neighbouring tetrahedral sites. On this basis, the configurational entropy was a maximum for the composition $MH_{0 \cdot 75}$, if the hydrogens were occupying octahedral sites, while, if tetrahedral sites were occupied, the entropy was a maximum for the composition, $MH_{1 \cdot 66}$. In addition, the configurational entropy was greater if the hydrogen was in octahedral positions than it was for tetrahedral hydrogen up to a composition $MH_{0 \cdot 6}$.

These calculations show that the entropy effect may be important in determining the stable structure at moderate temperatures, and also plays a part in determining the temperatures and compositions at which phase changes take place. This is especially marked where the metal-hydrogen system has a significant 'solution' region before the first hydride phase separates and is discussed further in the case of the vanadium Group hydrides and palladium hydride.

With the general ideas of the first section and this one in mind, we turn to a more detailed discussion of the transition metal hydrides, starting with the hydrides of the lanthanide elements. Then follow the actinide hydrides and the chapter is concluded with the hydrides of the transition metals proper, with the zinc Group providing a bridge to the covalent hydrides of the next chapter.

3.3 The Hydrides of the Lanthanide Elements

All the lanthanide elements, with the exception of promethium which does not seem to have been studied, are known to form hydrides readily. With pure samples of the metal in an appropriate condition, hydriding will take place at room temperature and normal pressures (e.g. [15]). Scandium, yttrium and lanthanum also form hydrides which may be conveniently discussed here. Yttrium hydrides correspond in properties to those of the heavier lanthanides in a way similar to the matching of yttrium to these elements in general chemistry. The scandium hydrogen system is not well-known. Pre-1959 work is reviewed [86], and later work discussed [187].

Scandium [119, 120] and europium as discussed in the last chapter, form hydrides up to the composition MH_2 only, while all the other elements can be hydrided up to compositions approaching, or reaching, MH_3. The difficulties in attaining the stoicheiometric composition reported for some elements, especially by earlier workers, probably reflect the difficulties found until recently in obtaining pure samples of the elements, rather than any specific chemical property of these lanthanide hydride systems.

All lanthanides except Eu form a cubic hydride phase up to the composition MH_2, with the hydride ions occupying the tetrahedral sites in the cubic close packed metal lattice at random. Thus, the composition MH_2 corresponds to the fluorite structure. Above this composition, the hydride ions enter the octahedral sites. In the lighter lanthanides, and in lanthanum itself, the cubic phase persists up to the composition MH_3, but for yttrium and the heavier, smaller, lanthanides a hexagonal phase separates at higher hydrogen contents. The Table below shows the approximate compositions at which these changes occur.

Table 3.4. *Compositions of Lanthanum Hydride Phases*

H/La	Phases (H/La 0·0 → 1·0 → 2·0 → 3·0)
La, Ce, Pr, Nd	M + C → C
Sm	M + C → C → C + H → H
Eu	M + C → C
Gd, Tb	M + C → C → C + H → H
Dy, Ho	M + C → C → C + H → H
Er, Tm, Lu and Y	M + C → C → C + H → H
Yb	M + C → C → not known

M + C = metal + cubic MH_2: C = cubic MH_2 (containing octahedral H above H/Ln = 2): C + H = cubic plus hexagonal phases: H = hexagonal MH_3 phase. For EuH_2 and the stable form of YbH_2, the C phase is orthorhombic.

The metal and the cubic phase coexist up to compositions in the range H/Ln = 1·8–2·0, while the composition at which the hexagonal phase separates, and the composition range over which the cubic and hexagonal phases coexist, are much more variable. The hexagonal phase alone is usually found above a H/Ln ratio of 2·8, but it may separate earlier. In addition, there is an initial range where the metal phase exists alone, taking hydrogen into solid solution. At room temperature, to which the compositions given in the Table correspond, this solid solution range is very short but it becomes more extensive at higher temperatures, reaching $MH_{0\cdot1}$ at 600°C and about $MH_{0\cdot2}$ at 700°C [16]. The data on which the Table is based come from references [17, 18] for La and Ce, [19] for Gd, and [20] for the remaining lanthanide hydrides and for yttrium.

Most of these results are based on X-ray studies, but the position of the hydrogen in CeH_2 has been confirmed by neutron diffraction [21]. This study shows the hydrogen to be in tetrahedral sites, so that the complete structure of CeH_2 is the fluorite one. (It might be noted here that this study, and the majority of other cases quoted later, was carried out on the deuteride, as deuterium has superior neutron scattering properties to ordinary hydrogen.) The same study showed that, in the cubic hydride of higher hydrogen content, $CeH_{2\cdot7}$, the additional hydrogen atoms were in octahedral positions.

However, a neutron diffraction study of a hexagonal trihydride, HoH_3, has shown for this case that the conclusion, based on X-ray data, that the hydrogens in this structure were also in tetrahedral and octahedral sites, is not strictly correct [185]. The unit cell found by neutron diffraction is three times the pseudo-cell reported in the X-ray work [20], the c_0 length remaining the same, but the a_0 length being increased by $\sqrt{3}$. The new, larger, unit cell contains 6 Ho and 18 H atoms. The structure is derived from the ideal one, with 12 tetrahedral and 6 octahedral H atoms, by slight displacements of the tetrahedral atoms, to provide the required space of the Ho^{3+} radii, and by a more substantial displacement of the octahedral hydrogens. The latter are moved from the octahedral positions between the planes of Ho atoms towards these planes, and 1/3 of the hydrogens are actually in the Ho planes, and three-coordinated. Thus, of the eighteen hydrogen atoms in the unit cell, twelve are in slightly distorted tetrahedral positions, two are in trigonal positions, and the remaining four are in distorted octahedral positions. The hydride ions are approximately close-

Table 3.5. *Lattice Parameters for the Lanthanide Hydrides*

	MH_2 a_0 (Å)		$MH_{2\cdot9\ 3\cdot0}$ a_0 (Å)		c_0 (Å)	d_c/d_h [all from ref. 20]
			X-ray [20]	neutron [185]		
La	5·667 [21]	5·663 [22]				
Ce	5·581 [21]					
Pr	5·517 [21]	5·518 [20]				
Nd	5·470 [21]	5·464 [20]				
Sm	5·376 [21]	5·375 [20]	3·782	6·551*	6·779 [20]	1·082
Gd	5·303 [19]		3·73	6·46*	6·71 [19]	1·084
Tb	5·246 [20]		3·700	6·409*	6·658 [20]	1·093
Dy	5·201 [20]		3·671	6·359*	6·615 [20]	1·097
Ho	5·165 [20]		3·642	6·308	6·560 [20]	1·094
Er	5·123 [20]		3·621	6·272*	6·526 [20]	1·102
Tm	5·090 [20]		3·599	6·234*	6·489 [20]	1·104
Lu	5·033 [20]		3·588	6·163*	6·443 [20]	1·108
Y	5·205 [20]		3·672	6·360*	6·659 [20]	1·103
	5·200 [23, 24]		3·674		6·599 [23]	

In addition, some data for cubic phases with H/Ln above 2·0 is available. Goon [22] points out the diffuse nature of the LaH_3 pattern at room temperature and obtains a_0 for LaH_3 = 5·604 Å by extrapolation of his high temperature data. The authors of [21] give a_0 for $CeH_{2\cdot47}$ = 5·540 Å, for $CeD_{2\cdot48}$ = 5·530 Å and calculate in the latter that there are eight Ce-D spacings of 2·40 Å, and three of 2·77 Å. (The latter authors calculate metal-hydrogen distances on the basis of metallic radii and a tetrahedral radius for hydrogen which is reasonably consistent for the dihydrides from LaH_2 to SmH_2: this is one example of the point made in section 3.1 that radii other than ionic ones may well give a good fit to the observed data.) For $CeH_{2\cdot97}$, a = 5·539 Å [30] and the same authors report a = 3·573, c = 6·434 Å for $LuH_{2\cdot9}$ in good agreement with the above values. ScH_2 is cubic with a = 4·783 Å [119].

*These values are calculated from the X-ray data by analogy with the HoH_3 value.

packed, with the three types having respectively 9, 14, and 11 hydrogen neighbours for the tetrahedral, trigonal, and octahedral hydrides. Each Ho atom has nine nearest hydrogens at 2·10–2·29 Å, and two further away at 2·48 Å. This structure is unusual in having three-coordinated hydrogen, the only other example being Th_4H_{15}.

It is probable that the hexagonal hydrides, MH_3, of samarium, gadolinium, terbium, dysprosium, erbium, thulium, lutetium, and yttrium have similar hydrogen arrangements, as X-ray studies show them to be isomorphous with HoH_3. In Table 3.5, the X-ray parameters, as reported [20] for the MH_3 hexagonal phases, are shown, as well as the unit cell calculated on the assumption that all the hexagonal MH_3 species are isostructural with HoH_3.

The unit cell dimensions of the hydrides vary with the lanthanide element, and with hydrogen content above the LnH_2 composition. For the elements up to samarium, there is a relatively rapid contraction in unit cell length as the hydrogen content increases. For example, for LaH_{2+x}, the cell constant, a_0, decreases by 0·001 Å for an increase of 0·017 in x [22]. For the heavier lanthanides, the decrease in a_0 for the cubic phase is much more gradual and is difficult to distinguish from experimental error, especially in the composition range where the hexagonal phase coexists with the cubic one. The lattice constant data are collected together in Table 3.5. In the last column of the Table, the density of the cubic phase, d_c, extrapolated to the composition LnH_3, is given as a ratio of the density of the hexagonal phase, d_h, at the LnH_3 composition for those elements where the hexagonal phase is formed. It is clear that the formation of the hexagonal trihydride allows a decrease in density, and thus an increase in M-H distances, of the order of ten per cent. As the lanthanide elements show the effect of the lanthanide contraction in their M-H distances in all the hydride phases (compare Table 3.5 and reference [20]), the formation of the hexagonal trihydride phase by the smaller lanthanides and yttrium is governed by the need to relieve the crowding imposed by the cubic structure.

The contraction observed in the composition range between the dihydride and the trihydride is ascribed to the withdrawal of the one electron per metal atom in the conduction band in MH_2 as further H^- ions are formed. This decreases the shielding between the cations and the hydride ions, due to the conduction electrons, and the lattice contracts. In addition, the quasi-free electrons in the conduction band themselves cause a lattice expansion. The fact that the lattice contraction is linearly proportional to the added hydrogen is in accord with the ionic theory of the hydrides.

Mulford, [16] and see also Figure 58 of ref. [5], has proposed a tentative phase diagram for the lanthanide-hydrogen systems (see also Bacur [188]). The metals which form only the cubic hydride phase show a two-phase (metal + hydride) region which decreases in extent with rising temperature. The initial region, where the hydrogen is in solution in the metal, increases with temperature, as does the range over which the cubic hydride phase exists alone. On

Table 3.6. *Thermodynamic and Other Properties of the Lanthanide Hydrides*

	H_f° (kcal/mole)	Dissociation Pressures *A*	*B*	Density (g/cc)
LaH_2	−49·7 [16], −49·6 [189]	10,858 10,850	10·756 [16] 10·64 [189]	5·14 [21]
CeH_2	−33·9 [16], −49·2 [189] (the latter value is to be preferred by comparison with the other MH_2 data)	7,417 10,760	7·608 [16] 10·63 [189]	5·43 [21]
PrH_2	−47·8 [16], −49·7 [189]	10,446 10,870	10·229 [16] 10·53 [189]	5·65 [21]
NdH_2	−44·8 [16], −50·5 [189]	9,796 11,030	9·370 [16] 10·48 [189]	5·94 [21]
SmH_2				6·52 [21]
EuH_2 and YbH_2 (different structures – see Table 2.8)				
GdH_2	−46·9 [19], −47·59 [188]	10,250 10,400	9·72 [19] 8·14 [188]	7·08 [19]
ErH_2	ca. −54 [190]	11,780	10·91 [180]	
TbH_2, DyH_2, HoH_2, TmH_2, LuH_2 – no data available.				
ScH_2	−16·62 [119]	1,137	2·788 [119]	2·851 [119]
YH_2	−44·42 [25]			4·237 [27] (YD_2 = 4·397 [27])
$LaH_{2\cdot76}$	−40·09 [16]			LaH_3 = 5·26 [16]
$CeH_{2\cdot69}$	−42·26 [16]			CeH_3 = 5·5 [26]
$PrH_{2\cdot84}$	−39·52 [16]			PrH_3 = 5·5 [26]
GdH_3	−17·94 [19], −21·52 [188]	3,135	5·71 [188]	6·57 [19]
YH_3		4,370	10·10 [28]	3·946 [28]

Further data are available for yttrium di- and tri-hydrides as follows [27, 28]:

	YH_3	YD_3	YH_2	YD_2	
Heat capacity at 25°C, C_p	10·363	13·727	8·243	10·773	cal/°/mole
Entropy at 25°C, S	10·019	12·028	9·175	10·294	cal/mole
Enthalpy function, $H^\circ - H_0^\circ$	1613	2025	1403	1659	cal/°/mole
Gibbs function $(G^\circ - H_0^\circ)/T$	−4·608	−5·237	−4·470	−4·279	cal/°/mole

extrapolation, the two-phase region would seem to disappear above 1000°C. In the case of those lanthanide elements which form the hexagonal phase at high hydrogen content, the effect of increasing temperature is again to widen the composition ranges over which the single phases – metal with dissolved hydrogen, cubic hydride, and hexagonal hydride – exist, and to decrease the composition ranges within which the two-phase regions occur. On extrapolation, the (metal plus cubic hydride) two-phase region would disappear above about 100°C, and the (cubic plus hexagonal) two-phase region would disappear about 600°C. These diagrams are generalized and tentative. One point of interest is that the solution region, of hydrogen in the parent metal lattice, becomes significant at higher temperatures although it is negligible at room temperature. In other hydride systems, particularly those of the vanadium

Group metals, this solution region is an important one at low temperatures as well.

A relatively limited amount of information is available on heats of formation and other thermodynamic properties of the lanthanide hydrides and this is collected in Table 3.6, together with other properties. Data for EuH_2 and YbH_2 have already been given in Table 2.8.

Full heat capacity studies of YH_2 and YD_2 [27] and of YH_3 and YD_3 [28] are reported. At temperatures up to about 100°K, the heat capacities of the hydride and deuteride are equal, but above that temperature the heat capacity of the deuteride exceeds that of the hydride for both the dihydride and the trihydride. The difference is satisfactorily accounted for in terms of the optical lattice vibration. For the dihydride, the difference in heat capacities corresponds to a vibration frequency of 1030 $\pm$ 30 cm^{-1} for the hydride, (and this frequency multiplied by $1/\sqrt{2}$ for YD_2) and this value corresponds to the value of 984 $\pm$ 50 cm^{-1} derived from slow neutron scattering experiments [29]. A similar explanation holds for YH_3 and YD_3, but in this case it is actually possible to observe the lattice vibrations (which were unobservable in the infra-red of the dihydride because of scattering by the conduction electrons). In YH_3, only three rather broad bands are observed in the infra-red between 4000 and 400 cm^{-1}. These have maxima at 1295, 920, and 640 cm^{-1}, of half-widths of 100–200 cm^{-1}. On the assumption that there are two hydrogens in tetrahedral sites and one in an octahedral site in YH_3, these frequencies were assigned; 1295 cm^{-1} to two of the tetrahedral modes, 920 cm^{-1} to the third tetrahedral mode, and the lowest one to the three octahedral modes of lattice vibration. (The mass difference between hydrogen and yttrium is so great that the hydrogens can be regarded as vibrating against essentially stationary metal atoms.) These assignments, and the corresponding values multiplied by $1/\sqrt{2}$ for the deuteride give calculated heat capacity differences in agreement with those found for YH_3 and YD_3. For example, the calculated difference at 300°K is 3·45 and the measured one is 3·38 cal/degree/mole. The comparison between the lattice frequency calculated from heat capacity differences for hydride and deuteride, and that derived from slow neutron scattering has been carried out for a number of hydrides (compare section 3.5) but the yttrium trihydride system is the first case where the lattice vibration has actually been found in the infra-red (as all the other hydrides examined contained conduction electrons).

Preparation. As far as the data are known, all the lanthanide hydride phases form exothermically and reversibly. With pure samples of the metal, especially in an activated or powder form, it is probable that all the lanthanide elements will react at room temperature to form the dihydride phase, although an induction period is usually observed [15] which varies in length with the condition of the metal. To form hydrides with a hydrogen content exceeding MH_2, more vigorous conditions are necessary. For example, it was found that reaction between YH_2 and hydrogen started at 350°C, and then proceeded at 200°C and was complete in forty-eight hours [28]. In general, methods described in Chapter 2 for ionic hydrides will serve equally well for lanthanide hydrides. The hydrides, especially those with an H/M ratio greater than two, react with air and have to be handled in an inert atmosphere. The dihydride phases are less reactive and similar to calcium hydride in this respect, but the trihydride phases are pyrophoric. All the hydrides are reported as dark solids or powders.

Attempts to react scandium or europium dihydrides with further hydrogen have been unsuccessful, even at hydrogen pressures up to fifty atmospheres, but YbH_2 reacted with more hydrogen under such conditions [30]. In the Yb-H system below 13 atmospheres and 320°, the dihydride and higher hydride coexisted, but above these values only a single hydride phase was found. This new phase in the ytterbium hydride system had a maximum hydrogen content of $YbH_{2\cdot55}$ and a face centred cubic structure with $a_0 = 5\cdot192$ Å. On thermal decomposition, a metastable cubic dihydride phase was formed with $a_0 = 5\cdot253$ Å, which passed over into the normal orthorhombic dihydride phase on annealing at 400°C. Samples of ytterbium hydrides with compositions in the range H/Yb 1·88 to 2·55, showed magnetic properties which were interpreted on the basis of a mixture of diamagnetic YbH_2 and strongly paramagnetic higher hydride phase containing Yb^{3+} ions.

It is clear from these results that ytterbium behaves in a similar way to the other heavy lanthanides in forming a trihydride (although this is cubic and not hexagonal) and it is interesting that a cubic dihydride phase was also observed, corresponding to those formed by its congeners in the lanthanide series. However, much more severe reaction conditions are required to form the trihydride phase and the cubic dihydride passes over into the orthorhombic form analogous to CaH_2, so that the resemblance to europium, and the stability of the II state, are still the most important features in the ytterbium hydride system. In its general chemistry, ytterbium shows a less stable II state than does europium.

Magnetic and electrical properties: the MH_2–MH_3 composition range. A number of studies by Wallace and his coworkers [33, 34, 35, 36] on the heavier lanthanides, and by Stalinski [37, 18] on the lighter ones have shown that all behave in a similar manner on hydrogenation. The dihydride has metallic properties which gradually disappear as the hydrogen content approaches the trihydride composition. Thus, LaH_2 [37] exhibits a metallic conductivity of about 1/100th that of the metal (10 ohm^{-1} cm^{-1} at 80°K) while the conductivity of LaH_3 is 10^{-1} ohm^{-1} cm^{-1}, in the range of the semiconductors. Another study gives the conductivity of pressed pellets of $LaH_{2\cdot88}$ as 10^{-1} ohm^{-1} cm^{-1} with similar values for $CeH_{2\cdot7}$ and $PrH_{2\cdot7}$ [30]. All the lanthanide hydrides exhibit a similar change in properties as their composition approaches the MH_3 value – except for EuH_2 and YbH_2 which become non-conducting at the MH_2 composition (a resistance of 30,000 ohm per cm is reported for $YbH_{1\cdot9}$ [30]). Similarly, while the dihydrides exhibit magnetic susceptibilities similar to those of the metals, these disappear for the trihydrides, which become diamagnetic. (Note that $YbH_{2 \cdot 5}$ discussed above is anomalous in this respect, in that magnetic susceptibility increases between H/Yb ratios of 2·0 and 2·5: it would be interesting to know if it falls again at higher hydrogen concentrations.)

This disappearance of metallic and magnetic properties is ascribed to the use of all the conduction electrons to form H^- ions in the MH_3 hydrides. In addition, as two-thirds of the electrons are so used in the dihydrides, Wallace points out [33, 36] that magnetic ordering, as shown by the appearance of ferromagnetism or anti-ferromagnetism, should appear at lower temperatures in the dihydrides than in the metals, and at still lower temperatures–if at all–in the trihydrides, as such ordering occurs via the conduction electrons. This was indeed found to be the case. For example, holmium metal shows a Néel point at 135°K, HoH_2 has one at 8°K, while HoH_3 shows no sign of ordering above 4·2°K, the lowest temperature available [33]. DyH_2 also has a Néel point at 8°K, while TmH_2 and ErH_2 showed none above 4·2°K [33]. ErH_2 was reported to go antiferromagnetic below 2·6°K [39]. TbD_2 and HoD_2 [36] had Néel points at 40°K and 8°K respectively. A neutron diffraction study of TbD_2 allowed the ordering to be described in more detail (at 4°K) as due to antiferromagnetic coupling between adjacent (001) layers which were ordered ferromagnetically. In none of the systems investigated were trihydrides found to be magnetically ordered.

In three systems, a study has been made of the heat of the reaction

$$2MH_3 \rightleftharpoons 2MH_2 + H_2.$$

The values given, per mole H_2, are [30]

$LaH_{2 \cdot 70}$	$LaH_{2 \cdot 80}$	$CeH_{2 \cdot 80}$	$CeH_{2 \cdot 90}$	$YbH_{2 \cdot 5}$
6·6	6·8	6·5	6·8	3·3 kcal/mole.

These values illustrate the markedly lower stability of the higher ytterbium hydride.

A nuclear magnetic resonance study of the lanthanum/hydrogen system is reported [40] which also shows the change in properties of the highly hydrided system. Relaxation time studies show that proton self-diffusion occurs at moderate temperatures, with an activation energy which is fairly constant up to the MH_2 composition and then decreases abruptly from about 23 kcal/mole to about 3 kcal/mole at $LaH_{2 \cdot 85}$. The line widths are constant for H/La up to 1·95 and then increase linearly with hydrogen concentration. (All the MH_2–MH_3 changes were found to start at the composition $MH_{1 \cdot 95}$: the authors suggest that this shows that 0·05 of the tetrahedral sites are inaccessible, due to lattice defects.) The lanthanum resonance confirms the change in properties observed with the hydrogen resonance. Octahedral sites are occupied only above H/La = 1·95, and the lifetime of a diffusing proton in an octahedral site, at compositions below this, is much less than 10^{-7} seconds. They suggest their results are not incompatible with the model of H^+ in the hydride.* They remark that a crystal field splitting of the lanthanum levels is apparent. Similar crystal field effects were remarked in some of the magnetic studies above and in a heat capacity study of CeH_2 [38].

Mixed Lanthanide-Other Element Systems. Mikheeva reports some results of hydriding alloys of cerium with aluminium [41] and magnesium [42]. In the case of magnesium, alloys containing up to 50% Mg could be completely hydrided (to $CeH_3 + MgH_2$) at room temperature and ordinary pressures, although the induction time and time of hydriding were longer than those for cerium alone. Magnesium alone, as discussed in section 2.5c, requires high pressures and temperatures for hydriding. Alloys containing only up to 25% Al could be hydrided. Again the reaction occurred at room temperature and ordinary pressure with extended induction time compared with cerium alone. Rather more hydrogen was absorbed than required to form CeH_3 and compositions such as $CeH_3.AlH_{0{\cdot}16}$ were found. A cerium-aluminium-magnesium alloy would also hydride under similar conditions to give $CeH_3 + MgH_2 + AlH_{0{\cdot}1-1{\cdot}7}$. The hydrided compounds had the properties of a mechanical mixture of the separate hydrides.

It is reported that solutions of yttrium, lanthanum and cerium (and also calcium and thorium) in liquid magnesium react with hydrogen at elevated temperatures with the precipitation of the hydride [43]. At 650°C, 0·034% Y, 2·9% La and 3·3% Ce were the residual concentrations of these metals in magnesium, with hydrogen at one atmosphere pressure. Addition of zinc or aluminium to the solvent decreased the amount of hydride formation.

Summary. Scandium, yttrium, and lanthanum, and all the lanthanide elements react exothermically with hydrogen. Europium and ytterbium give dihydrides similar to CaH_2. Scandium and europium form only dihydrides, ytterbium gives an unstable higher hydride, $YbH_{2{\cdot}5}$, and all the others form both dihydrides and trihydrides. The dihydrides form relatively easily and are face centred cubic with tetrahedral hydrogen – the calcium fluoride structure. The cubic phase persists up to the MH_3 composition for the lighter lanthanides but is replaced by a hexagonal phase for YH_3 and the heavier element trihydrides. In the trihydride phases, the third hydrogen enters approximately octahedral sites. All the lanthanide hydrides (except EuH_2 and YbH_2) are less dense than the metal, in contrast to the ionic hydrides of the first two Groups. Magnetic and electrical properties change from metallic for the dihydrides to those typical of ionic compounds (or semi-metals) for the trihydrides. The trihydride phases require more forcing conditions for their formation, and they are more reactive than the dihydride phases. At higher temperatures, a phase at low hydrogen concentration corresponding to a solid solution of hydrogen in the metal

* On this theory, the observed diamagnetism is the result of the *filling* of the conduction band by the electrons from the hydrogens, whereas the ionic postulates its emptying.

becomes a significant component of the metal-hydrogen system. These hydrides show many resemblances to the alkali and alkaline earth hydrides in general stability and reactivity. The most striking differences are the presence of metallic properties and the wide departure from stoicheiometry.

3.4 The Hydrides of the Actinide Elements

All the actinide elements up to americium are known to form hydrides, but the uranium and thorium hydrides are very much better known than the others. Dihydrides and trihydrides are found, as well as Th_4H_{15}. *Actinium* [80] is known to form a dihydride, AcH_2, which is cubic and similar to the lanthanide dihydrides. *Protactinium* [81] reacts readily with hydrogen to form the black trihydride, PaH_3, which is isostructural with UH_3. Little else is reported for these two hydrides and they are not discussed further.

Of the other systems, the *plutonium* hydrogen system is most similar to those already encountered. Plutonium combines with hydrogen to form a dihydride which is face-centred cubic and of the fluorite structure. In the composition region from H/Pu = 0 to 2, the cubic dihydride and the metal coexist in a two phase system [44]. In the range from H/Pu = 2 to 2·75, the extra hydrogen atoms enter octahedral sites in the cubic lattice while, above this composition, a hexagonal phase separates which is the trihydride, PuH_3 [45]. The system is thus very similar to that of a heavier lanthanide element. Further, even a contraction in the size of the cubic phase above the PuH_2 composition is noted, with the lattice constant a_0 decreasing from 5·395 Å at $PuH_{2\cdot0}$ to 5·34 Å for $PuH_{2\cdot5}$. Other physical data are given in Table 3.7.

A plutonium hydride sample of composition $PuH_{2\cdot7}$ is reported to be relatively unreactive [47]. There was no reaction with cold water or with air below 150°C. Hydrogen was evolved with water at 90°C, and the hydride dissolved with hydrogen evolution in HCl and H_2SO_4 to give plutonium III solutions. The hydrogen evolution with hydrochloric acid was quantitative and could be used for analysis. The hydride reacts with nitrogen at 250°C to give PuN. These reactions are similar to those observed for the other actinide hydrides, and for the lanthanide hydrides, but the reactivity is lower than for lanthanide trihydrides. The one report of americium hydride gives the structure of AmH_2 as cubic, like PuH_2, and unlike ThH_2 which is tetragonal. This is some indication that the heavier actinides may well form hydrides similar to the lanthanides with cubic MH_2 and possibly hexagonal trihydrides. If such behaviour emerges, it would be in accord with the general tendency of the heavier actinides to resemble the lanthanides rather more closely than the earlier members do.

Uranium forms one hydride, UH_3, which is very well known, and exists in two forms, α and β. (A number of reports of UH_4, and other MH_4 phases, have appeared but without substantiation.) This is formed directly, by passing hydrogen over heated uranium at moderate temperatures, and no lower hydride exists. UH_3 is formed in stoicheiometric composition at least up to 350°C, as a black powder. Its formation and decomposition is a well-established

Table 3.7. *Parameters of the Actinide Hydrides*

Hydride	Crystal Structure (Ångströms)	Density (g/cc)	Heat of Formation (kcal/mole)	Decomposition Pressures *A*	*B*
AcH_2 ?	fcc $a_0=5{\cdot}670$	8·35 [80]			
ThH_2	bct $a_0=4{\cdot}10$, $c_0=5{\cdot}03$	9·20 [64, 65]	−36·9 [67] −34·4 [68]	8060 7700	10·47 [68] 9·54 [67]
ThH_2(4% ThO_2)	fcc $a_0=5{\cdot}489$ [64]: 5·492 [66]				
Th_4H_{15}	cubic $a_0=9{\cdot}11$ (Th−3H=2·46: Th−9H=2·29)	8·24 [63]	−19·3 [67] (from ThH_2)	4220	9·50 [67]
ThC.ThH_2	hcp $a_0=3{\cdot}816$, $c_0=6{\cdot}302$		−48·2 (from ThC.Th) [75]		
ThC,2ThH_2	monocl. $a=6{\cdot}50$, $b=3{\cdot}80$, $c=10{\cdot}91$, $\beta=119°$		−38·3 (from ThC.ThH_2.Th) [75]		
PaH_3	cubic $a_0=6{\cdot}648$ (UH_3 str) [81]				
α-UH_3	cubic $a_0=4{\cdot}160$ (U−12H=2·32)	11·11 [56]			
β-UH_3	cubic $a_0=6{\cdot}631$ ($U_{I,II}$−12H = 2·32)	10·95 [55]	−30·800 [48]		
			−30·5 [84]	4460	9·21 [84]
UH_3			−30·35 [51]	4590	9·39 [26]
UD_3			−31·02 [51]	4500	9·43 [26]
UT_3			−31·14 [51]	4471	9·46 [26]
NpH_2	cubic [183]		−28 [183]		
NpH_3	hexagonal [183]		−8·6 (from NpH_2)		
PuH_2	fcc $a_0=5{\cdot}359$: 5·34	10·40 [82][46]	−37·4 [44]	8165	10·01 [44]
PuD_2			−35·5 [44]	7761	9·71 [44]
PuH_3	hex $a_0=3{\cdot}78$, $c_0=6{\cdot}76$	9·61 [83][46]	−37·0? [26]		
AmH_2	cubic $a_0=5{\cdot}322$	10·7 [79]			
$AmH_{2{\cdot}7\pm10\%}$	cubic				

UH_3 : free energy of formation = −17·35 kcal/mole: entropy = 15·27 eu [51, 53]
At 25°C, heat capacity = 11·78 cal/degree/mole, $H° - H_0° = 2155$ cal/mole and the Gibbs Free energy function = 8·01 cal/degree/mole [53]
A study of UH_3 and UD_3 [85] gives dissociation pressures of 760 mm at 415 and 445°C respectively (A = 4255, B = 9·08 $\Delta H_f° = -29.1$ kcal/mole for UH_3: A = 4401, B = 9·01, $\Delta H_f° = -30{\cdot}1$ kcal/mole for UD_3)

method of producing pure hydrogen [48], and many recent studies of metal hydrides have used this method. The hydriding-dehydriding reaction is also used to produce finely powdered and reactive uranium (for example [49]), and similar use of hydriding-dehydriding reactions for formation of other actinide metal powders is reported [50].

In a study of the heat of formation by an adiabatic calorimetric method, using finely-divided uranium and hydrogen or its isotopes, it was found that there were distinct, though small, differences in the heat of formation of UH_3, UD_3, and UT_3 [51]. Similar effects have been remarked previously in the last chapter. The values are shown in Table 3.7: it is worth noting that the UH_3 value was confirmed in a quite separate study at higher pressures and temperatures [52]. This, and other studies [53], showed that the heat of the $\alpha \rightarrow \beta$ transformation is low, not more than 3 kcal/mole [53]. It is probably much less, as an independent study of UH_3/HD exchange [54] (using βUH_3 in place of the α/β mixture of the above study [51]) found a difference in the UH_3 and UD_3 heats of formation of 641 $\pm$ 50 cal/mole, which is close to the 669 $\pm$ 60 cal/mole from the values [51] given in Table 3.7. The crystal structures of the two forms also show only small differences.

Normal, or β-UH_3, has an unusual and quite complicated crystal structure. The uranium lattice is cubic with length 6·631 Å [55] and there are two types of uranium atom, in the positions of the β-tungsten structure. One type, U_I, has two other U_I atoms at a distance of 3·316 Å (compare distances of 3·27 and 3·36 Å for the longer interactions in α-uranium) and has four U_{II} atoms at 3·707 Å. The U_{II} atoms have a more symmetrical environment with twelve U_I atoms in slightly distorted icosahedral coordination, all at 3·70 Å. UD_3 has exactly the same structure except that a_0 is slightly less, at 6·620 Å (compare the heats of formation).

The hydrogen positions were found by neutron diffraction on UD_3. The hydrogens are all in equivalent positions in the centre of a flattened tetrahedron of uranium atoms at 2·32 Å distance. Each U_I is surrounded by an icosahedron of twelve deuteriums, while the U_{II} atoms are also surrounded by twelve deuterium atoms, in sets of three, making up the faces of four different icosahedra. The U_I-U_I distance corresponds to weak uranium-uranium bonding; otherwise the hydride presents a puzzle on the metallic (or protonic) theory of hydrides, in that the hydrogen atoms are in very large holes, and that the uranium lattice is considerably expanded to form the hydride, (so there is no case that the hydrogens fill holes already present: the density of uranium metal is about 19g/cc, almost twice that of the hydride). The ionic theory does seem to give better agreement with the structure. Gibb [5, p. 389] gives diagrams of the UH_3 structure according to both the atomic and ionic models.

The β-form of UH_3 is the only one found when the preparation is carried out above 200°C, but preparations at or below room temperature produce a mixture of β-hydride with a new, cubic, α-form. By carrying out the preparation at -80°C, mixtures containing over 50% of the α-form may be obtained [56].

This form has a unit cell of 4·160 Å and is slightly denser than the β-form. The structure is probably P_{m3n}, with each uranium surrounded by twelve hydrogens at 2·32 Å, the same distance as in the β-form. The hydrogens are coordinated tetrahedrally by four uranium atoms. The structure is therefore similar to that of β-UH_3, but without the rather short U–U distance. The α-form is completely converted to the β-form at 250°C, but is unchanged at 100°C. The conversion is irreversible, and no conditions have been reported for either β to α conversion or for preparation of pure α-UH_3.

A number of magnetic studies on UH_3 are reported [57, 58, 59] and it has been shown to be ferromagnetic below 173°K. Above this temperature, it is paramagnetic with a moment of 2·79 Bohr magnetons [59]. The paramagnetic transition has also been observed in the heat capacity curve [52]. The relatively high temperature of the onset of ordering, compared with those observed in the lanthanide hydrides, may indicate that the metal-metal interaction, also implied by the unusual structure, is stronger than in the metallic dihydrides of the lanthanides and underlines the unique nature of the uranium hydride. The elementary magnets in UH_3 are thought to be the electrons whose orbital angular momenta are completely quenched [59].

Uranium hydride is commonly used as a starting material for the preparation of uranium compounds, as its finely powdered state makes it extremely reactive. Similar reactivity is found for most of the other actinide hydrides, although the properties quoted above for $PuH_{2\cdot7}$ shows these properties are not universal–or possibly that the hydride becomes protected by an oxide layer under some conditions, see below. Uranium hydride ignites in oxygen to form U_3O_8 and gives tetrahalides at 200–300°C with Cl_2, Br_2 and HF. With HCl and HBr, the trihalides are formed at these temperatures. Reaction with water or H_2S, about 400°C, gives UO_2 and US_2 respectively [60].

In a more detailed study of the reaction of UH_3 with aqueous oxidizing agents, [61], it was found that there was little hydrogen exchange with the solvent and evidence for a surface barrier layer of UO_2 was obtained. A similar phenomenon would explain the varied reactivities reported for a number of hydrides. It was found that UD_3 with concentrated HCl in H_2O gave HD as the principle product, while reaction with ceric solution in H_2O gave D_2 as the only gaseous product. At lower acidities, the surface film may be U(O)XH, similar to that found for thorium [62].

As well as uranium, the hydrogen compounds of *thorium* have been fully studied. It is now established that two thorium hydrides exist, ThH_2 and Th_4H_{15}. Reports of ThH_3 and ThH_4 presumably refer to impure forms of the latter. The formula of Th_4H_{15} was confirmed by the X-ray study [63], and in later work [64] in which samples of the actual composition were synthesized for the first time. The higher hydride is prepared from ThH_2 and hydrogen at high temperatures, around 700°C. The dihydride was prepared from the metal and hydrogen at about 350°C.

The crystal structure of Th_4H_{15} shows a cubic lattice of side 9·11 ± 0·02 Å.

This contains four molecules. There are two different types of hydrogen position. One is surrounded by four thorium atoms at a distance of 2·46 Å, while the other has only three thorium neighbours at 2·29 Å. Each thorium has three hydrogens at 2·46 Å and nine at 2·29 Å, showing twelve-coordination as found in uranium hydride. The shorter Th-H distance is less than that in ThH_2 (with Th-8H = 2·41 Å) and of the same order as in PaH_3 (2·31 Å) and in UH_3. This partly reflects the effect of twelve-coordination on the metal, and partly arises from the unusual three-coordination of the hydrogen (which is tri-angular, not pyramidal). This and HoH_3 are the sole examples of three-co-ordinated hydrogen in hydrides. The shortest Th-Th distance is 3·87 Å in Th_4H_{15}, which is much greater than that in the metal (3·59 Å) so metal-metal interaction is insignificant.

Thorium dihydride forms, not a cubic lattice as in all the other actinide dihydrides, but a body-centred tetragonal lattice with a = 4·10 Å and c = 5·03 Å [64, 65]. If these dimensions are converted to the face-centred tetragonal cell, a = 5·80, c = 5·03. Now, a face-centred cubic dihydride phase *is* formed, when the sample contains about four atoms per cent ThO_2, and this cubic cell has a = 5·492 Å [66]. These two cells have almost the same volume, 164 cubic Ångströms for the tetragonal cell and 166 Å^3 for the cubic cell, and so repres-ent very similar structures. It is clear therefore, that although the tetragonal structure is adopted by pure ThH_2, very little constraint, in the form of a small admixture of the slightly larger ThO_2, is required to convert this to the cubic fluorite structure of the other dihydrides. The tetragonal cell varies in size with hydrogen content and changes (in the face-centred tetragonal notation) of a_0 = 5·735 to 5·715, c_0 = 4·971 to 5·009 were observed as the composition changed from $ThH_{1\cdot 93}$ to $ThH_{1\cdot 73}$. The cubic form became more pronounced at the lower hydrogen contents.

The pressure–temperature–composition variation of the thorium/hydrogen system has been studied over the whole range of composition by Nottorf [67] and up to the dihydride stage by Mallet and Campbell [68]. The results are included in Table 3.7. Both sets of data agree that ThH_2 is formed exothermic-ally with a heat of formation of 34 to 35 kcal/mole, and Th_4H_{15} is formed exothermically from the dihydride and hydrogen. Schumacher [69] has dis-cussed the problem of finding a theoretical expression for the hydrogen pres-sure over a hydride which shows a two-plateau isotherm, as the thorium and gadolinium systems do. (This is a development of earlier work on the single plateau case, as in the uranium system [70].) The non-stoicheiometric regions are ascribed to hydrogen vacancies, rather than interstitial metal atoms, and allowance is made for vacancy-vacancy interactions. The derived isotherms agree quite successfully with the observed ones. Petersen and Rexer calculate the heat of formation of a hydrogen vacancy in ThH_2 as 9·95 kcal, a value that is much lower than that of 68·2 kcal for UH_3 [71].

In studies of the low hydrogen content end of the thorium hydride system, it has been calculated that thorium/thorium dihydride mixtures contain Th metal dissolving about 2×10^{-3} atoms per cent H, and $ThH_{2 \cdot 00}$. At higher temperatures, the solubility of hydrogen in thorium rises to 1% at 300°C and 26% at 800°C (and the equilibrium composition of the hydride phase at the latter temperature is $ThH_{1 \cdot 73}$) [71, 72]. These data for solid solutions of hydrogen in thorium are similar in type to those found for the lanthanides, with the room temperature solubility very low. The rate law for reaction of Th and hydrogen is parabolic, showing that reaction is diffusion controlled by a protective hydride layer. This yields an activation energy for diffusion of hydrogen in ThH_2 of 19·6 kcal [73], of the same order as the diffusion activation energies in ZrH_2 (11·4 kcal) and TiH_2 (10·2 kcal) [74].

Among studies on ternary systems may be mentioned the work on hydriding Th/ThC systems [75]. ThC.ThH$_2$ and ThC.2ThH$_2$ are formed, the former hexagonal with $a_0 = 3 \cdot 816$, $c_0 = 6 \cdot 302$, and the latter monoclinic ($a = 6 \cdot 50$, $b = 3 \cdot 80$, $c = 10 \cdot 91$, $\beta = 119°$: the thorium atoms being in slightly distorted hexagonal close packing). The heats of formation were calculated as $-48 \cdot 2$ kcal/mole and $-38 \cdot 3$ kcal/mole for Th + ThC + H_2 = ThC.ThH$_2$ and Th + ThC.ThH$_2$ + H_2 = ThC.2ThH$_2$ respectively. These values are a little higher than those for the formation of the dihydride. It is noted that hexagonal phases reported in other hydride systems at low hydrogen content may be due to similar compounds. In the case of $AlTh_2$ [76], hydrogen was readily absorbed homogeneously up to a composition $AlTh_2H_4$. The deuterides were made and examined by neutron diffraction. In $AlTh_2D_4$, all the deuterium atoms completely fill a set of equivalent thorium tetrahedra, quite like those in thorium dihydride. At lower deuterium contents, these tetrahedral sites are occupied at random, with one of each pair of sites with a common base being occupied first. After completion of these, at $AlTh_2D_2$, the second member of the pair is occupied, again at random. The Th-D distances range from 2·36 Å to 2·42 Å, for various compositions, compared with 2·41 Å in ThH_2. Hydriding ThCe, on the other hand, is reported to yield primarily CeH_2 with ThH_2 in equilibrium with a solution of hydrogen in thorium as a secondary constituent of the system [76]. More recent work on the Th/Al system, and on systems containing cerium [191], provides evidence for more complex phases such as $Th_8Al_4H_x$ (x = 5, 8, 9, 13). The hydrogen again occupies tetrahedral sites.

Thorium hydrides may be used as starting materials in the preparation of thorium compounds, in a similar manner to UH_3 above. It has been shown [62] that the so-called lower oxide of thorium, which forms as a voluminous black precipitate when thorium is dissolved in hydrochloric acid, is actually a hydridic material of formula corresponding to Th(O)ClH.

In early studies on *neptunium* chemistry, a black powder was reported to result when the metal was heated to 50°C in hydrogen. The analysis gave $NpH_{3 \cdot 6-3 \cdot 8}$, but the sample contained oxide [77]. On this rather inadequate basis, the hydride was regarded as Np_4H_{15} [60]. A very recent paper removes this anomaly and shows that neptunium, like plutonium, forms a dihydride and a trihydride [183]. The dihydride is cubic, and the cubic structure persists up to a hydrogen content of 2·7 H/Np. The trihydride, NpH_3, is hexagonal and isomorphous with PuH_3. Solubility of hydrogen in neptunium was small.

Americium is also reported to react with hydrogen at 50°C to give a voluminous black hydride of composition $AmH_{2\cdot 7}$ (within ten per cent) [78]. In addition, a cubic lower hydride, AmH_2, is reported [79].

Thus, plutonium and neptunium, and presumably americium, give di- and tri-hydrides analogous to those of the heavier lanthanide elements. The later actinides, in their hydrogen chemistry, resemble the lanthanides as they do in their general chemistry.

Summary. The most fully-studied actinide hydrides are those of uranium and thorium, reflecting the greater accessibility of these elements. Thorium dihydride resembles the zirconium and hafnium dihydrides in structure, but otherwise the thorium, uranium, and protactinium hydrides appear to be unique. The other actinides show more resemblance to the lanthanides, as expected, although only a limited amount of work has been done on these hydride systems. Thus the hydride chemistry of the actinides reflects their general chemistry (Table 3.8 gives a brief summary of this) in showing unique chemistry at the start of the series, and then tending to resemble the lanthanide elements from about americium onwards.

Table 3.8. *Actinide Hydrides in Relation to the General Chemistry of the Elements*

Element	Ac	Th	Pa	U	Np	Pu	Am	Cm onward
Most stable Oxidation State	III	IV	V	VI	V	IV	III	III
Other Oxidation States		(III) (II)	IV	(V) IV III	VI,IV III	VI,V III	(VI) V,IV	IV
Hydrides	AcH_2? (cubic)	ThH_2 (tetrag.)	PaH_3 (as UH_3)	UH_3 (cubic) (complex)	NpH_2 (cubic)	PuH_2 (cubic)	AmH_2 (cubic)	none reported
		Th_4H_{15} (cubic) (complex)			NpH_3 (hex)	PuH_3 (hex)	AmH_3?	

Apart from Th_4H_{15} and UH_3 and PaH_3, all the cubic structures are fcc (fluorite) in form and the hexagonal PuH_3 is also approximately close-packed. The structures can be rationalized in terms of the competing processes (*a*) to resemble the lanthanide hydrides and (*b*) the specifically actinide characteristics such as showing twelve-coordination (U,Pa,Th) and the tendency (possibly) of thorium to reach the IV oxidation state. The most obvious prediction is that an AcH_3 will be discovered: it also seems possible that any hydrides formed by the later elements will be cubic MH_2 and hexagonal MH_3 types.

3.5 The Hydrides of the Transition Elements

Hydride phases become less stable, and contain less hydrogen, across the *d* block and also down each Group. Although hydrogen is strongly adsorbed by the elements in the centre of the transition series, the formation of hydrides is dubious to the right of, and below, chromium, with the exception of the unique palladium hydride. At the right of the *d* block, the hydrides CuH, ZnH_2 and CdH_2 are found, with metals having a d^{10} configuration, and these hydrides have their closest affinities with the hydrides of aluminium and gallium. There is thus what may be termed a 'hydride gap' in the middle of the Periodic Table for elements with five or more *d* electrons. This gap need not imply a discontinuity in bonding in the hydride itself, and probably reflects more the increase in stability of the metal-metal bonding in the non-hydride forming elements. This matter is better discussed with the properties of the transition metal hydrides in mind. It is therefore convenient to discuss the properties of each group of hydrides individually, starting with the titanium Group, and then compare the general properties and trends at the end of the section.

Hydrides of Titanium, Zirconium, and Hafnium. These three elements combine exothermically with hydrogen to form hydrides with the usual metallic appearance, usually as black brittle solids. All three elements have been shown clearly to form the stoicheiometric dihydride, MH_2, as long as the temperature is not too high (with the usual reservation that a small number of hydrogen sites may be unavailable due to lattice defects). Rather more vigorous preparation methods are required than for the lanthanides and actinides, although the ease of hydriding reaction again depends sensitively on the purity of the metal. In particular, samples obtained from the van Arkel iodine process are more readily hydrided than those from the Kroll process which may contain small amounts of the calcium, aluminium or sodium used in the reduction. Typical conditions involve outgassing the metal above 1000°C, and then reacting with hydrogen at about one atmosphere pressure at 400°C for several hours. Slow cooling in a hydrogen atmosphere is necessary to attain the maximum hydrogen content. There seen to be no reports of any attempt to make a higher hydride phase, for example, by working at more than atmospheric pressure (excluding the volatile TiH_4 discussed in the next chapter).

At room temperature, zirconium and hafnium dihydrides are tetragonal and isomorphous with thorium dihydride. Titanium dihydride is cubic above 310°K and tetragonal below that temperature, so that the room temperature form is slightly distorted cubic. At lower hydrogen contents, a number of phases are found for each metal, and the lattice parameters vary with hydrogen content and temperature. In addition, the presence of small amounts of oxide, carbide, or nitride may cause changes in the symmetry of the lattice, as remarked also in the case of thorium [75], and has probably been responsible for some spurious phases reported in the earlier literature [96]. The position has therefore been rather confused, and a number of distinct 'hydrides' such as Zr_2H or Zr_4H have been reported. It is now clear that these are not different compounds but are arbitrarily selected points on the phase diagram. Details of the room temperature structures are given in Table 3.9, and the dihydride phases shall be discussed first.

At 78°K, TiH_2 is tetragonal [87] and the ration of the sides of the unit cell, (taken as face-centred tetragonal (fct) for ease of comparison with the face-centred cubic (fcc) phase)* c_0/a_0, equals 0·945. As the temperature rises, a_0 decreases, and c_0 increases, smoothly, until $a_0 = c_0$ at 310°K and the structure is face-centred cubic. Above the transition, the length of the cubic cell increases slowly with temperature. The volume of the unit cell increases steadily with temperature, through the tetragonal-cubic transition, with no apparent discontinuity [87]. A neutron diffraction study of the deuteride, [88], confirms that the hydrogens are in the tetrahedral sites, so the cubic structure is of the fluorite type. The titanium has eight deuterium atoms at 1·932 Å, and its next neighbours are twelve Ti atoms at 3·140 Å–a significantly greater distance than the Ti-Ti distances in the metal where there are six neighbours at 2·889 Å and six more at 2·952 Å. In this, as in all the transition element hydrides, the density of the hydride is less than that of the metal.

ZrH_2 is tetragonal at room temperature [89], and at all temperatures between 78°K and 780°K [87]. The tetragonality decreases as the temperature rises, with $c_0/a_0 = 0{\cdot}89$ at 78° and 0·91 at 780°K. This suggests that the tetragonal phase may transform to a cubic phase at some higher temperature, in a manner analogous to the titanium system. In an unpublished report [110], it appears that this is indeed the case and a second order transformation at 900°C is reported with a high temperature, cubic, fluorite phase.

HfH_2 resembles ZrH_2 and is tetragonal at room temperature [88, 92]. Again, a transformation to a high-temperature cubic form is reported [110], this time at 407°C. In view of the similarity of the room temperature structures, it seems not unlikely that ThH_2 might have a similar high temperature form. In HfH_2, as in the other dihydrides, the deuteride, MD_2, has a slightly smaller unit cell, and a higher density, than the hydride, MH_2, (see Table 3.9). This effect seems common among the metallic and ionic hydrides.

At hydrogen concentrations below the dihydride stoicheiometry, a number of phases are observed. A very detailed study of the zirconium hydrogen

*The smallest unit cell, and thus the correct description, is that of the body-centred tetragonal (bct) arrangement. However, if the structure is rotated about the *c* axis by 45°, a face-centred tetragonal (and larger) unit cell can be defined. The latter, with $a = b \neq c$, passes into face-centred cubic when $a = c$; it is thus useful when a comparison with fcc is desired to use fct in place of bct to describe the tetragonal structure. The c_0 length is the same for bct and fct, but a_0 in the fct unit cell is $\sqrt{2}$ times a_0 in the bct unit cell.

Table 3.9. *Properties of the Titanium Group Hydrides*

A. *Crystallographic Properties* (a)

	Unit Cell (Å) (a)			Density (g/cc)	
$TiH_{2\cdot0}$	fcc (CaF_2)	$a_0 = 4{\cdot}454$		3·752	[87]
$TiH_{2\cdot0}$	tetragonal, bct	$a_0 = 3{\cdot}202$	$c_0 = 4{\cdot}279$		
	(at 79°K) fct	$a_0 = 4{\cdot}528$		3·779	[87]
	Transformation temperature, tetragonal↔cubic = 310 ± 4°K				
$TiD_{2\cdot0}$	fcc (CaF_2)	$a_0 = 4{\cdot}440$		3·940	[87, 88]
$TiD_{2\cdot0}$	tetragonal, bct	$a_0 = 3{\cdot}187$	$c_0 = 4{\cdot}267$		
	(at 79°K) fct	$a_0 = 4{\cdot}516$		3·963	[87]
	Transformation temperature, tetragonal↔cubic = 310 ± 4°K				
$ZrH_{2\cdot0}$	tetragonal, bct	$a_0 = 3{\cdot}520$	$c_0 = 4{\cdot}449$		
	fct	$a_0 = 4{\cdot}977$		5·62	[89]
	bct	$a_0 = 3{\cdot}522$	$c_0 = 4{\cdot}451$	5·61	[90, 91]
		3·519	4·450		[102]
		3·530	4·455		[93]
$ZrD_{2\cdot0}$	tetragonal, bct	$a_0 = 3{\cdot}516$	$c_0 = 4{\cdot}447$		
	fct	$a_0 = 4{\cdot}972$		5·75	[90]
$HfH_{2\cdot0}$	tetragonal, bct	$a_0 = 3{\cdot}478$	$c_0 = 4{\cdot}361$		
	fct	$a_0 = 4{\cdot}918$		11·37	[92]
		4·882	4·384		[94]
$HfD_{2\cdot0}$	tetragonal, bct	$a_0 = 3{\cdot}456$	$c_0 = 4{\cdot}345$		
	fct	$a_0 = 4{\cdot}887$		11·68	[88]

TiH_x	fcc $a_0 = 4{\cdot}397$ at $x = 1$, to $4{\cdot}460$ at $x = 1{\cdot}65$	
$(Ti + Zr)_1H_2$	fct a_0, c_0 decrease smoothly from 100% Zr to 40% Zr, then two tetragonal phases separate to ca. 5% Zr. Low Zr concentrations soluble in tetragonal TiH_2.	[93]
ZrH_x	(ϵ) bct $x = 1{\cdot}66$ to $2{\cdot}0$, $a_0 = 3{\cdot}469$ to $3{\cdot}519$, $c_0 = 4{\cdot}560$ to $4{\cdot}450$	[102]
	(δ) cubic $x = 1{\cdot}59$ to $1{\cdot}67$, $a_0 = 4{\cdot}779$	[96]
	($\alpha + \gamma + \delta$) bct $x = 1{\cdot}0$ $a_0 = 3{\cdot}527$, $c_0 = 4{\cdot}449$ (but note that the phase diagram [96] shows this region as three-phase)	[97]
	(β) bcc $x = 0$ to $1{\cdot}5$ (high temperature β phase above 900°K) $a_0 = 3{\cdot}65$ at $x = 0{\cdot}4$ and $3{\cdot}72$ at $x = 1{\cdot}5$	[91]
ZrNiH	cubic $a_0 = 7{\cdot}04$, $ZrNiH_3$ $a_0 = 7{\cdot}40$ (both sl. distorted) (cf. ZrNi with $a = 6{\cdot}98$)	[98]
HfH_x	$x = 0$ to $x = 1{\cdot}53$ Hf + deformed cubic HfH_2 $x = 1{\cdot}53$ to $x = 1{\cdot}70$ deformed to fcc phase with $a = 4{\cdot}702$, $c = 4{\cdot}678$ at $x = 1{\cdot}53$ and $a = 4{\cdot}708$ at $x = 1{\cdot}70$ $x = 1{\cdot}70$ to $x = 1{\cdot}87$fcc plus tetragonal HfH_2 phases x above $1{\cdot}87$, tetragonal phase only, $a = 3{\cdot}461$, $c = 4{\cdot}395$ at $x = 1{\cdot}87$ and $a = 3{\cdot}478$, $c = 4{\cdot}361$ at $x = 2$	[92, 94]
$HfD_{1\cdot628}$	cubic, $a_0 = 4{\cdot}680$	[88]

Table 3.9—*continued*

(B) *Thermodynamic Data* (At 25°C)

		ΔH_f° (kcal/mole)	ΔG_f° (kcal/mole)	S° (cal/degree/mole)	
TiH_2		− 4·870	− 0·709	14·96	[105] (b)
$TiH_{1\cdot75}$		−18·850	−10·03	32·3	[105]
		(kcal/mole H_2) −31·1			[112] [184]
		(kcal/mole hydride)			
ZrH_2	(ε)	−39·7			[103] (c)
$ZrH_{1\cdot85}$	(ε)	−38·2			[103]
		(kcal/mole hydride)			
$ZrH_{1\cdot70}$	(δ + ε)	−34·7			[103]
		(kcal/mole hydride)			
$ZrH_{1\cdot43}$	(α + γ + δ)	−30·05			[103]
		(kcal/mole hydride)			
$ZrH_{1\cdot23}$	(α + γ + δ)	−25·3			[103]
		(kcal/mole hydride)			
ZrH_2		−38·90	−29·32	32·13	[101] (d)
ZrD_2		−40·22	−29·68	34·75	[101]
ZrH_2		−40·5	−30·9	C_p difference at 100–350°K gives lattice vibration of 1190 ± 30 cm^{-1}	[90] (b)
ZrD_2		−41·5	−31·2		[90]
$HfH_{1\cdot0}$	δ	− 8·00 (kcal/gatom at 1052°K)		6·32	[113] (e)
$HfH_{1\cdot33}$	δ	− 9·73 (kcal/gatom at 1052°K)		8·00	

Notes (a) The relation between bct and fct alignments of the tetragonal structure is given in the footnote on page 72.

Methods (b) from decomposition pressures; (c) from heat of reaction with HF in water; (d) from oxygen combustion.

(e) These values, with the heat of the δ → ε change, give −23 kcal/mole for ε$HfH_{1\cdot33}$.

system has been made [96], and rather more tentative phase diagrams of the titanium system [111, 112] and of the hafnium system [113] are available. The principle features are best described in terms of the generalized phase diagram shown in Figure 2. (This is based largely on the zirconium diagram.) The zirconium-hydrogen system shows all the regions marked, and five phases have been identified which are tabulated below.

Phase	α	β	γ	δ	ε	Region H
Symmetry	hcp	bcc	bct	fcc	bct	fcc
Description	Zr saturated with H	High temperature Zr, saturated with hydrogen	hydride (metastable)	hydride	hydride	high temperature hydride (part of δ?)

Region (1) on the Figure is the α-phase which is the hexagonal metal with hydrogen in solid solution. At room temperature, this occurs for only a minute proportion of hydrogen, less than 0·1 atom per cent, but it becomes more stable at higher temperatures. Region (6) in Figure 2 is the high temperature, bcc, form of the metal, saturated with hydrogen, and region (5) is the $(\alpha+\beta)$ two-phase region. In the zirconium system, region (3) is the cubic hydride of the δ phase which transforms to the ε tetragonal hydride at increasing hydrogen

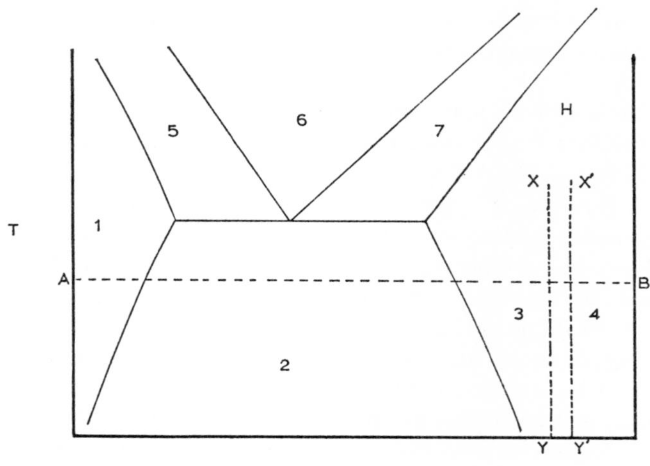

Figure 2. Generalized phase diagram for the metal-hydride systems of titanium, zirconium, and hafnium.

concentration in region (4). The phase boundary between these two regions, XY, varies only slightly with temperature, as far as is known [96]. It is not yet established whether the high temperature cubic form [110] is part of the δ region or a new phase. With pure zirconium, the transition between the δ and ε regions occurs at 62·5 atoms per cent hydrogen and is sharp, occurring over less than 0·1 atoms per cent at room temperature. However, in the presence of oxygen, [11], this transition becomes much less sharp and a broad $(\delta + \varepsilon)$ region exists between (3) and (4). The δ to ε transformation is a diffusionless transfer [96] and related to the increasing occupation of the tetrahedral sites. Region (7) in Figure 2 is the two-phase $(\beta + \delta)$ region. Finally, region (2) has to be considered. This transforms into the cubic δ hydride at 61·4 atoms per cent hydrogen. It contains the α and δ phases, but also a third, metastable phase, the tetragonal γ phase. The structures of the hydride phases are discussed below. A partial study of Zr/D_2 shows no isotope effect on the phase boundaries. [117].

The titanium-hydrogen phase diagram [111, 112] is somewhat simpler than the zirconium one, and corresponds to cutting off the diagram in Figure 2 along the line XY. At temperatures above 100°C, there is no tetragonal phase corresponding to (4), although if the diagram was prolonged below room temperature, a tetragonal hydride phase appears as described above. Thus, the titanium diagram corresponds in general terms to the zirconium one with a shift of the temperature axis. The eutectoid temperature is lower, at about 300°C and shows hysteresis. The zirconium eutectoid temperature is sharp at 580°C. There is also no indication of a metastable phase in region (2) so that the designations of the phases are different. The α and β phases are similar to the zirconium ones, while the stable hydride phase is called γ, and occurs from 50 atoms per cent hydrogen upwards. Region (7) then becomes the ($\beta + \gamma$) two-phase region.

In the hafnium-hydrogen system [113], no eutectoid has been identified (although hafnium metal does have a high-temperature bcc form) in the temperature range 250–870°C. There is an indication of a phase change at about 100°C [114] but it is not known how this fits the general diagram. The phase diagram for Hf/H from 200–800°C is that of Figure 2 cut off along the line AB. The room temperature crystallographic results [92, 94], which are given in Table 3.9, agree with such a diagram. Both cubic and tetragonal hydride phases–regions (3) and (4)–are found, although the transformation XYX′Y′ does not occur so sharply as in the zirconium system. The cubic δ phase extends from 60·5 to 64·8 atoms per cent H, and transforms into the tetragonal ε phase at 65·3 atoms per cent, giving a narrow two-phase (Y-Y′) region at room temperature. Region (1) is hydrogen saturated metal (α) and region (2) is two-phase metal plus cubic hydride ($\alpha + \delta$). In this system, there is no report of any metastable hydride in region (2), but the naming of the phases is chosen to correspond to the zirconium ones. The absence of any β region seems surprising and it may be found at higher temperatures. If this was so, the three phase diagrams would be simply related by a shift of the temperature axis upwards from titanium to zirconium to hafnium (although it will be recollected that the tetragonal-cubic transformation in MH_2 was at a *lower* temperature for hafnium than for zirconium).

A number of questions arise from these structural data. In particular, what is the relation between the structures of the different phases reported, and what is the explanation of the cubic-tetragonal transformation in the dihydride? Both these questions may well have their answer in the same phenomenon, the degree of ordering of the hydrogens entering the tetrahedral sites in the metal structure (which has the metal atoms in cubic close-packed positions, or a tetragonal distortion of this, in all phases except the α one). A study of the mixed titanium-zirconium dihydride system [93] showed that all the $(Ti + Zr)_1H_2$ phases prepared were tetragonal. A single phase was obtained for zirconium concentrations above 40% and below 5%, while a two-phase region, containing tetragonal TiH_2 and tetragonal ZrH_2, occurred between.

It was suggested that this tetragonal/cubic transition in the stoicheiometric dihydride is due to magnetic ordering, and there is a magnetic anomaly–and a specific heat one – in the region of 310°K in TiH_2 [99]. However, the size of this anomaly is too small for it to be a Néel point, and it is unlikely that zirconium dihydride would remain antiferromagnetic up to 900°. It has been suggested instead [93] that the transformation corresponds to the onset of hydrogen diffusion in the lattice, which would equalize the 'occupancy' of the tetrahedral sites and increase the overall symmetry. The nuclear magnetic resonance data [8] show that the protons in TiH_2 become mobile at about the transformation temperature.

The structural relation among the various hydride phases has also been related to the occupancy of the tetrahedral sites by hydrogen. In the zirconium system, Beck [96] points out that the fcc δ hydride is simply related to the fct γ and ε hydrides, transforming sharply into the latter, and forming the former as a metastable decomposition product. The sizes of the unit cells are (in Ångströms)

γ (fct)	δ (fcc)	ϵ (fct)
a_0 = 4·5951 c_0 = 4·9686	a_0 = 4·7783 : 4·8708	a_0 = 4·8854 : 4·9702 c_0 = 4·582 : 4·452
H = 50%	H = 61·4% : 62·5%	H = 62·5% : 65·8%

Thus the δ phase goes into the γ one with a decrease in a_0 and an increase in c_0, and into the ε one with the reverse changes. That is, there is a continual expansion of a_0 and a contraction of c_0 with addition of hydrogen. If the hydrogen is in tetrahedral sites in all three hydride phases, and if the 'ideal' composition of the γ hydride is ZrH, Beck [96] proposes that all the phase differences correspond to variable occupation of the tetrahedral sites, with ZrH having one in every two of the ZrH_2 hydrogen sites occupied. (The alternative of octahedral hydrogen in γ hydride is regarded as less probable.) Thus, increase in the hydrogen content increases the unit cell in the a direction, and contracts it in the c direction, and the cubic phase corresponds to the compositions where $a = c$ out of a range from $a < c$ to $a > c$.

The high temperature, β, body centred cubic phase is also structurally related to the tetragonal phase (in its bct orientation) and the correlation has been discussed [91] by Douglas. He points out that there are many more tetrahedral sites in the cubic cell (in which there are only six H atoms around the Zr, while there are eight in the ε form, the Zr-H distance being 2·08 Å in each case) so that configurational entropy is considerably enhanced in the β phase. If the entropy is maximized (compare Gibb [14] who uses a different calculation) and the further assumption is made that the closest H-H distance in the β phase is the same as that in the ε phase, the maximum hydrogen content of the β phase should be $ZrH_{1\cdot5}$, in agreement with the phase diagram. Douglas, in these calculations, treats the bonding as covalent (similarly to Pauling's theory of metals) and finds good agreement with experiment. In a further calculation, the difference between the configurational entropy and the total entropy leads to a value of 1440 cm^{-1} for the lattice vibration for $ZrH_{1\cdot5}$, in reasonable agreement with the value of 1190 cm^{-1} from heat capacity measurements for ZrH_2 [90]. The good agreement with experimental values found in these calculations based on covalency, and the different route to the configurational entropy from Gibb's ionic model, again emphasizes that a number of theoretical models of the metal hydrides can be constructed and each made to yield acceptable parameters.

Less work has been done on the defect hydride phases of the titanium and hafnium systems, but there is nothing in the zirconium studies to imply that the above conclusions cannot be applied, as appropriate, to the other two systems.

Turning to thermodynamic properties, which are recorded in Table 3.9, the zirconium system is again the most thoroughly studied, and is the only one we shall discuss in detail. All three hydrides form exothermically, and the zirconium and hafnium dihydrides have as high heats of formation as the dihydrides of the earlier Groups. Titanium dihydride is less stable. Turnbull [103] has published a thorough study of the zirconium hydride system, and gives a full review of the somewhat contradictory heats of formation given by earlier authors. His value for ZrH_2, by measuring the heat of reaction with hydrofluoric acid, is in good agreement with the recent combustion value [101]. The combustion data for ZrH_2 and ZrD_2 show a small difference of 1·3 kcal/mole in the heats of formation, and this is similar to the value of 1·0 kcal/mole found from dissociation pressure data in the heat capacity study [90]. In his discussion of the phases of lower hydride content, Turnbull calculates a number of heats of formation of the lower hydride phases from literature data and shows that these values lie on the smooth curve which can be drawn through his own values for various compositions (Table 3.9) and which extrapolate down to zero hydrogen content. Thus, using Douglas and Westlake's [106] correlation of several sets of data, a heat of reaction of $-14\cdot55$ kcal/mole can be calculated for

$$ZrH_{0\cdot755} + 0\cdot285H_2 \xrightleftharpoons{873°K} ZrH_{1\cdot325}\ (\delta)$$

giving a calculated heat of formation at 25°C for $ZrH_{1\cdot325}$ of $-27\cdot35$ kcal/mole, in agreement with the interpolated value from his own data [103]. Turnbull [103] also shows that the metastable γ hydride phase can have only a small heat of formation from the δ phase, and that intermediate compositions, such as $ZrH_{1\cdot6}(\delta)$ are stable with respect to disproportionation into $ZrH_2(\varepsilon)$ and metal. A further point is that, except in the vicinity of a phase transition, the high temperature heat of formation $\Delta H_{T,f}$ is close to the standard heat $\Delta H_{298\ f}$. This is also found for other hydrides, such as UH_3, and means that enthalpies calculated from dissociation pressure data at high temperatures may be relied on. These recent papers [101, 103, 106, 107], which combine and review much earlier data and add their own careful studies, mean that the zirconium-hydrogen system is one of the most fully and critically studied of all the hydrides, from the point of view of thermodynamic properties. The system is also understood in fair detail from the structural point of view, and the phase diagram [96, 108] is established over a wide range of conditions.

Among the ternary phases involving these elements, the results of some studies may be mentioned to indicate the variety of effects that may be expected. The titanium-zirconium dihydride has already been mentioned, and hysteresis in the decomposition of the zirconium-hafnium system has been remarked [109]. Further studies of the zirconium-oxygen-hydrogen system, in addition to [11], have extended and confirmed the earlier results, particularly as to the effect of oxygen in widening the $(\delta + \varepsilon)$ region [118]. Of more varied systems, the study of the zirconium-nickel system with hydrogen is interesting [98]. Here is a case where one component of the alloy has a strong affinity for hydrogen, while the other forms no hydride on its own. NiZr, NiZrH, and $NiZrH_3$ were found in the Ni-Zr-H_2 system, all with slightly distorted cubic structures (Table 3.9). The density of the hydride was less than that of the ZrNi alloy. Thus the alloy forms two hydrides, isomorphous with it, and with an H/Zr ratio rising above that found in zirconium hydride. Thus nickel, although forming no hydride itself, considerably modifies the behaviour of zirconium. The reaction of zirconium-silver alloys has also been studied [116]. ZrAg readily reacts with hydrogen and ZrAgH is formed at 250°C. The unit cell of the hydride shows a marked expansion along the c axis: $a = 3{\cdot}47$, $c = 6{\cdot}61$ for AgZr, and $a = 3{\cdot}36$, $c = 7{\cdot}35$ Å for AgZrH. The hydrogen is thought to be between the sheets of Ag and Zr in the alloy structure, in a site which is coordinated to five zirconium atoms and one silver one. In reactions at higher temperatures, silver is precipitated and a new ternary hydride $ZrAg_xH$ is formed (x less than one). Other alloys were also shown to absorb hydrogen and the probable existence of hydrides, $Zr_3AgH_{4{\cdot}5}$ and Zr_2CuH_2, or related compounds with these Zr/H ratios, was claimed. As far as the evidence goes, these silver, nickel, and copper ternary hydrides with zirconium are all new phases. On the other hand, it is well known that magnesium/zirconium alloys absorb hydrogen with the formation of ZrH_2, which leads to embrittlement [115].

The possible use of zirconium hydride as a neutron moderator in an atomic pile has led to studies of the zirconium-uranium-hydrogen system [186]. The addition of one per cent uranium, by weight, to the zirconium merely shifts all the phase boundaries of the zirconium-hydrogen diagram to slightly lower temperatures–for example, the eutectoid temperature is lowered from 547° to 541°C. No new phases, and no uranium hydride phase, were detected. At higher uranium contents–25 and 50 per cent by weight–the general behaviour with hydrogen was found to be a breakdown of the intermetallic alloy. The zirconium reacted with the hydrogen giving polyphase regions of uranium, zirconium, and zirconium hydride phases, mainly the cubic δ hydride. The phase boundaries of the zirconium hydrogen diagram were relatively unaffected in the region of high hydrogen content, but the α and β phases were markedly shifted. The main effect of the added uranium in this low hydrogen content region was to considerably increase the range of the α phase (of hydrogen dissolved in the metal). Uranium hydride phases were not observed, but one unknown phase appeared at about 700°C, 30 atom per cent hydrogen and 25 weight per cent uranium. This phase was thought to be a complex uranium-zirconium hydride. The presence of uranium increased the heat of 'solution' of the hydrogen in the zirconium. For example, for 25% U, the 'heat of solution' in the δ zirconium hydride was −47·2 kcal/mole, while for the 1% U alloy in the same region, the heat was only 41·2 kcal/mole. Ternary phase diagrams for the Zr-U-H systems are proposed [186]. It would be of interest to extend these studies to alloys of higher uranium content, to explore more fully the possible existence of ternary hydrides.

Hydrides of Vanadium, Niobium and Tantalum. The elements of the vanadium Group all combine with hydrogen directly, under similar conditions to those required for the titanium Group elements. However, hydrogenation does not proceed so far under normal conditions and the usual product is the monohydride, MH, mostly in a non-stoicheiometric form. Under proper conditions hydrogen is readily taken up to this point. Thus Maeland [121] reports that vanadium powder (prepared by first hydriding the pure metal, grinding the hydride, and then decomposing the hydride at 700°C and 10^{-6} mm pressure) reacts exothermically with hydrogen at room temperature and atmospheric pressure. The more conventional preparation direct from the metal requires that this be outgassed at about 1000° under high vacuum and then hydrided at several hundred degrees, with slow cooling in hydrogen (compare [122] for $NbH_{<1}$ or [123] for $TaH_{<1}$). Hydrogen can be taken up beyond the MH composition but only under special conditions. Thus, hydriding vanadium hydride ($VH_{0\cdot40}$) at 70 atmospheres pressure at room temperature gave $VH_{1\cdot45}$, and higher pressures and lower temperatures allowed the preparation of $VH_{1\cdot64}$ [124]. Niobium dihydride could be prepared by cathodic hydrogenation of niobium [125] or by treatment of Nb_2O_5, or better, NbH, with 10% hydrofluoric acid [125, 126]. The hydrofluoric acid treatment yielded a vanadium hydride, $VH_{1\cdot77}$, [124]. There are no reports of any attempts to make a higher tantalum hydride, and indeed, most of the work on tantalum has been on samples around the Ta_2H composition. Brauer [125] notes that hydrofluoric acid treatment of Ta_2O_5 yielded only $TaH_{0\cdot9}$. It may well be that high pressure methods, or the hydrofluoric acid treatment of TaH, would yield a higher tantalum hydride. The dihydrides of niobium and vanadium are much less stable than the monohydrides: for example, half the hydrogen may be removed from NbH_2 by pumping the sample for a short time at room temperature [125].

The elements of the vanadium Group differ further from the elements discussed so far, in the much wider range of hydrogen content over which the α or solution phase occurs. Whereas the other metals formed the α phase over only a very narrow range of hydrogen content at room temperature, in the vanadium Group, the α phase exists for a much wider range of hydrogen content, being found up to $TaH_{0.15}$ at room temperature [127], while some authors have put it as high as $TaH_{0.5}$ [128]. At higher temperatures the α phase is much more extensive, and is the only one observed above about 200°C for all three metals, up to the highest compositions studied.

Information about the phases and their structures in these metal-hydrogen systems is much less complete than that for the earlier Groups, and there is considerable conflict about the occurrence, extent, and symmetry of hydride phases. In the vanadium system, three phases have been identified: the α solid solution phase, the β phase which is a tetragonal hydride phase, and the γ phase which is a cubic hydride phase which probably corresponds to the ideal stoicheiometry VH_2. The data on these phases, at room temperature, are collected in Table 3.10.

For niobium, the α phase accurs along with a phase which is orthorhombic at room temperature, although the departure from the tetragonal angle is very small, and the ratio of the sides is also close to unity. Thus the orthorhombic phase is only slightly distorted from cubic. The corresponding phase in the tantalum system is very similar, but slightly more tetragonal. The niobium dihydride is reported to be cubic.

A number of points should be made about these structures. First, in all cases, the structural parameters of the β hydride phases are obtained from powder photographs with only relatively low accuracy, due to diffuse lines. In the case of the niobium and tantalum systems, this is due to the slight angular distortion of the unit cell, and a similar effect may possibly occur in the tetragonal β phase of the vanadium system. This diffuseness is one cause of the uncertainty of the phase boundary between the α and $(\alpha + \beta)$ regions remarked in the niobium and tantalum systems [123]. In all cases, the two-phase $(\alpha + \beta)$ region disappears at moderate temperatures and the orthogonal distortion of the β phases of the niobium and tantalum systems also disappears on heating. The pure VH_2 has not been prepared [124] and, although $NbH_{2.0}$ has been prepared [125], its relation to the rest of the niobium-hydrogen system is not established, and it is not clear how extensive the (presumed) $(\beta + \alpha)$ two-phase region is. Considerable uncertainty exists in this structural work, especially about the positions of the phase boundaries. Forthcoming work of Hardcastle [134] on the $V\text{-}D_2$ system may help to clarify the situation. The phase diagram has been determined from pure V to $VD_{1.8}$, using X-ray techniques, and the structures of $VD_{0.5}$ and $VD_{0.75}$ have been determined at several temperatures by neutron diffraction. The $V\text{-}D_2$ system is similar to that of $V\text{-}H_2$ [121], except for a shift in the temperature axis; 75°C in the $V\text{-}H_2$ system corresponding approximately to 0°C in the $V\text{-}D_2$ system. The structures of $VD_{0.5}$ and $VD_{0.75}$ are pseudo-cubic, similar to that for Ta_2D.

It is clear that the distortion of the unit cell in the niobium hydride β phase is very slight, and accurate work using line profiles on the X-ray diffractometer [122] shows that the variations with composition are subtle, and not completely regular. The tetragonal distortion passes from $c < a$ through $c = a$

Table 3.10. *Structural Parameters of the Group V Hydrides*

Phase	Composition range	Structure	
Vanadium [121]			
α	V to $VH_{0\cdot05}$	bcc	a = 3·027 to 3·037 Å
α + β	$VH_{0\cdot05}$ to $VH_{0\cdot46}$		
β	$VH_{0\cdot46}$ to $VH_{0\cdot90}$	bct	a = 3·002, c = 3·302 for $VH_{0\cdot05}$ a = 3·03, c = 3·42 for $VH_{0\cdot80}$ parameters same for $VH_{>0\cdot80}$ Compare, a = 2·96, c = 3·28 ($VH_{0\cdot43}$) [129] a = 3·00, c = 3·31 ($VH_{0\cdot82}$) [129] a = 3·02, c = 3·36 ($VH_{0\cdot94}$) [130] a = 2·996, c = 3·342 (VH) [131] a = 3·081, c = 3·280 ($VH_{0\cdot25}$) [174]
β + γ	$VH_{0\cdot90}$ to $VH_{1\cdot80}$		
γ	(VH_2)	fcc	a = 4·270 [124]

The β phase disappears above 200°C. At H/V above 0·8, it is proposed that an eutectoid exists involving a low-temperature (β + γ) phase, and high temperature phases with α and (α + γ) regions. The eutectoid temperature is about 80°C [121].

Phase	Composition range	Structure	
Niobium [126]			
α	Nb to $NbH_{0\cdot11}$	b.c.c.	a = 3·295 to 3·307 (compare 3·305 [132])
α + β	$NbH_{0\cdot11}$ to $NbH_{0\cdot70}$		
β	$NbH_{0\cdot70}$ to $NbH_{>0\cdot9}$	ortho-rhombic (a) (slightly deformed bcc)	a = 4·83, b = 4·89, c= 3·44, γ = 89·4° (for $NbH_{0\cdot89}$) (Compare similar data in [122] in Figures) c/a_b = 1·004 for $NbH_{0\cdot84}$ (a) [122] 0·9995 for $NbH_{0\cdot73}$ 0·9975 for $NbH_{0\cdot67}$ Compare a = 4·849, b = 4·854, c = 3·383 for $NbH_{0\cdot85}$ [174]
β + γ	???		
γ	$NbH_{2\cdot00}$	fcc	a = 4·536 [125]

The β phase transforms to full cubic symmetry at about 100°C and with H content above $NbH_{0\cdot6}$. The (α + β) region disappears above 140°C – at a lower temperature than with V.

Notes (a) The orthorhombic a and b parameters are divided by $\sqrt{2}$ to convert to the sides of the corresponding deformed cube, a_b and b_b: the c side remains unaltered.

(b) Taking the β phase as essentially cubic, a = 3·42 for $NbH_{0\cdot68}$ [132].

Phase	Composition range	Structure	
Tantalum [126]			
α	Ta to $TaH_{0\cdot22}$	bcc	
α + β	$TaH_{0\cdot22}$ to $TaH_{0\cdot6}$		
β	$Tah_{0\cdot6}$ to $TaH_{>0\cdot9}$	ortho-rhombic (distorted bcc)	a = 4·718, b = 4·768, c = 3·421, γ = 89·2° (for $TaH_{0\cdot89}$) Compare a = 4·804, c = 3·382 for $TaH_{0\cdot8}$ taken as fct [174]

It is calculated that a = (3·306 + 0·146n) in the nearly cubic alignment of the β phase (from the data of [133] for TaH_n) for hydrogen contents up to $TaH_{0\cdot75}$ [123].

to $c > a$ with increasing hydrogen content, and the angular distortion also increases by about $\frac{1}{2}°$ between H/Nb = 0·6 to 0·8. A similar, but rather greater, distortion is found in the β tantalum hydride phase.

It is not even completely clear what the hydrogen positions are in these hydrides. It is assumed that the MH_2 phases are fluorite structure, and the vanadium-hydrogen work [121], and recent neutron scattering experiments on $TaD_{0·5}$ [136], are based on tetrahedral hydrogen. However, the suggestion in earlier papers [135] of octahedral hydrogen in tantalum hydrides has not been specifically refuted. There is a conflict between this neutron diffraction study, and work from the same laboratory on the heat capacity of $TaH_{0·5}$ [137]. The latter showed a residual entropy of $-0·39$ cal/degree/mole, while the neutron diffraction study showed an *ordered* arrangement of deuterium in $TaD_{0·5}$ at low temperatures. The unit cell (pseudo-cubic) was of side 6·67 Å from 4°K to about room temperature, and the 'normal' cell of 3·37 Å was found only at temperatures above room temperature. The change was ascribed to the change from ordered filling of tetrahedral sites at the lower temperatures, to disordered occupation at higher temperatures. An attempt to reconcile the two types of result, and the fact that three discontinuities occur in the heat capacity curve, was made by postulating local ordering which was not sufficiently extensive to show up in the diffraction experiments. This would also account for the fact that the configurational entropy for the α phase was found to be only 4·9 eu, compared with a calculated value of 6·4 eu for random tetrahedral site occupation.

There is little thermodynamic data available for the vanadium Group hydrides. The defect monohydrides form exothermically, but the heats of formation are probably fairly low. A value of 3·2 kcal/gram-atom has been reported for $TaH_{0·5}$ [138], at a temperature which indicates the compound was probably α phase.

The important feature of this group of hydrogen systems is that the 'solution' region or α phase is more extensive than with the earlier hydrides, even at room temperature. Thus these hydrides, especially TaH_x with $x =$ about 0·5, have been studied fairly extensively in the investigation of the diffusion of hydrogen in the metal [123, 139], using magnetic resonance techniques. The general results of these studies will be discussed, along with those for other systems, at the end of this section. Here it might be noted that the results suggest the transitions observed in the niobium and tantalum systems, including the heat capacity anomalies [137], may all reflect different degrees of order, governed by the ease of diffusion of hydrogen in the lattice.

Much of this uncertainty about the structures in the Group V monohydride phases, and a major factor in the difficulty of interpreting the neutron diffraction results, arises from the fact that these monohydrides are body-centred cubic (to a first approximation), whereas all the hydride phases previously encountered (except the high temperature β phase of the Group IV hydrides) have been based on close packing. In the latter, there are only two tetrahedral sites and one octahedral site per metal atom, while in the body-centred cube, there are many more possible sites–six tetrahedral and three octahedral sites per metal atom. Thus the possibilities for disorder, for local ordering, and for superstructure formation are much greater. The number of alternative configurations to which the diffraction results could be matched is also considerably increased.

Supposed Hydrides of the Remaining Transition Elements (*Excluding Pd and Cu*). The uncertainty which appears in the case of the Group V elements, is even more pronounced in the remaining part of the *d* block up to the zinc Group–with the exception of palladium and copper hydrides which are discussed separately. The problems arise because many of the transition elements can adsorb and occlude considerable volumes of hydrogen, especially when they are finely divided, and it is difficult to distinguish such systems from non-stoicheiometric hydrides by purely chemical means, especially when the 'hydride' preparation involves a complex reaction system. To quote one example, the anhydrous halides of many of the later transition metals form a dark, finely crystalline, powder when treated with Grignard reagents in ether in a hydrogen atmosphere under anhydrous conditions [140]. These systems certainly absorb hydrogen, and the preparation of a variety of hydrides, such as NiH_2, CoH_2, FeH_2, CrH_3 and even FeH_6, has been claimed. Later work on the nickel system showed that part of the observations were accurate, in that hydrogen was absorbed, but this went (*a*) to hydrogenate the organic group of the Grignard reagent and (*b*) to form RMgH [141]. The H/Mg ratio was found to be 0·5 under a variety of conditions (MgX_2 formed as well) but no constancy was observed in the H/Ni ratio. Clearly, the presence of hydridic magnesium compounds in the residue could account for many of the metal-hydride observations. The presence of NiH_2 as a reaction intermediate is postulated by the latter authors [141].

To be acceptable, reports of metal hydrides must show clear structural changes in the hydride phase, and, on this criterion, the postulate of hydrides of all the elements in the later transition Groups (from chromium through to copper) must be regarded as not proven, with the exceptions of chromium, palladium, and copper hydrides. There are sometimes reports of permanent structural changes in other metals, for example in nickel [142, 171], on cathodic hydrogenation, but these amount to changes in the lattice constant of the metal structure rather than the formation or a hydride phase of different structure. Thus, hydrogenated metals corresponding to the α phase solid solutions of the earlier transition elements probably occur.

The solubility of hydrogen in these metals varies widely from one element to the next, and also with the state of the metal. A critical review is given by Smith [149], to which the reader must be referred for details. Hydrogen contents of up to 60cc/100g of metal have been observed for manganese, to quote an average case. Calculations of the heats of formation of the hypothetical hydrides of such elements show that in a number of cases, especially iron, cobalt, nickel and platinum, these are approximately zero, not endothermic, which may account for the ready absorption of hydrogen which gives rise to the well-known catalytic properties of the elements.

The case of *chromium* is rather more certain than for the other metals, though considerable doubts still exist about the details of composition of the chromium hydrides. Snavely [143] showed twenty years ago that the reported hexagonal allotrope of chromium metal was, in fact, a hydride phase, and he also identified a second hydride phase [144]. These were both formed in the course of the electrolysis of chromic acid solutions, when bcc chromium metal, hexagonal hydride, or fcc hydride, were formed depending on the conditions. He measured the crystal structure of his hydride phases and found (Å),

hexagonal hydride: $a = 2{\cdot}722$, $c = 3{\cdot}441$, (density $= 6{\cdot}198$ g/cc.)
face-centred cubic hydride: $a = 3{\cdot}861$ (density $= 6{\cdot}236$ g/cc.).

The hexagonal hydride was identified as CrH and the fcc one as CrH_2, largely by analogy with known hydrides and structures. More recent work has confirmed the existence of both hydride phases, shown that the hexagonal phase is approximately CrH [145], but the composition CrH_2 was not confirmed for the cubic phase. It was shown that the bcc metal takes up hydrogen in solid solution to a composition $CrH_{0{\cdot}04}$, then a two-phase region exists with this 'α' phase and the hexagonal hydride. The hexagonal hydride exists as a single phase only in the composition range $CrH_{0{\cdot}95-1{\cdot}00}$ [146]. The hydrides were prepared by electrolysis of CrO_3 in dilute acid, with high CrO_3 concentration, high current density, and temperatures in the range 2–4°C. The apparent unreactivity of the hydrided samples was ascribed to rapid formation of a protective oxide layer. At low oxygen pressures, there was rapid decomposition at room temperature. This author [145] still has reservations about the existence of a 'true hydride' of chromium in this hexagonal phase, apparently because of the high mobility of the hydrogen in the lattice. In a neutron diffraction study of the hexagonal phase [147] it was found that the structure was not wurtzite, as postulated by Snavely [144], but anti-NiAs with six-coordinated hydrogen. The structure has a minimum Cr-Cr distance of 2·71 Å, as compared with 2·55 Å calculated for twelve-coordinated chromium. The Cr-H distance was 1·91 Å. This is the first case encountered so far, where the hydrogen in a hydride is six-coordinated without there first being four-coordinated hydrogen in the lattice (as there was in the MH_3 lanthanide phases). It may be that there is here an indication of one reason contributing to the instability of hydride phases in this region of the Periodic Table. There is a big decrease in radius between vanadium and chromium [89] and then a further decline to nickel and this suggests that steric effects, such as a diminution in the size of the tetrahedral site, may be one cause of the 'hydride gap', though not the only factor as the bonding also alters and the bonding ability of the *d* orbitals is changing.

A critique of the existence of an iron hydride has been given recently [148]: no Fe-H material was found in Grignard preparations.

A mixed, or complex, hydride of lithium and rhodium has been reported briefly [150], and this is discussed with K_2ReH_7 in the chapter on transition metal hydride complexes.

The Palladium-Hydrogen System. The absorption of large volumes of hydrogen by palladium was observed over a hundred and fifty years ago. The system has been extensively investigated for more than a century, and the results are still not fully understood in the sense that there is no uniformly accepted account of the various phenomena. Smith [149] reviews the work up to 1945, and Gibb [5] has given an account of more recent developments. Aston discusses the structure in [186] and see also [172]. Wicke and Nernst give a very useful short review in their 1964 paper [151].

There are two phases in the palladium-hydrogen system, both with cubic close packed palladium atoms. The α phase, which occurs to the extent of three atoms per cent hydrogen at room temperature, has a lattice constant close to that of the parent metal, and may be regarded as the solution phase, analogous to that observed in all other hydride systems. The β phase has a much larger unit cell ($a = 4{\cdot}018$ Å for a composition $PdH_{0{\cdot}6}$ at room temperature compared with $a = 3{\cdot}890$ Å for $PdH_{0{\cdot}03}$) and occurs up to the highest hydrogen content so far obtained, of $PdH_{0{\cdot}83}$ at -78°C. A two-phase region exists for hydrogen contents up to about $PdH_{0{\cdot}5}$ at room temperature, but diminishes in range with temperature. Above 300°C, only one phase is found up to 1000 atmospheres hydrogen pressure. The phase diagram is thus qualitatively similar to that of the Group V hydrides below the composition MH. A full pressure-composition-temperature diagram covering the composition range $PdH_{0-0{\cdot}9}$, temperatures up to about 500°C and pressures up to 1000 atmospheres is given by Levine and Weale [152], incorporating their own and earlier work [153–5]. A complementary diagram of composition, as reflected in the lattice parameters, against decomposition pressure is given by Maeland and Gibb [156]. A neutron diffraction study [157] shows that the hydrogen in the β phase is octahedrally coordinated, so that this phase is a defect sodium chloride lattice, with an extrapolated lattice constant of $a = 4{\cdot}11$ Å, for the hypothetical PdH stoicheiometry. A number of workers have reported lattice constants [156–159, among others] and all are in substantial agreement. As the pressure of hydrogen above the sample varies, the lattice constants alter in a regular manner, as the following examples indicate [156]:

Temperature				
206°C	Pressure (atm)	22·3—5·1	3·8—1·7	0·0
	alpha a_0 (Å)	*	3·916—3·909	3·903
	beta a_0 (Å)	4·043—4·022		

*The α phase appears faintly at this pressure.

346°C	Pressure (atm)	33·7—4·1
	single phase, a_0	3·997—3·916

The 206° isotherm passes through the two phase region. The cell size of the β phase decreases quite rapidly with hydrogen content, while the change in the α phase is much slower. At the higher temperature, only one phase occurs which decreases in size with hydrogen content.

In the two-phase region, hysteresis occurs in the isotherms, and this has been the subject of much work. A recent contribution [160], suggests that it results from compressive strains arising in the α phase as the much larger β lattice forms. This strain exceeds the elastic limit of the α lattice which deforms plastically. Then, on desorption, the system is β plus deformed α and the pressures differ from those for absorption. Calculation of the position and size of the hysteresis loop from the yield strength of the metal proved to be successful. This model is only one of a number which have been proposed, and the merits of each are discussed [160, 173]. The more commonly accepted theory to account for the hysteresis deals with the attraction of vacancies and hydrogen atoms in the lattice. It is found that there is a zero-point entropy in the α phase, of 0·6 eu [158], and this is also accounted for by an interaction between atoms. A calculation of the chemical potential of the dissolved gases as the composition tends towards PdH_0 gives excess values which were attributed to attractive interactions in the α phase, while the excess values for the β phase indicated a repulsive interaction [151].

The heat of formation of the hydride is exothermic and various determinations agree quite closely. The values for the deuteride are lower than those for the hydride:

Heat of Formation	$PdH_{0\cdot5}$	9·66 [158] :	9·5 [156] :	9·32 [151]
(kcal/mole H_2)	$PdD_{0\cdot5}$	8·63 [158] :		8·88 [151]

Entropy of Formation: $PdH_{0\cdot5}$, 21·8 eu; $PdD_{0\cdot5}$, 23·4 eu, per mole H_2 [151].

These values imply considerable differences in the pressures of hydrogen or deuterium over palladium. At 30°C, pressures are 8·4 torr and 39·0 torr, and at −78°C, they are $1{\cdot}56 \times 10^{-3}$ torr and $10{\cdot}6 \times 10^{-3}$ torr, respectively for hydride and deuteride. These values give a separation factor for equimolar mixtures of H_2/D_2 of 2·3 at 50°C and 3·7 at −78°C.

Among other parameters of the system which have been studied, mention may be made of the magnetic susceptibility which falls linearly with increased hydrogen content to a value of zero at about $PdH_{0\cdot6}$ [5]. This has been attributed to the effect of the expansion of the palladium lattice in the β form [5], or to the effect of adding hydrogen electrons to the conduction band [161]. It may be objected that the latter account requires the limiting composition, where diamagnetism sets in, to be $PdH_{0\cdot55}$, while the experimental results show that the composition is above 0·6 H/Pd. In addition, there is the result of Michel and Gallissot [162], that the susceptibility of 'β-palladium' (that is, the expanded metal form produced by carefully dehydriding the β hydride phase at low temperatures) is itself diamagnetic.

In an elegant paper by Aben and Burgess, it has been shown that the changes observed in the voltage of the palladium/hydrogen electrode reflect formation of hydride on the surface. The voltage of a palladium electrode (in contact with one atmosphere pressure H_2 and normal acid) is about 100 millivolts when freshly set up. It drops sharply in the first few minutes (I) to a constant value of about 45 mv (II) which remains for some time, of the order of an hour, and then falls off gradually in a third region (III) to zero. Aben and Burgess [159] showed by X-ray diffraction that the region I corresponded to the formation of a surface layer of α hydride, region II, to a two-phase layer, with the α component diminishing with time, and region III to a build up of β hydride as a single phase in the surface layer.

The above account is no more than a cursory account of the vast volume of work on the palladium-hydrogen system. As one of the first metal-hydrogen systems to be discovered, the properties of the palladium system are the most extensively studied, and have given rise to many of the theories of the metal hydrides which have gained currency in the last half-century. In view of this, it must be emphasized that the palladium system is atypical in a number of ways. It is the only hydride where the hydride phase and the α metallic solution phase have a metal lattice of the same symmetry. It is the only hydride, apart from CrH, in which the hydrogen is in octahedral co-ordination, without first filling the tetrahedral sites. It is the only hydride of the transition metals where the stoicheiometric composition has never been attained (and, as such, gave rise to the whole impression of non-stoicheiometric, interstitial solutions, with variations between samples being due to rifts and inclusions).

Palladium hydride and the vanadium Group hydrides have the most extensive range over which the α phase occurs at moderate temperatures, and they show the highest mobility of hydrogen at moderate temperatures and compositions. Furthermore, because of its electrical properties, palladium has tended to reveal its hydriding character in electrical studies, and it has been natural to prepare the hydrides electrolytically. Thus, the purity of samples has been more variable than with compounds prepared by direct combination. All these factors have combined to give rise to Gibb's conclusion [5] that 'the present consensus is that additional study of the several proposed models must be made in order to reconcile the many observed properties of the Pd-H_2 system'. It also means, from the general point of view of all the metal hydrides, that the palladium-hydrogen system is the worst one to use in the construction of models of the hydrides. Its unique properties may well mean that it is an extreme case, and general theories would do better to start from the more 'average' hydrides of Groups III and IV.

In this context, Aston's theory of the palladium hydride may be mentioned, as it does satisfy the criterion of being unique to the palladium system [165]. Aston regards the basic unit in palladium hydride as square planar PdH_4, as in general palladium chemistry. These units are arranged in sheets, so that all the sheets in one direction would be filled at $PdH_{0.5}$. Cross-sheets in the perpendicular direction would then form, giving ultimately the NaCl structure. In any one region, there would be a tendency for sheets to be parallel, but right-angled bends would be common, retaining the overall cubic symmetry. This basic model is used to explain the conductivity and specific heat properties of the hydride, and diffusion between PdH_4 units sets in at 150°K and accounts for the observed mobility of the hydrogen.

A large variety of studies have been made of mixed systems of palladium with other metals. Among the most fully studied systems are the palladium/platinum system [163] and the palladium/silver system [164]. In both cases, increasing the amount of added metal decreases the hydrogen uptake, but the qualitative features of the palladium/hydride system remain, and cubic α and β phases are observed up to about 12% Pt and 30% Ag. Alloys containing as much as 50% Ag still absorb about fifteen atoms per cent hydrogen.

Copper Hydride. Copper hydride has been known almost as long as palladium hydride, and was first prepared by Wurtz in 1844. His method, the reduction of copper sulphate solution by hypophosphorous acid, still remains one of the most effective preparations. The hydride, CuH, is produced as a reddish-brown powder, of varying degrees of purity and stability, so there has been some controversy as to its identity. This is now regarded as established.

Among the more recent studies on copper hydride, is the Russian investigation of various preparation reactions [166]. In this, diborane, and sodium borohydride were confirmed to be effective in the reduction, while phosphorous acid and sodium hydrotrimethoxyborate $NaH(OMe)_3$, were not effective in producing CuH from copper sulphate, confirming Schlesinger's observation in the former case. The hydride is also prepared electrolytically, or by reaction with atomic hydrogen, but cannot be prepared by direct combination between the elements. As commonly prepared, copper hydride contains copper, water, and phosphorus-containing ions. Preparations free of copper can be obtained, while those of low water content are very unstable and pyrophoric. Attempts to remove the last 0·1% of phosphorus led to decomposition. The decomposition is irreversible, and has been shown by Warf [167] to be first order, and catalyzed by base or fluoride ion and retarded by small amounts of the other halide ions. Warf proposes that the surface of each copper hydride particle is protected by adsorbed water, phosphorus oxyanion, and halide if present. The action of hydroxide or fluoride is to remove copper at the surface, producing metal in the process, and the decomposition nucleates at these surface sites. Then the whole particle reacts (as the decomposition is exothermic). Halide ions in large concentrations catalyze the decomposition because copper halo-complexes, CuX_2^-, are formed. This mechanism is in accord with the observation that CuH in D_2O does not exchange hydrogen on decomposition with NaOD.

Copper hydride, as solid or suspension, may be kept indefinitely at -78°C, or in solution in the presence of the optimum amount of halide ion, but otherwise decomposes rapidly. Even the dry solid kept in an inert atmosphere is completely decomposed in a few hours.

The structure of copper hydride has been determined by X-ray and neutron diffraction methods [168]. Müller and Bradley [169] found the copper atoms were in an hexagonal unit cell with $a = 2{\cdot}89$ Å, $c = 4{\cdot}61$ Å. This was confirmed by Goedkoop and Andresen [168] who located the hydrogen atoms in the (0,0,3/8) and (1/3, 2/3, 7/8) positions by neutron diffraction, to give the wurtzite structure. Warf and Feitknecht [170] find $a = 2{\cdot}89$ Å, $c = 4{\cdot}63$ Å, density = 6·39 g/cc for CuH, and $a = 2{\cdot}93$ Å, $c = 4{\cdot}68$ Å, density = 6·28 g/cc for CuD.

Copper hydride is intermediate between the transition metal hydrides and the polymeric hydrides of the main Group elements, and has many affinities with the latter. It is formed endothermically ($\Delta H_f = 5{\cdot}12$ kcal) and decomposes irreversibly, and has not been found in the direct reaction between the metal and hydrogen.

Further Studies on the Transition Metal Hydrides. Sakamoto [174] has reported the results of thermal neutron scattering by a number of transition metal hydrides and correlated a number of earlier studies. Measurements on a variety of compositions in the titanium hydride system, in the range $TiH_{1\cdot3-2\cdot0}$, and at temperatures above and below the cubic-tetragonal transition in TiH_2, gave results which were independent of composition and symmetry. The scattering curves gave minima due to the optical vibration of the hydride lattices, with the values listed:

	$TiH_{1\cdot3-2\cdot0}$	0·135 eV (1090 cm^{-1})
	$VH_{0\cdot25}$	0·165 eV (1332 cm^{-1})
	$NbH_{0\cdot50}$	0·150 eV (1210 cm^{-1})
	$TaH_{0\cdot70}$	0·145 eV (1170 cm^{-1})
Compare	YH_2	984 cm^{-1} [29]
	YH_3	1295, 920, and 640 cm^{-1} ([28]–from infra-red)
	$ZrH_{1\cdot5-1\cdot8}$	1105 cm^{-1} [90][175].

Sakomoto shows that the lattice vibrations bear a linear relation to the M-H distance in the solid, for all the transition metal results listed, and also for CaH_2 and UH_3. The only result which does not fall on, or very near, his straight line is that for $PdH_{0\cdot6}$, and this is the only hydride where the hydrogen is in an octahedral site rather than a tetrahedral one. The value for YH_2 also fits Sakamoto's relation. The correlation between the two parameters is expected as both give a measure of the 'bond strength' of the metal-hydrogen interaction. This supports the general use of the Einstein model in dealing with these hydride lattice vibrations, in which the hydrogens are regarded as vibrating against the stationary metal atoms.

A variety of nuclear magnetic resonance studies on transition metal hydrides have appeared. Results for lanthanum, titanium and tantalum hydrides have been discussed by Pedersen [176]. Briefly, there are three parameters derived from the nmr experiment: the line width, the position of the absorption–which, in the case of these metallic hydrides, corresponds to a Knight shift–and the spin-lattice relaxation time. These can be interpreted to give structural information (from line widths), information on the mobility of the proton (shown by a narrowing of the nmr line, and its temperature variation), and information about the electron distribution in the hydride (mainly from the Knight shift). The structural information derived from the nuclear magnetic resonance experiments is complementary to that derived from diffraction results, as the latter correspond to long-range ordering while the former reflect short-range order. Thus, as we have seen, neutron diffraction results on non-stoicheiometric lanthanum hydride and titanium hydride show that the hydrogens are occupying the tetrahedral sites in a random manner, and this reflects the overall statistical occupation of these positions. The nmr measurements, at low temperatures before proton diffusion sets in, on these systems [40, 8, 177] also show random occupation of the tetrahedral sites, so the statistical distribution of the hydrogens is short range. On the other hand, neutron diffraction results on tantalum hydride [136] indicate superstructure and the nmr study [123] shows rapid proton motion at low temperatures. The results are combined to indicate a highly correlated motion of the protons, made possible by the large number of sites available.

The spin-lattice relaxation time for the tantalum hydride [123] showed discontinuities at the same temperatures as the thermal anomalies were found [137], and these intermediate transformations could correspond to the breakdown of the correlation of the proton motion.

From the nmr results, a number of values have become available for the activation energy of proton diffusion. These are approximately

20 kcal/mole in the La/H system [40]
10 ,, ,, ,, Ti/H system [8]
12·5 ,, ,, ,, Zr/H system [180]
5 ,, ,, ,, Nb/H system (low temperature phase) [139]
3·7 ,, ,, ,, Nb/H system (high temp. cubic phase) [139]
2·5 to 3·7 for $TaH_{0\cdot75-0\cdot10}$ (low temperature phase) [178, 123]: 6·3 for the intermediate β' phase and 1·6 for the high temperature α phase (all kcal/mole: the latter two independent of H concentration) [123].
3·9 kcal/mole for the Pd/H system [179].

These values reflect the higher hydrogen content (and the smaller number of proton sites in the cubic close packed lattice) of the LaH_2, TiH_2, and ZrH_2 systems compared with the lower proton content in the other $MH_{<1}$ systems. The niobium and tantalum hydrides also have available the much larger number of hydrogen sites of the body-centred cubic lattice.

Final Remarks on the Bonding in Transition Metal Hydrides. The Knight shifts measured in the nmr experiments, and the variations in the other two parameters, have all been interpreted in terms of the protonic or alloy theory of the hydrides [8, 40, 137, 177, 180, 181, 182, 178, 179]. That is, the hydrogen in the metal hydride is regarded as ionizing to H^+ and an electron, which then enters the conduction band of the metal as in the model of Isenberg [2]. The close correlation observed in the Knight shifts of the V-H and V-Cr systems has been adduced as additional evidence for the proton theory. The Cr is regarded as *providing* an extra conduction electron in its vanadium alloys, and the curves, of Knight shift versus concentration of 'alloying' element, follow the same path, whether the added element is H or Cr. However, it is remarked that the same model leads to a calculated charge separation in the sense $Ti^{\delta-} - H^{\delta+}$ [8] and $Ta^{\delta+} - H^{\delta-}$ [123] for these two hydride systems.

In recent papers, the proton theory has been mainly used in the interpretation of nuclear magnetic resonance experiments on a variety of metal hydrides, and in the interpretation of the palladium-hydrogen system. The hydridic hydrogen theory has been used, equally successfully, in the calculation of lattice energies and configuration interactions, and has been applied in theories of long- and short-range ordering in the highly defect phases. The hydride theory also gives a direct explanation of the magnetic studies on the lanthanide hydrides [35]. Here, the observed differences in the temperatures at which magnetic ordering takes place in the metal, dihydride, and trihydride, can be explained only on the basis that addition of hydrogen to the metal *removes* electrons from the conduction bands.

Thus, the position of the two theories, postulating respectively $H^{\delta+}$ and $H^{\delta-}$ in the metallic hydrides, seems to be about 'all square at the turn'. It appears that either theory, if developed rigorously, will give a sufficient explanation of the phenomena. Certainly, no experiment has yet been reported which clearly eliminates one or the other. At present, the hydride theory is very successful when applied to 'static' situations like the calculation of lattice energies and interionic distances, while the protonic theory succeeds when discussing the mobile hydrogen species in diffusion and relaxation processes.

It has been assumed so far, in the literature and in the above, that a single theory should be able to account for all the hydrides which show metallic properties. It is quite likely that this may not be the case, and the nature of the hydrogen in the solution (or α) phases, and in palladium hydride, and the low-hydrogen-content phases of the vanadium Group elements, is not the same as in the lanthanide, actinide and titanium Group hydrides. In particular, it seems dangerous to assume that theories which account for the behaviour of the unique palladium-hydrogen system can necessarily be extended to other metal hydrides.

Possibly much of this apparently contradictory series of results can be reconciled by Gibb's proposal that H^+ is an excited state of H^- and exists in minute proportion in equilibrium with H^- at experimental temperatures. Then all the steric and bonding interactions in the hydrides are determined by the properties of hydride ions, while motion of the hydrogen and related effects are governed by the unique size of the proton.

Summary. The elements of the titanium Group form hydrides of ideal stoicheiometry MH_2. These are tetragonal at lower temperatures but probably become cubic close packed at higher temperatures, and also at H-M ratios of less than two. They are isomorphous with ThH_2. The phase relations are fairly complex but now seem to be firmly established, at least in the case of zirconium. The vanadium Group elements form hydrides of ideal formula MH, and vanadium and niobium probably give an MH_2 hydride as well. The MH hydrides are relatively stable and have a body-centred cubic structure, or one slightly distorted from this. The higher hydrides are much less stable and are assumed to be cubic, with the fluorite structure. Of the remaining transition elements, chromium forms a monohydride and a dihydride is also possible. CrH has the nickel arsenide structure with six-coordinated hydrogen. Palladium forms a hydride of composition $PdH_{0\cdot 6}$ at room temperatures, in which the hydrogen is octahedrally coordinated. The ideal form, PdH, (which has never been prepared) would have the sodium chloride structure. Copper hydride, CuH, decomposes irreversibly and has the wurtzite structure.

Theories postulating either positive or negative hydrogen in the hydrides (including the lanthanide and actinide hydrides) have been advanced and each succeeds in accounting for part of the observed phenomena.

REFERENCES

[1] A. R. UBBELOHDE, *Proc. Roy. Soc.*, 1937, **159A**, 295: *J. Chem. Soc.*, 1950, 1143.
[2] I. ISENBERG, *Phys. Rev.*, 1950, **79**, 736.
[3] C. K. COOGAN and H. S. GUTOWSKY, *J. Chem. Phys.*, 1962, **36**, 110.
[4] W. B. HILLIG, Thesis, University of Michigan, 1954. (Quoted in [5]).
[5] T. R. P. GIBB Jr., "Primary Solid Hydrides" in *Progress in Inorganic Chemistry.* Edited by F. A. Cotton, Inter-science, 1962, **3**, 315.
[6] T. R. P. GIBB Jr., Lecture at Nottingham University, 1964.
[7] M. A. GARSTENS, *Phys. Rev.*, 1950, **79**, 397.
[8] B. STALINSKI, C. K. COOGAN, and H. S. GUTOWSKY, *J. Chem. Phys.*, 1961, **34**, 1191.
[9] T. R. P. GIBB Jr. and D. P. SCHUMACHER, *J. Phys. Chem.*, 1960, **64**, 1407: T. R. P. GIBB Jr. and G. G. LIBOWITZ, *J. Phys. Chem.*, 1956, **60**, 510.
[10] R. J. CLARK and J. D. CORBETT, *Inorg. Chem.*, 1963, **2**, 460.
[11] R. K. EDWARDS and P, LEVESQUE, *J. Amer. Chem. Soc.*, 1955, **77**, 1312.
[12] G. V. SAMSONOV, *Russ. J. Inorg. Chem.*, 1963, **8**, 685.
[13] J. S. ANDERSON, 1963 Liversidge Lecture, *Proc. Chem. Soc.*, 1964, 166.
[14] T. R. P. GIBB Jr., *J. Phys. Chem.*, 1964, **68**, 1096.
[15] K. H. GAYER and W. G. BOS, *J. Phys. Chem.*, 1964, **68**, 2569.
[16] R. N. R. MULFORD and C. E. HOLLEY Jr., *J. Phys. Chem.*, 1955, **59**, 1222.
[17] K. DIALER and W. ROTHE, *Zeit. Elektrochem.*, 1955, **59**, 970.
[18] B. STALINSKI, *Bull. Acad. Polon. Sci.*, 1955, **III 3**, 613.
[19] G. E. STURDY and R. N. R. MULFORD, *J. Amer. Chem. Soc.*, 1956, **78**, 1083.

[20] A. PEBLER and W. E. WALLACE, *J. Phys. Chem.*, 1962, **66**, 148.
[21] C. E. HOLLEY Jr., R. N. R. MULFORD, F. W. ELLINGER, W. C. KOEHLER, and W. H. ZACHARIASEN, *J. Phys. Chem.*, 1955, **59**, 1226.
[22] E. J. GOON, *J. Chem. Phys.*, 1959, **63**, 2018.
[23] E. S. FARSTON, *Met. Soc. Amer. Inst. Mining, Spec. Rept. Ser.*, 1960, **7**, no. 10, 51.
[24] K. DIALER and B. FRANK, *Zeit. Naturf.*, 1960, **15B**, 58.
[25] C. E. LUNDIN, and J. P. BLACKLEDGE, *J. Electrochem. Soc.*, 1962, **109**, 838.
[26] R. E. ELSON, H. C. HORNIG, W. L. JOLLY, J. W. KURY, W. J. RAMSEY and A. ZALKIN, *Some Physical Properties of the Hydrides*, University of California, UCRL–4519, Revised, 1956.
[27] H. E. FLOTOW, D. W. OSBORNE, K. OTTO, *J. Chem. Phys.*, 1962, **36**, 866.
[28] H. E. FLOTOW, D. W. OSBORNE, K. OTTO, and B. M. ABRAHAM, *J. Chem. Phys.*, 1963, **38**, 2620.
[29] W. L. WHITTEMORE and A. W. MCREYNOLDS, *Phys. Rev.*, 1959, **113**, 806.
[30] J. C. WARF and K. HARDCASTLE, Proc. 2nd Conf. Rare Earth Research, 1961, 261 (*Chem. Abs.* 1964, **61**, 1496): U.S. Dept. Comm., Tech. Ser., A.D. 265,232 and A.D. 265,321 (1961).
[31] T. R. P. GIBB Jr., *J. Inorg. Nucl. Chem.* Edited by F. A. Cotton, 1962, **24**, 349.
[32] T. C. WADDINGTON, "Lattice Energies" in *Advances in Inorganic Chemistry and Radiochemistry*, Academic Press 1959, **1**, 157.
[33] Y. KUBOTA and W. E. WALLACE, *J. Chem. Phys.*, 1963, **39**, 1285: *J. Appl. Phys. Suppl.* 1962, **33**, 1348: *J. Appl. Phys.*, 1963, **34**, 1.
[34] R. L. ZANOWICH, and W. E. WALLACE, *Phys. Rev.*, 1962, **126**, 536.
[35] W. E. WALLACE, Y. KUBOTA, and R. L. ZANOWICH, *Adv. Chem. Ser.*, 1963, **39**, 122.
[36] D. E. COX, G. SHIRANE, W. J. TAKEI, and W. E. WALLACE, *J. Appl. Phys.*, 1963, **34**, 1352.
[37] B. STALINSKI, *Bull. Acad. Polon. Sci.*, 1959, **7**, 269; 1957, **5**, 997, 1001; 1954, **2**, 245.
[38] B. STALINSKI and Z. BIEGANSKI, *Bull. Acad. Polon. Sci.*, 1964, **12**, 331.
[39] W. KOEHLER, private communication reported in [33].
[40] D. S. SCHREIBER and P. M. COTTS, *Phys. Rev.*, 1963, **131**, 1118.
[41] V. I. MIKHEEVA, Z. K. STERLYADKINA and A. A. CHERTKOV, *Russ. J. Inorg. Chem.*, 1963, **8**, 888 (Russian 1710): idem, *ibid*, 890 (Russian 1715).
[42] V. I. MIKHEEVA, Z. K. STERLYADKINA, A. I. KONSTANTINOVA, and O. N. KRYUKOVA, *Russ. J. Inorg. Chem.*, 1963, **8**, 682 (Russian 1314).
[43] P. CHIOTTI and P. F. WOERNER, *J. Less-Common Metals*, 1964, **7**, 111, 120.
[44] R. N. R. MULFORD and G. E. STURDY, *J. Amer. Chem. Soc.*, 1955, **77**, 3449.
[45] idem, *ibid*, 1956, **78**, 3897.
[46] B. MCDONALD and J. B. FARDON, *J. Chem. Soc.*, 1956, 781.
[47] F. BROWN, H. M. OCKENDEN, and M. WELCH, *J. Chem. Soc.*, 1955, 3936.
[48] F. H. SPEDDING, A. S. NEWTON, J. C. WARF, O. JOHNSON, R. W. NATTORF, I. B. JOHNS, and A. H. DAANE, *Nucleonics*, 1949, **4**, 10.
[49] R. DE ANCA, G. GERBOLES, and J. M. JIMENEZ, *Energia Nucl.* (*Madrid*), 1963, **7**, 4.
[50] S. FREID and H. L. BAUMBACH, U.S. Patent, 2,915,362 (1959): R. H. WITT, J. NYLER, and H. M. MCCULLOUGH, *U.S. Atomic Energy Comm.*, SEP 221 (1956).
[51] B. M. ABRAHAM and H. E. FLOTOW, *J. Amer. Chem. Soc.*, 1955, **77**, 1446.
[52] G. G. LIBOWITZ and T. R. P. GIBB Jr., *J. Phys. Chem.*, 1957, **61**, 793.
[53] H. E. FLOTOW, H. R. LOHR, B. M. ABRAHAM, and D. W. OSBORNE, *J. Amer. Chem. Soc.*, 1959, **81**, 3529.
[54] J. BIGELEISEN and A. KANT, *J. Amer. Chem. Soc.*, 1954, **76**, 5957.
[55] R. E. RUNDLE, *J. Amer. Chem. Soc.*, 1947, **69**, 1719; 1951, **73**, 4172.
[56] R. CIALLAT, H. CORIOU, and P. PERIO, *Comptes rendus*, 1953, **237**, 812: R. N. R. MULFORD, F. H. ELLINGER, and W. H. ZACHARIASEN, *J. Amer. Chem. Soc.*, 1954, **76, 297.**

[57] W. TRZEBIATOWSKI, A. STIWA, and B. STALINSKI, *Roczniki Chem.*, 1952, **26**, 110; 1954, **28**, 17.
[58] M. K. WILKINSON, C. G. SHULL, and R. E. RUNDLE, *Phys. Rev.*, 1955, **99**, 657.
[59] D. M. GRUEN, *J. Chem. Phys.*, 1955, **23**, 1708.
[60] J. J. KATZ and G. T. SEABORG, *The Chemistry of the Actinide Elements*, Methuen 1957.
[61] J. B. HUNT and H. TAUBE, *Inorg. Chem.*, 1964, **3**, 1431.
[62] L. I. KATZIN, I. KAPLAN, and T. STEITZ, *Inorg. Chem.*, 1962, **1**, 963.
[63] W. H. ZACHARIASEN, *Acta Cryst.*, 1953, **6**, 393.
[64] W. L. KORST, *Acta Cryst.*, 1962, **15**, 287.
[65] R. E. RUNDLE, C. G. SHULL, and E. O. WOLLAN, *Acta Cryst.*, 1952, **5**, 22.
[66] D. T. PETERSON, D. G. WESTLAKE, and J. REXER, *J. Amer. Chem. Soc.*, 1959, **81**, 4443.
[67] R. W. NOTTORF, Thesis, Quoted in [60] and [5].
[68] M. W. MALLET and I. E. CAMPBELL, *J. Amer. Chem. Soc.*, 1951, **73**, 4850.
[69] D. P. SCHUMACHER, *J. Chem. Phys.*, 1964, **40**, 153.
[70] G. G. LIBOWITZ, *J. Chem. Phys.*, 1957, **27**, 514.
[71] D. T. PETERSON and J. REXER, *J. Less-common Metals*, 1962, **4**, 92.
[72] D. T. PETERSON and D. G. WESTLAKE, *Trans. Amer. Inst. Min.* (*Metals*), 1959, **215**, 444.
[73] idem, *J. Phys. Chem.*, 1959, **63**, 1514.
[74] E. A. GULBRANSON and K. F. ANDREWS, *J. Electrochem. Soc.*, 1954, **101**, 560.
[75] D. T. PETERSON and J. REXER, *J. Inorg. Nucl. Chem.*, 1962, **24**, 519.
[76] J. BERGSMA, J. A. GOEDKOOP and J. H. N. VAN VACHT, *Acta. Cryst.*, 1961, **14**, 223; J. H. N. VAN VACHT, *J. Inst. Met.*, 1958, **87**, 94.
[77] S. FRIED and N. DAVIDSON, *J. Amer. Chem. Soc.*, 1948, **70**, 3539; 1953, **75**, 1236.
[78] E. F. WESTRUM Jr., and L. EYRING, *J. Amer. Chem. Soc.*, 1951, **73**, 3396.
[79] F. H. ELLINGER, quoted in [60] and [26].
[80] J. D. FARR, A. L. GIORGI, M. G. BOWMAN, and R. K. MONEY, *J. Inorg. Nucl. Chem.*, 1961, **18**, 42.
[81] P. A. SELLERS, S. FRIED, R. E. ELSON, and W. H. ZACHARIASEN, *J. Amer. Chem. Soc.*, 1954, **76**, 5933.
[82] F. H. ELLINGER, private communication quoted in [44] (with A. S. Coffinberry).
[83] F. H. ELLINGER, private communication quoted in [45].
[84] J. BESSON and J. CHEVALLIER, *Comptes rendus*, 1964, **258**, 5888.
[85] M. DESTRIAU and J. SERIOT, *Comptes rendus*, 1962, **254**, 2982.
[86] V. I. MIKHEEVA and M. E. KOST, *Uspekki Khim.*, (*Russian Chemical Reviews*) 1960, **29**, 55 (28 in Eng. Trans.).
[87] H. L. YAKEL, *Acta Cryst.*, 1958, **11**, 46.
[88] S. S. SIDHU, L. HEATON, D. D. ZAUBERIS, *Acta Cryst.*, 1956, **9**, 607.
[89] L. PAULING, *The Nature of the Chemical Bond*, (Oxford University Press) Third Edn. 1960.
[90] H. E. FLOTOW and D. W. OSBORNE, *J. Chem. Phys.*, 1961, **34**, 1418.
[91] T. B. DOUGLAS, *J. Chem. Phys.*, 1964, **40**, 2248.
[92] S. S. SIDHU, *Acta Cryst.*, 1956, **7**, 447: *J. Chem. Phys.*, 1954, **22**, 1062.
[93] A. D. MCQUILLAN and N. PESSALL, *Acta. Cryst.*, 1961, **14**, 1287.
[94] S. S. SIDHU and J. C. MCGUIRE, *J. Appl. Phys.*, 1952, **23**, 1257.
[95] T. P. EHRLICH, *Z. angew. Chem.*, 1947, **59**, 163.
[96] R. L. BECK, *Trans. Amer. Soc. Met.*, 1962, **55**, 542, 556.
[97] G. A. MEERSOV and S. ROI, *Poroshkovaya Met. Akad. Nauk. Ukr. SSR.*, 1963, **3**, 71. (Chem. Abs., **60**, 8994).
[98] G. G. LIBOWITZ, H. F. HAYES, and T. R. P. GIBB Jr., *J. Phys., Chem.*, 1958, **62**, 76.
[99] Z. BIEGANSKI and B. STALINSKI, *Bull. Acad. Polon. Sci.*, 1960, **8**, 243.
[100] idem., *ibid*, 1961, **9**, 367.

[101] D. R. FREDERICKSON, R. L. NUTTALL, W. HUBBWARD, and H. E. FLOTOW, *J. Phys. Chem.*, 1963, **67**, 1506.
[102] W. TRZEBIATOWSKI and B. STALINSKI, *Roczniki Chem.*, 1956, **30**, 691.
[103] A. G. TURNBULL, *Australian J. Chem.*, 1964, **17**, 1063.
[104] J. F. HON, *J. Chem. Phys.*, 1962, **36**, 739.
[105] T. R. P. GIBB Jr., J. J. MCSHARRY and R. W. BRAGDON, *J. Amer. Chem. Soc.*, 1951, **73**, 1751.
[106] T. B. DOUGLAS and D. G. WESTLAKE, *J. Nucl. Mater.* 1962, **7**, 346.
[107] T. B. DOUGLAS, *J. Res. Nat. Bur. Standards*, 1963, **67**, A 403: *J. Amer. Chem. Soc.*, 1958, **80**, 5050.
[108] D. A. VAUGHAN and D. R. BRIDGE, *Trans. Amer. Inst. Mın. (Metall.) Engrs.*, 1956, **206**, 528.
[109] O. M. KATZ and J. A. BERGER, *Nature*, 1964, **203**, 1163.
[110] E. J. GOON and J. MAXLGIOLIO, *U.S. At. En. Comm.* TID 5913, (1959): (*Nucl. Sci. Abs.* 1960, **14**, 14768)
[111] G. A. LENNING, C. M. CRAIGHEAD, and R. I. JAFFEE, *Trans. Amer. Inst. Min. (Metall.) Engrs.*, 1954, **200**, 367.
[112] R. M. HAAG and F. J. SHIPKO, *J. Amer. Chem. Soc.*, 1956, **78**, 5155.
[113] R. K. EDWARDS and E. VELECKIS, *J. Phys. Chem.*, 1962, **66**, 1657.
[114] L. ESPAGNO, P. AZOA, and P. BASTIEN, *Comptes rendus*, 1960, **250**, 4352.
[115] J. E. HARRIS, P. G. PARTRIDGE, W. T. EALES, and G. K. RICKARDS, *J. Nucl. Mater.*, 1963, **9**, 339: G. T. HIGGINS, and B. W. PICKLES, *ibid*, 1963, **8**, 160.
[116] A. DESCHANVRES and G. DESGARDIN, *Revue de Chimie minerὰle*, 1964, **1**, 439.
[117] K. P. SINGH and J. G. PARR, *Trans. Faraday Soc.*, 1963, **59**, 2256.
[118] idem. *ibid*, 1963, **59**, 2248.
[119] J. C. MCGUIRE and C. P. KEMPTER, *J. Chem. Phys.*, 1960, **33**, 1584.
[120] M. L. LIEBERMAN and P. G. WAHLBECK, *Abstracts 148th Amer. Chem. Soc. Meeting*, 1964, 12V.
[121] A. J. MAELAND, *J. Phys. Chem.*, 1964, **68**, 2197.
[122] C. A. WAINWRIGHT, A. J. COOK, and B. E. HOPKINS, *J. Less-Common Metals*, 1964, **6**, 362.
[123] B. PEDERSON, T. KROGDAHL, and O. E. STOKKELAND, *J. Chem. Phys.*, 1965, **42**, 72.
[124] A. J. MAELAND, T. R. P. GIBB Jr., and D. P. SCHUMACHER, *J. Amer. Chem. Soc.*, 1961, **83**, 3728.
[125] G. BRAUER and H. MILLER, *J. Inorg. Nucl. Chem.*, 1961, **17**, 102; *Angewandte Chem.*, 1958, **70**, 534.
[126] G. BRAUER and R. HERMANN, *Zeit. an. Chem.*, 1953, **274**, 11.
[127] G. HÄGG, *Zeit. phys. Chem.*. 1931, **B11**, 433; **B12**, 33.
[128] F. H. HORN and W. T. ZIEGLER, *J. Amer. Chem. Soc.*, 1947, **69**, 2762.
[129] R. L. ZANOWICK and W. E. WALLACE, *J. Chem. Phys.*, 1962, **36**, 2059.
[130] W. ROSTAKER, *The Metallurgy of Vanadium*, Wiley, New York 1958.
[131] M. M. ANTONOVA and G. V. SAMSONOV, *Zhur. Priklad. Knim.*, 1960, **33**, 1407.
[132] W. M. ALBRECHT, M. W. MALLETT, and W. D. GOODE, *J. Electrochem. Soc.*, 1958, **105**, 219.
[133] B. STALINSKI, *Bull. Acad. Polon. Sci.*, 1954, **2**, 245.
[134] K. I. HARDCASTLE, private communication. The X-ray results are in the press in *J. Phys. Chem.*, see reference [121].
[135] T. R. WAITE, W. E. WALLACE, and R. S. CRAIG, *J. Chem. Phys.*, 1956, **24**, 634.
[136] W. E. WALLACE, *J. Chem. Phys.*, 1961, **35**, 2156; also comment by G. J. PALINEK, *ibid*, 1964, **41**, 3260; W. E. WALLACE, 3261.
[137] W. G. SABA, W. E. WALLACE, H. SANDMO, and R. S. CRAIG, *J. Chem. Phys.*, 1961, **35**, 2148.

[138] P. KOFSTAD, W. E. WALLACE, and L. J. HYVONEN, *J. Amer. Chem. Soc.*, 1959 **81**, 5015.
[139] D. ZAMIR and R. M. COTTS, *Phys. Rev.*, 1964, **134**, A666.
[140] B. SARRY, *Z. anorg. Chem.*, 1955, **280**, 65; 78.
[141] V. P. MADYKIN, *Vestsi Akad. Navuk Beloris S.S.R.*; *Ser. Fiz-Tekh. Navuk*, 1960, *No.* 2, 50 (*Chem. Abs.* **56**, 8282d).
[142] A. JANKO, *Bull. Acad. Polon. Sci.*, 1962, **10**, 613.
[143] C. A. SNAVELY, *Trans. Electrochem. Soc.*, 1947, **92**, 552.
[144] C. A. SNAVELY and D. A. VAUGHAN, *J. Amer. Chem. Soc.*, 1949, **71**, 313.
[145] A. KNOEDLER, *Metalloberfläche*, 1963, **17**, 331.
[146] idem, *ibid*, 1963, **17**, 161.
[147] G. ALBRECHT, D. DOENITZ, K. KLEINSTUCK and M. BETZL, *Phys. Status Solidi*, 1963, **3**, K249.
[148] M. E. KOST, N. N. MAL'TSEVA, and V. I. MIKHEEVA, *Zhur. neorg. Khim.*, 1964, **9**, 1053. (English 576).
[149] D. P. SMITH, *Hydrogen in Metals*, University of Chicago Press, 1948.
[150] J. D. FARR, *J. Inorg. Nucl. Chem.*, 1960, **14**, 202.
[151] E. WICKE and G. H. NERNST, *Ber. Bunsengesellschaft Phys. Chem.*, 1964, **68**, 224.
[152] P. L. LEVINE and K. E. WEALE, *Trans. Faraday Soc.*, 1960, **56**, 357.
[153] L. J. GILLESPIE and L. S. GALSTAUN, *J. Amer. Chem. Soc.*, 1936, **58**, 2565.
[154] L. J. GILLESPIE and F. P. HALL, *J. Amer. Chem. Soc.*, 1926, **48**, 1207.
[155] P. S. PERMINOV, A. A. ORLOV, and A. N. FRUMKIN, *Dokl. Akad. Nauk. S.S.S.R.*, 1952, **84**, 749: J. A. FEDEROVA and A. N. FRUMKIN, *Zhur. Fiz. Khim.*, 1953, **27**, 247.
[156] A. J. MAELAND and T. R. P. GIBB Jr., *J. Phys. Chem.*, 1961, **65**, 1270.
[157] J. E. WORSHAM, M. K. WILKINSON, and C. G. SHULL, *J. Phys. Chem. Solids*, 1957, **3**, 303.
[158] D. M. NACE and J. G. ASTON, *J. Amer. Chem. Soc.*, 1957, **79**, 3619–33.
[159] P. C. ABEN and W. G. BURGESS, *Trans. Faraday Soc.*, 1962, **58**, 1989.
[160] N. A. SCHOLTUS and W. K. HALL, *J. Chem. Phys.*, 1963, **39**, 868.
[161] N. F. MOTT and H. JONES, *The Theory of the Properties of Metals and Alloys*, Oxford, 1936; Dover Publications 1958.
[162] A. MICHEL and M. GALLISSOT, *Comptes rendus*, 1939, **208**, 434; 1945, **221**, 551.
[163] A. MAELAND and T. B. FLANAGAN, *J. Chem. Phys.*, 1964, **68**, 1419: also, A. W. CARSON, T. B. FLANAGAN, and F. A. LEWIS, *Trans. Faraday Soc.*, 1960, **56**, 363; 1311; 1324; 1332.
[164] E. WICKE and G. BOHMHOLDT, *Zeit. phys. Chem.*, (*Frankfurt*), 1964, **42**, 115: S. D. AXELROD and A. C. MAKRIDES, *J. Chem. Phys.*, 1964, **68**, 2154; A. C. MAKRIDES, *ibid*, 2160.
[165] J. G. ASTON and P. MITACEK, *Nature*, 1962, **195**, 70.
[166] V. I. MIKHEEVA and N. N. MAL'TSEVA, *Zhur. Neorg. Khim.*, 1961, **6**, 3 (English p. 1)
[167] J. C. WARF, *J. Inorg. Nucl. Chem.*, 1961, **19**, 304.
[168] J. A. GOEDKOOP and A. F. ANDRESEN, *Acta Cryst.*, 1955, **8**, 118.
[169] H. MÜLLER and A. J. BRADLEY, *J. Chem. Soc.*, 1926, 1669.
[170] J. C. WARF and W. FIETKNECHT, *Helv. Chim. Acta*, 1958, **33**, 613.
[171] B. BARANOWSKI, *Roczniki Chem.*, 1964, **38**, 1019, 1419; *Naturwiss.*, 1964, **51**, 262: Z. SZKLAVSKA-SMIALOWSKA and M. SMIALOWSKI, *J. Electrochem. Soc.*, 1963, **110**, 444.
[172] H. BRODOWSKI, *Z. Phys. Chem.* (*Frankfurt*), 1965, **44**, 129.
[173] J. C. BARTON, F. A. LEWIS, and I. WOODWARD, *Trans. Faraday Soc.*, 1963, **59**, 1201; 8.
[174] M. SAKAMOTO, *J. Phys. Soc. Japan*, 1964, **19**, 1862.
[175] W. L. WHITTEMORE and A. W. MCREYNOLDS, *Phys. Rev.*, 1959, **113**, 806.
[176] B. PEDERSON, *Tidsskr. Kjemi. Bergv. Metallurgi*, 1965, **25**, 63.
[177] D. S. SCHREIBER, *Phys. Rev.*, 1965, **137**, A860.

[178] H. C. TORREY, *Nuovo Cimento Suppl.*, 1958, **9**, 95.
[179] R. E. NORBERG, *Phys. Rev.*, 1952, **86**, 745.
[180] J. F. HON, *J. Chem. Phys.*, 1962, **36**, 739.
[181] H. BETSUYAKU, Y. TAKAGI, Y. BETSUYAKU, *J. Phys. Soc. Japan*, 1964, **19**, 1089.
[182] R. A. ORIANI, E. MCCLIMENT, and J. F. YOUNGBLOOD, *J. Phys. Chem.*, 1957, **27**, 330.
[183] R. N. R. MULFORD and T. A. WIEWANDT, *J. Phys. Chem.*, 1965, **69**, 1641.
[184] J. R. MORTON and D. S. STARK, *Trans. Faraday Soc.*, 1960, **56**, 351.
[185] M. MANSMANN and W. E. WALLACE, *J. Physique et Radium*, 1964, **25**, 454.
[186] *Nonstoichiometric Compounds*, American Chemical Society Symposium, Published in the *Advances in Chemistry* series, 1963, **39**. Articles of relevance include, 'Current Problems', J. S. ANDERSON, 1–22; 'Nonstoichiometry in Metal Hydrides' G. G. LIBOWITZ, 66–73; 'Neutron Diffraction Studies' (mainly on Zirconium-Deuterium), S. S. SIDHU et al, 87–98; 'Interstitial-Atom, Proton, and Hydride-Anion Models', T. R. P. GIBB, Jr., 99–110; 'Hydrogen in Palladium', J. G. ASTON et al, 111–121; 'Magnetic Characteristics of Lanthanide hydrides–quoted as ref. [35] above; 'Zr–H–U System', H. H. KRAUSE et al, 131–143.
[187] G. G. LIBOWITZ, *J. Nucl. Materials*, 1960, **2**, 1 (review on transition metal hydrides).
[188] R. V. BACUR, *Revue de Physique, Acad. Rep. Pop. Roumaine*, 1963, **8**, 395 (in German).
[189] W. L. KORST and J. C. WARF, 129th Meeting A.C.S., 1956 (quoted in [187]).
[190] R. N. R. MULFORD, AECU–3813 (quoted in 187).
[191] J. H. N. VAN VUCHT, *Phillips Research Report*, 1963, **18**, 1; 21; 35; 53.

CHAPTER 4

Covalent Hydrides

4.1 Introduction

This chapter includes the remaining binary hydrides of the metals, which fall into two general groups. There are the volatile hydrides of the metals of the carbon, nitrogen and oxygen Groups, where the number of valency electrons is equal to, or greater than, the number of orbitals, and there are the non-volatile solid hydrides of beryllium, aluminium and gallium, where the number of valency electrons is insufficient to give electron pair bonds with hydrogen which will use all the valence shell orbitals. Included in this latter group of 'electron-deficient' molecules are the boron hydrides, although they are relatively volatile, and it is proposed that zinc and cadmium dihydrides are intermediate in character between this type of hydride and the metallic hydrides, with properties more in accord with the covalent end of the metallic-covalent spectrum. The transient volatile hydride of titanium, TiH_4, is to be included with the covalent hydrides of the first type.

The volatile hydrides, for example GeH_4, SbH_3 or Sn_2H_6, are relatively simple and are comparable to their well-known non-metallic analogues like the paraffins and ammonia. The hydrides of the Group IV elements are tetrahedral, and chains can be built up analogous to the paraffins, but only a limited number of members are known–up to $M_{10}H_{22}$ in the cases of silicon and germanium. These hydrides make complete use of the valence shell *s* and *p* orbitals, forming four electron pair bonds. However, they are not completely analogous to the carbon compounds as the possibility is open to them of using the higher energy *d* orbitals of the valence shell. This has some steric effects, as shall be seen, especially in the case of silicon compounds, and also offers a possible low-energy reaction path by allowing increase in the coordination number above four, without the marked weakening of existing bonds which is required in the analogous carbon intermediates. Further, in the silicon, germanium, and tin chain compounds, the metal-metal bonds are weaker than the C–C bond, and become progressively weaker down the Group. The metal-hydrogen bond also becomes weaker, so much so that the existence of PbH_4 is not fully established, while the bonds to oxygen and halogens remain relatively strong. Thus, the Group IV hydrides are very reactive in air and to oxidizing agents, both because of the thermodynamic effects, and probably because of the ready kinetic pathway afforded. However, it is becoming clear, with the development of handling techniques, that the instability of the hydrides, especially of the silicon and germanium chain compounds, has been exaggerated in the past and a considerable chemistry of these hydrides is possible. The metallic hydrides of the following Groups are substantially similar, with the additional effects of the unshared electron pairs on the metal. The metal-metal and metal-hydrogen bonds in the hydrides of Groups V and VI are weak, and few chain compounds are known.

No case of π bonding involving the *s* or *p* orbitals of the heavier members of the Main Groups is known, so that there are no analogues of the olefins, acetylenes, or of species like azides, but π bonding involving the *d* orbitals is well-established in the case of silicon and is possible for germanium compounds. It is, however, important to resist the tendency, which is occasionally apparent, to explain all differences between carbon or nitrogen and their heavier congeners in terms of the participation of *d* orbitals in the compounds of the latter, without taking account of other differences, of electronegativity and the like.

In the hydrides of the boron Group elements, a new situation appears. Although we omit detailed discussion of the boron compounds, it is convenient to introduce the bonding in these compounds by reference to diborane, which is the most fully discussed and best understood example.

The simplest hydride of boron is diborane, B_2H_6, and all attempts to isolate BH_3 have been unsuccessful [1], although it is frequently proposed as a reaction intermediate [2], and has been identified as a transient species in the mass spectrometer [3]. In diborane, all the chemical [4], spectroscopic [5, 6] and finally structural [7] evidence has demonstrated the bridge structure

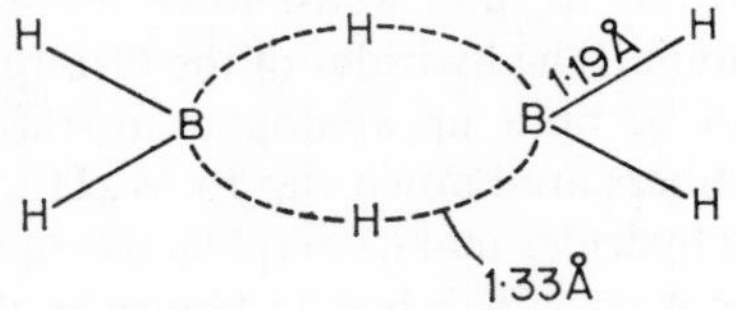

H H
B B 1·19Å
H H
H H
1·33Å

with normal single bonds for the terminal BH_2 groups. This leaves only four electrons to form the bridges, whereas normal bonding would require eight (assuming that hydrogen could be divalent), hence the term 'electron deficient'. It might be noted that the analogy between hydrides and simple alkyl compounds holds – approximately – here in that trimethylaluminium is dimeric with a very similar bridge structure [9]. A number of theories have been proposed to describe the bridge structure, but the two most acceptable were Pitzer's idea of the 'protonated double bond' (emphasizing the similarity found in the infra-red spectrum between diborane and ethylene) and Longuet-Higgins's theory of the three-centre bond [10]. As Longuet-Higgins has shown that the two theories are equivalent, the wave functions describing the one being simply transformable into those describing the other [11], only the three-centre bond description need be given. The boron atoms are hybridized tetrahedrally (with the two orbitals forming the terminal bonds not exactly equivalent to the two forming the bridges). The bridge bonds, and the corresponding anti-bonding orbitals, then result from combinations of the hydrogen $1s$ orbital with an orbital from each boron.

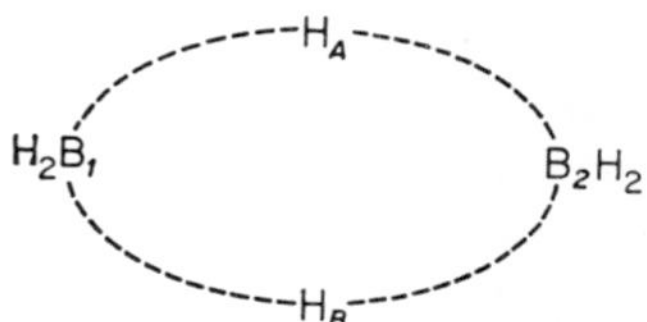

$$\left.\begin{aligned}\psi_1 &= \tfrac{1}{2}(t_1 + t_2 + \sqrt{2}s_A)\\ \psi_1^* &= \tfrac{1}{2}(t_1 + t_2 - \sqrt{2}s_A)\\ \psi_2 &= \tfrac{1}{2}(t_3 + t_4 + \sqrt{2}s_B)\\ \psi_2^* &= \tfrac{1}{2}(t_3 + t_4 - \sqrt{2}s_B)\end{aligned}\right\}$$

where t_1 and t_3 are tetrahedral hybrids on B_1, t_2 and t_4 are the hybrids on B_2, and the s orbitals on H_A and H_B are s_A and s_B.

The hydrogen electron, and the boron electron not used in the terminal B-H bonds, four in all, are placed two into ψ_1 and two into ψ_2 giving two three-centre, two-electron bonds. The two anti-bonding orbitals, ψ_1^* and ψ_2^*, remain empty. As two electrons bind three atoms, the molecule is susceptible to attack by electron pair donors, but otherwise is relatively stable. The more stable boron hydrides survive temperatures of several hundred degrees.

In the boron hydrides, other types of electron deficient bonds are postulated. These include 'linear' B-B-B bonds formed by overlap of a p orbital on the central atom with hybrids on the outer atoms, a 'central' bond between three borons involving overlap of orbitals on each boron pointing toward a common centre (with the borons in a triangle), and higher order bonds, such as five-centred boron-boron bonding in pentaborane-9. This is becoming similar to the metallic bonding in cluster molecules such as $Mo_6Cl_8^{4+}$.

In the hydrides of elements related to boron, electron deficient bonding is also postulated, but it is more difficult to demonstrate as the hydrides are polymers which are relatively unstable, insoluble, and difficult to free from coordinating molecules, such as ether, used in the preparation. It is proposed, however, that beryllium hydride is an infinite chain molecule of bridges like the diborane one,

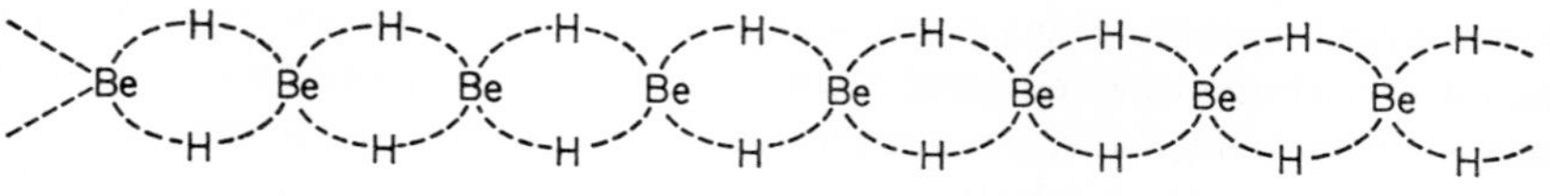

analogous to beryllium dimethyl, $(BeMe_2)_x$, [12], and to beryllium borohydride, which has B-H-Be-H-B bridges (see Chapter 5). Similarly, aluminium hydride $(AlH_3)_x$ is regarded as a three-dimensional bridged polymer, possibly with aluminium six-coordinated to hydrogen as in $Al(BH_4)_3$. The status of gallium hydride is dubious, as it has been shown that claims for Ga_2H_6 were incorrect, but unstable oily compounds are reported which may be similar to the aluminium or beryllium compounds. Similar doubts apply to reports of indium and thallium hydrides. It is possible that ZnH_2 and CdH_2, which are like beryllium or aluminium hydrides in general properties, also have bridged structures.

All these electron-deficient hydrides very easily form adducts with donor molecules, such as $Me_3N.AlH_3$ or $Et_2O.GaH_3$, and also form complex hydrides by acceptance of the electron pair in H^- to give MH_4^- (M = B,Al,Ga). The electron pair donor makes up the electron deficiency in the parent hydride, and all these compounds are tetrahedral. Coordination is not limited to four, for aluminium and gallium, and the existence of five-coordinated compounds such as $(Me_3N)_2AlH_3$ is established. The existence of these adducts is of importance from the point of view of the properties of the simple hydrides, as they are more stable than the parent hydride, and also more easily manipulated as they are soluble and volatile. They provide useful guidance to the stability of the metal-hydrogen bond and other properties of the pure hydrides.

There exists the possibility that the electron pair donor hydrides, such as SbH_3, could form adducts with the acceptor hydrides. This possibility has been studied in the case of boron and, while H_3MBH_3 adducts probably exist at temperatures below $-100°C$, they readily lose hydrogen on warming. This, of course, is one route to the ring compound borazine, $B_3N_3H_6$, though not an efficient one. The ultimate product is BM (M = N,P,As). If some of the hydrogen is replaced by alkyl groups, rings analogous to cyclohexane form, such as $Me_6P_3B_3H_6$, with phosphorus or arsenic, but antimony gives only a monomeric adduct, Me_2SbBR_2 [13, 14, 15, 16].

In addition to these relatively well-understood hydrides, there are a number of compounds which have been reported but whose structures are largely unknown. These include all the 'lower hydrides' of these elements, such as GeH, GeH_2, As_2H, and the like. These compounds are produced in some of the preparation reactions [17], or as reaction products, as insoluble, unstable yellow or brown solids, which lose hydrogen on warming. They may include higher members of the homologous chains, just as some of Stock's boron subhydrides undoubtedly included some of the recently-discovered higher boron hydrides like $B_{20}H_{16}$. They may also involve polymeric chains like the germanium dihalides. There is also a strong implication in some cases, such as the lower hydrides of arsenic and bismuth [18], that the 'compound' is actually only a finely divided form of the element with adsorbed hydrogen. There is one recent report of a lead subhydride, $PbH_{0\cdot19}$ [19], which seems to be similar to the transition metal hydrides.

4.2 Preparation of the Covalent Hydrides

The covalent hydrides cannot be prepared by the method of direct combination, which was the general method for the ionic and metallic hydrides (except in trace amounts by the action of atomic hydrogen on the metals [34]). The electrolytic hydrogenation, used to prepare palladium hydride and the Group V hydrides, does produce the Main Group hydrides, but only in small yields. There are three important routes to these hydrides in common use; two of direct formation and one of transforming the simple hydrides to higher homologues. These are

(*i*) acid hydrolysis of an alloy of the metal with an active metal such as calcium or magnesium, for example,

$$Mg_2Ge + H_3PO_4 = H_2 + GeH_4 + Ge_2H_6 + Ge_3H_8 + \dots \quad ;$$

(*ii*) reduction of the metal halide, oxide, or other suitable compound with an active metal hydride or complex hydride, especially $LiAlH_4$ or $NaBH_4$, for example,

$$SnCl_4 + LiAlH_4 \xrightarrow{\text{ether}} SnH_4$$

$$Ge^{IV} \text{ in solution} + NaBH_4 \xrightarrow{\text{dil. acid}} GeH_4 \quad ;$$

(*iii*) the action of a discharge, (microwave, radiofrequency, or ozoniser-type) on the monohydride

$$SiH_4 \rightarrow Si_2H_6 + Si_3H_8 + Si_4H_{10} + \dots$$

$$GeH_4 + AsH_3 \rightarrow GeH_3AsH_2 + Ge_2H_6 + \dots \quad .$$

These methods are largely complementary, although method (*i*) is gradually being replaced by a combination of (*ii*) and (*iii*). The advantage of method (*i*) is its simplicity and low cost, and that it leads to the higher hydrides directly. However, the overall yields are low – of the order of 20% – and the yield of higher hydride falls with increasing chain length. The yields have been improved by changing the solvent, to liquid ammonia for example, but at the price of lower yield of the higher members of the series.

Method (*ii*), in one of its variations, is the most generally useful and flexible. Lithium aluminium hydride is used only in an ether, but the latter can be varied to allow the separation of the hydride by vacuum fractionation. Yields may be quantitative in favourable cases, and related compounds such as $LiAlH(OMe)_3$ may often be used with advantage. The borohydride method is analogous, with the additional advantage that water may be used as a solvent. Any metal compound may be used in solution thus avoiding the need to handle the readily hydrolyzed halides. The method can be adapted to produce the higher hydrides, though at the expense of the overall yield. Again, yields approaching 100% are possible in the best cases.

Method (*iii*) is used to form higher hydrides from the monohydride, which can be produced in high yield by method (*ii*). As the total yield can be above 50%, this method, coupled with a complex hydride reduction with 100% conversion presents the most efficient route to the higher homologues of the silanes and germanes, and to diphosphine. However, method (*i*) is a cheaper route, does not need special apparatus, and may well be the most convenient if the starting material available is the metal. In the production of the germanes, the author has found it convenient to use a combination of all three methods, using the metal to make the magnesium alloy which is hydrolyzed in phosphoric or sulphuric acid (slightly less efficient than hydrochloric acid but avoiding volatile HCl in the product). The unreacted germanium is precipitated as the hydroxide from the acid residue, after oxidation with hydrogen peroxide. This is then taken up in alkali, sodium borohydride added, and the whole run into acid to produce a further yield of hydride, mainly as monogermane. These two operations generally give about 90% conversion of germanium with a total of 12–15% digermane and 5% trigermane in the product. The monogermane may be converted to higher germanes by circulating it in an all-glass system through a 10–15 kv discharge at half an atmosphere pressure. Four or five hours suffices to convert about a litre of GeH_4 giving about 50% yield with about equal amounts of digermane and trigermane, together with small amounts of tetragermane and higher hydrides. There are indications that straight chain hydrides are produced preferentially in the alloy hydrolysis, while the discharge method gives statistical yields of all the isomers of tetragermane and the higher germanes.

Method (*iii*), commonly using a micro-wave discharge, may be used to convert the chlorides into higher members of the series, for example to prepare Ge_2Cl_6 [8]. This is stable and may be stored till needed and then converted by lithium aluminium hydride to digermane. The corresponding route has become the standard method of preparing disilane, Si_2H_6 [49]. The advantage is that the higher halide is stable and can be stored till needed, while the higher hydrides decompose slowly on standing.*

Method (*i*) is Stock's classic method for preparing the boron hydrides [1] (along with pyrolytic interconversion which is basically similar to method (*iii*)), and has been used to prepare the silanes [1, 4], (in liquid ammonia [24] by using NH_4Br as acid), the germanes [20], stannane, plumbane and bismuthine in small amounts [21], phosphine (from calcium phosphide, giving a considerable proportion of diphosphine: a purer product is obtained from calcium aluminium phosphide), arsine [22], and stibine [23]. Method (*ii*), with lithium aluminium hydride, has been shown to yield all the monohydrides [52] although the yields vary and the borohydride method is the better route to stibine [25] and to the germanes [17, 26]. Method (*iii*) has been used to prepare the higher silanes and germanes [27], and gives a ready route to diphosphine [28], or diarsine [18].

Methods (*i*) and (*iii*) have also been used to prepare mixed hydrides. Mixed silicon-germanium hydrides have been explored by several authors [29, 30], while SiH_3PH_2, GeH_3PH_2, SiH_3AsH_2 and GeH_3AsH_2 have been made in discharges, and by hydrolyzing mixed alloys [31].

The boron hydrides can be made by the above methods, but only method (*ii*) can be used for the other electron deficient hydrides as they are non-

*However, the suggestion [99] that Si_3Cl_8 similarly gives Si_3H_8 has been refuted [233].

volatile. Most preparations have used $LiAlH_4$ in ether, and the products obtained cannot be freed from the last traces of ether. Routes to almost pure BeH_2 [38] and AlH_3 [33] have been reported, by suitable modifications of the preparation–discussed under the individual hydrides–and a further preparation reaction is useful for the more stable hydrides. This is the pyrolysis of an alkyl compound (method (*iv*)) for example,

$$\mathrm{Be\,(t\text{-}Bu)_2} \xrightarrow{150°\mathrm{C}} \mathrm{BeH_2} \quad .$$

This route was also used to prepare MgH_2 (Chapter 2). The product can be obtained ether-free, but at the price of some decomposition.

The individual hydrides will now be discussed, in the order in which they occur in the Periodic Table.

4.3 Beryllium Hydride

Beryllium hydride was made by modifications of method (*ii*), by the action of lithium aluminium hydride in ether on beryllium dimethyl [35]. An earlier claim to have prepared it by the action of lithium hydride on beryllium chloride [36] has been criticized [37]. This route gives a product which is about 60 mole per cent BeH_2, with ether as the main contaminant. Pyrolysis of di-t-butylberyllium etherate gave an improved product with 96·5 mole per cent BeH_2 [32], and this reaction was further improved, by using ether-free di-t-butylberyllium, to give a product containing 98% BeH_2 [37]. The best product so far reported, containing 99·5 mole per cent BeH_2 was made by removing BH_3 from $Be(BH_4)_2$ with triphenylphosphine [38]

$$2\,\mathrm{Ph_3P} + \mathrm{Be(BH_4)_2} \xrightarrow[180°\mathrm{C},\ \mathrm{N_2}]{\text{sealed tube}} 2\,\mathrm{Ph_3PBH_3} + \mathrm{BeH_2}$$

or by a similar reaction in xylene at 150°C. The triphenylphosphineborine is dissolved out in benzene leaving beryllium hydride as a white insoluble material, which is amorphous to X-rays. Treatment with water showed that the impurity was the phosphineborine.

The purest beryllium hydride prepared by pyrolysis [37] had a density of 0·57 g/cc at −110°C, and was relatively inert to air. It reacts slowly with water and rapidly with acid, evolving hydrogen. It decomposes slowly at 190°C and rapidly at 220°C to hydrogen and beryllium. The hydride gave an infra-red spectrum [38] which showed only a very broad band (half-width 313 cm^{-1}) at 1758 cm^{-1}, and another broad, weak absorption at 880–660 cm^{-1}. This absorption is in reasonable accord with that found for MgH_2 at about 1100 cm^{-1} (Chapter 2), if magnesium hydride has substantial 'bridging' character in its bond to hydrogen (although this magnesium hydride vibration does not seem too high to be a lattice vibration similar to those of the transition element hydrides). The frequency also agrees with those assigned to the BH_2Be bridge modes in beryllium borohydride, at 2180 and 1450 cm^{-1} [39]. It is not in accord with the assignment of bridging mode vibrations at around 1300 and 1100 cm^{-1} in the adduct of methylberyllium hydride (I) nor in the sodium compounds $(NaR_2BeH)_2$ which are both formulated with a BeH_2Be bridge [40].

(I) 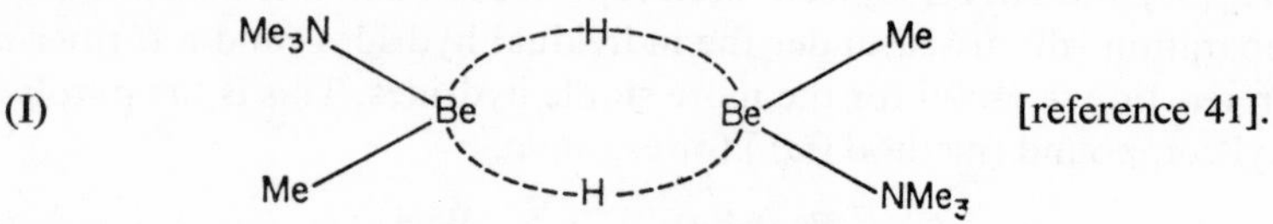

[reference 41].

It may well be, however, that all the assignments are correct, as the bridge modes must be very sensitive to the electronic environment and both the alkylberyllium hydride adduct and the sodium compounds differ considerably from the simpler bridged systems in beryllium borohydride. (The bridge modes in diborane are at 1915 and 1606 cm^{-1} [42].) If this assignment of the 1750 cm^{-1} mode is correct, then the weak band at 800 cm^{-1} is presumably a deformation mode. The great width of the bands in beryllium hydride reflect, in part, the amorphous nature of the hydride – which shows no X-ray pattern – and possibly also greater complexity in the beryllium hydrogen bonding than implied in the simple chain formulation. Resolution of these doubts must await further work. It would be interesting to know the data for the deuteride.

The sodium salt mentioned above precipitates when sodium hydride is added to a solution of dimethylberyllium in ether [40]. The earlier discovery of the corresponding ethyl compound [41] was made similarly, except that the latter is much more soluble. A preliminary crystal structure of the etherate has been reported [43]. The compound has one ether molecule per sodium atom (which is readily removed under vacuum) and crystallizes with two $(NaOEt_2)_2(Et_4Be_2H_2)$ units in a monoclinic cell. The structure contains normal Be-C bonds to the ethyl groups with a centro-symmetric

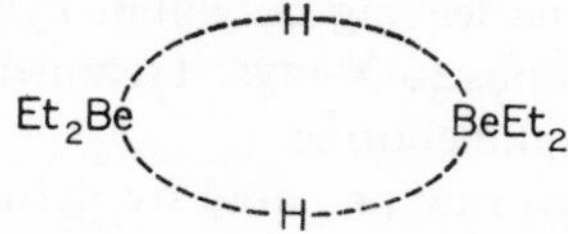

bridge structure with a Be-H distance of 1·4 Å (cf 1·33 Å for B-H bridges) and a Be-Be distance of 2·20 Å, similar to that in the free metal. This structural determination illustrates the existence of the hydrogen bridge, but the most interesting feature of the structure is that two sodium atoms are positioned at a distance of 2·4 Å from the bridging hydrogen, completing a distorted tetrahedron around it. This sodium-hydrogen distance is the same as in sodium hydride. To a first approximation, $Na(OEt_2)^+$ ions and $Et_2BeH_2BeEt_2^{2-}$ ions are present in the structure, but it would be 'unrealistic to differentiate too markedly' between the Be-H and Na-H bonding. Each sodium is linked to two hydrogens (from different BeH_2Be units) and to the ether and so is three-coordinate – or four-coordinate if the second sodium in the 'NaH_2Na' unit is counted.

Not much is reported of the chemistry of beryllium hydride, and known reactions were with impure samples. The most important reaction is with diborane [35] (compare Chapter 6)

$$BeH_2 + B_2H_6 = Be(BH_4)_2.$$

The sodium alkyl hydride mentioned above reacts with beryllium chloride with the precipitation of NaCl and the formation of a solution of '$R_4Be_3H_2$'. The nature of this solution is not known, but the etherate isolated from it loses most of its ether *in vacuo* at 50°C to give a compound which may reasonably be formulated with methyl and hydrogen bridges, in a chain stopped with ether molecules [40]

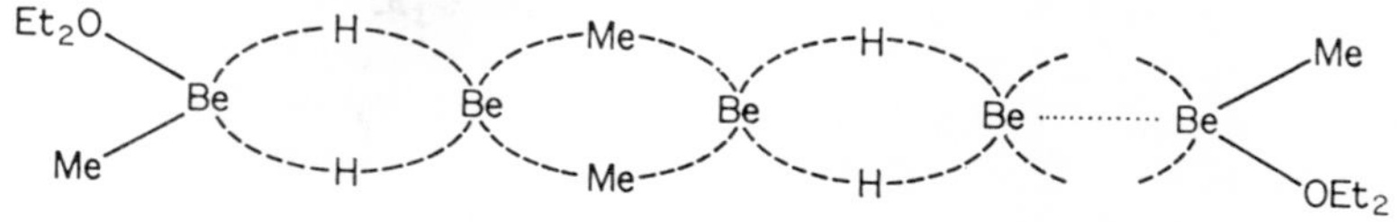

```
Et2O          H           Me           H                             Me
     \   ,-------.    ,-------.    ,-------.    ,-       -.    /
      Be          Be           Be           Be ........... Be
     /   `-------'    `-------'    `-------'    `-       -'    \
  Me          H           Me           H                             OEt2
```

The existence of a beryllium hydride anion, either Na_2BeH_4 or $Na_2Be_2H_6$, is indicated [40]. This would be the analogue of the well-known BH_4^- or AlH_4^- species.

4.4 Zinc, Cadmium, and Mercury Hydrides

Little work has been reported on the hydrides of the zinc Group elements since their discovery fifteen years ago. The first preparations of these hydrides were announced in 1951 by Wiberg and his colleagues [45, 48, 44] and by Schlesinger's group [35]. A general summary of these, and a wide variety of other main Group hydrides and double hydrides was given by Wiberg [6].

Zinc hydride is prepared by the reaction of lithium aluminium hydride in very dry ether on zinc dimethyl [35] or on zinc iodide [45]

$$ZnX_2\ (X = Me, I) + 2LiAlH_4 = ZnH_2 + 2\ \text{'}LiAlH_3X\text{'}.$$

The exact form of the aluminium product has not been determined, but it remains in solution in ether. The reaction is best carried out at −40°C; the zinc hydride precipitate is filtered off and ether removed under vacuum at 50°C. The analyses suggest that the final product contained 1–2% ether. The use of zinc chloride in the preparation is not satisfactory.

A later study, by conductimetric titration, of the reaction between zinc iodide and $LiAlH_4$ in ether showed two discontinuities in the titration curve, at $ZnI_2{:}LiAlH_4$ ratios of $\frac{1}{4}{:}1$ and $\frac{1}{2}{:}1$ [46]. The conductivity rose towards the first point and fell towards the second, leading to the interpretation

$$4\ LiAlH_4 + ZnI_2 = Li_2[Zn(AlH_4)_4]$$

$$\downarrow + ZnI_2$$

$$2\ Zn(AlH_4)_2\downarrow + 2\ LiI$$

$$\downarrow$$

$$ZnH_2\downarrow + 2\ AlH_3\ \text{(in solution)}.$$

Again, the exact form of the Li/AlH_3/I species in solution is not determined but the conductivity curve shows a further reaction between it and ZnI_2.

Zinc hydride is a white, non-volatile, insoluble material, which decomposes slightly at room temperature and quickly at 90°C. A suspension in ether reacts with diborane to form zinc borohydride $Zn(BH_4)_2$, [35]. There are also indications of an intermediate ZnHMe [35] and the preparation of ZnHI from ZnI_2 and LiH is claimed [45]. It is also reported that, in the presence of diethylzinc or zinc chloride, sodium hydride dissolves in glycol ethers, in the ratio $NaH.2ZnEt_2$ or $NaH.2ZnCl_2$, but attempts to isolate solids led to decomposition [47]. The diethyl, but not the dichloride, solution absorbs ethylene under pressure with reaction of all the hydride hydrogen.

Cadmium hydride was made by the same routes [35, 48] but the reaction had to be carried out at −78°C. A voluminous white precipitate resulted, which was insoluble in ether, tetrahydrofuran, pyridine or petroleum ether. It starts to decompose into its elements at −20°C [48] and decomposition was rapid at 0°C.

When similar preparations of mercury hydride were attempted, Schlesinger's group could isolate no product when working at −80°C [35], only mercury and hydrogen being produced–although a transient white product was observed in one run. Wiberg and Henle [44] prepared HgH_2 by allowing the reactants in frozen solution in ether-paraffin mixtures to warm up to −135°C. A white, insoluble, precipitate was formed which was stable to −125°C and then decomposed slowly, rapidly above −90°C. If the reaction was carried out at −100°C, only metallic mercury was produced, and this led to the decomposition of the aluminium hydride species in solution.

The decomposition temperatures of these three hydrides reflect a marked decrease in stability with the weight of the metal, in agreement with the properties of the Main Group hydrides. The low stability and ether insolubility indicate that these hydrides are probably electron-deficient bridged polymers, like beryllium hydride. They completely lack any metallic properties which would ally them with the transition metal hydrides. However, very little is known about these compounds. All the Wiberg papers are in the form of preliminary communications, and the Schlesinger paper announces the formation of half a dozen hydrides, although rather more is given in the way of experimental details. Much more work could be done in this field, especially on the relatively stable zinc hydride.

4.5 The Hydrides of Aluminium, Gallium, Indium and Thallium

A volatile hydride, AlH_3, and an analogue of diborane, Al_2H_6, have been identified in a time-of-flight mass spectrometer [50]. Aluminium was slowly evaporated from a hot tungsten filament into hydrogen (0.3 mm pressure) in the spectrometer and peaks with m/e = 30 at 1090°C, and of m/e = 60 at 1170°C were observed. Their identification as due to the parent ions, AlH_3^+ and $Al_2H_6^+$, was supported by the observation of increases of three and six respectively in the m/e ratio when deuterium was substituted for hydrogen. These two transient compounds apart, there are no volatile hydrides of aluminium analogous to the boron hydrides.

Aluminium hydride was first identified in the products from the action of an electric discharge on aluminium trimethyl and excess hydrogen [51], but is more easily prepared by the classic method of Finholt, Bond and Schlesinger [52], by the action of lithium hydride on aluminium trichloride in ether. The best preparation is to use an excess of lithium hydride to give a solution of $LiAlH_4$ which is then filtered from the precipitated LiCl and reacted with the calculated amount of $AlCl_3$ to give an immediate precipitate of LiCl:

$$AlCl_3 \xrightarrow{3LiH} 3LiCl\downarrow + AlH_3 \xrightarrow{LiH} LiAlH_4\ (\text{solution})$$

$$\downarrow 1/3AlCl_3$$

$$(AlH_3)_x\downarrow \xleftarrow[\text{few minutes}]{\text{standing a}} AlH_3\ (\text{solution}) + LiCl\downarrow$$

The solution can be quickly filtered from the lithium chloride, and, after a short time, deposits a white, insoluble, involatile form of aluminium hydride. Although the equations above are written with AlH_3 in solution, the species present is probably $AlH_3.OEt_2$ (or some more complex etherated hydride species) which polymerizes quite quickly. The polymeric form of the hydride also holds ether tenaciously, and was formulated as $3AlH_3.Et_2O$ [51]. In a modern preparation [53], the best product obtained was $2{\cdot}8AlH_3.OEt_2$. Although the ether in these products can be replaced by other donors, it is probably the case that no uncoordinated aluminium trihydride has ever been obtained. The closest attempt was in a preparation by Gibb and his colleagues [33], using the standard preparation. When they had separated the aluminium hydride solution from LiCl, they immediately ran it into a large excess of inert liquid, such as pentane, which was not a donor or a solvent for the hydride. The hydride precipitated immediately as a white fluffy solid. Analysis for aluminium showed a purity of 99·3%.

Direct reaction between hydrogen, atomized on a hot wire at 1100°C, with aluminium vapour gave a product of variable composition rising to $AlH_{1{\cdot}02}$ [34]. As this deposit certainly contained aluminium metal, the hydrogen content of the hydride was probably well above unity. The hydride decomposed slowly at 0°C and rapidly at 40°C.

A wide variety of reactions with aluminium hydride are known and these are, in general, the same as the reactions of $LiAlH_4$. Indeed, in many cases, it is not clear whether the reacting species is $LiAlH_4$, LiH, AlH_3, or even AlH_2Cl or related compounds. There is one report [62] of a study which deliberately distinguishes aluminium hydride from lithium aluminium hydride. It is shown that, while a double bond in conjugation with an aromatic ring is reduced along with a reducible group by $LiAlH_4$, the double bond is not attacked by AlH_3. (In all these examples, AlH_3 implies the solvated species, usually the polymer.) For example,

$$\begin{array}{l} C_6H_5CH{=}CHCHO \xrightarrow{AlH_3} C_6H_5CH{=}CHCH_2OH \text{ (I)} \\ \text{or } C_6H_5CH{=}CHCOOEt \\ \quad \downarrow LiAlH_4 \\ C_6H_5CH_2CH_2CH_2OH \text{ (II).} \end{array}$$

Similarly, the action of aluminium hydride on $C_6H_5C{\equiv}C.COOMe$ gives $C_6H_5C{\equiv}CCH_2OH$, while $LiAlH_4$ gives a mixture of (I) and (II). However, in most organic reactions, lithium aluminium hydride and aluminium hydride behave similarly [64], while hydride-halides such as AlH_2Cl show quite pronounced differences [64].

Aluminium hydride has been suggested for use in a variety of polymerisation catalysts. For example, [65], $AlH_3/TiCl_4$ or CrO_2Cl_2 mixtures catalyse the cyclisation of molecules such as butadiene or isoprene to give cyclododecatrienes. Gibb [66] and his colleagues have further examined the action of aluminium hydride on anhydrous halides of iron, cobalt, and nickel, and find that very finely divided black products were formed which may contain M-H bonds, (or be aluminohydrides). It is possible that analogous compounds participate in the catalytic reactions. Wiberg has noted that phosphorus oxybromide gives PH_3, possibly *via* PH_3O, by the action at low temperatures of aluminium hydride or lithium aluminium hydride. ($LiBH_4$ gave the interesting intermediate PH_3OBH_3 at $-115°C$ [67].) If phosphorus tribromide is treated, in place of the oxybromide, [68], yields of the order of 90% of the yellow $(PH)_x$ were obtained, with only 5–10% formation of phosphine.

Apart from the tetrahydroaluminates, the most fully investigated derivatives of aluminium hydride are its adducts, $AlH_3.D$ and $AlH_3.2D$, where D is a donor molecule such as trimethylamine, tetrahydrofuran, or a related compound. Diethyl ether is a relatively poor donor, probably because of steric effects, as tetrahydrofuran is much better. The amine adducts have been the most fully studied since their discovery by Wiberg [69], and considerable work has been reported on them recently. The system is rather complicated as the mono-amine and diamine adducts exist in equilibrium at room temperature, and this is one source of confusion in the earlier literature. In addition, many of the earlier studies were carried out in solution in donor solvents, so that the possibility of exchange with the solvent was present, Recently, the infra-red spectrum of Me_3NAlH_3, $(Me_3N)_2AlH_3$, and their deuterated analogues have been studied in the gas phase by different groups of workers [55, 57, 58] and a crystal structure determination has been carried out [56]. As this determination was not completely clear, because of disorder, the related tetramethylethylenediamine adduct was also investigated [59].

The amine adducts are made by the action of aluminium hydride, in ether, with the amine, and purified by distillation or sublimation. The trimethylamine adduct can also be prepared from $LiAlH_4$ [54], but the reaction is complex and depends on the stoicheiometries used; though Wiberg's formulation of the products as $Li(AlH_4)_xNMe_3$ [70] was shown to be only approximate. The corresponding alkylaluminiumhydride adducts may be made similarly [71]. It is even possible to synthesize the adducts directly, if a strongly coordinating ether such as triethylenediamine is used [61]. Aluminium heated with hydrogen and triethylenediamine for six hours at 70°C and 5000 psi pressure, gives the 1:1-triethylenediamine:aluminium hydride adduct. Other tertiary diamines behave similarly, giving products which are probably not monomeric and likely to be similar to the chain structure of the tetramethylethylenediamine adduct discussed below. (This direct synthesis is analogous to that of lithium aluminium hydride discussed in Chapter 6, and provides what will almost certainly become an important new route to the hydrides: for example, silicon or phosphorus halides heated under pressure with aluminium and hydrogen give silane and phosphine respectively [78].)

In the infra-red and Raman spectra of $AlH_3.NMe_3$ [55], and $AlD_3.NMe_3$, all the bands can be assigned on the basis of C_{3v} symmetry (with the methyls as pseudoatoms) giving the expected pyramidal arrangement of the hydrogens at the aluminium, (as found in BH_3 and AlX_3 adducts). The aluminium-hydrogen stretching modes occur at 1790 cm^{-1}.

The spectra of the diamine adducts may be assigned similarly on the basis of D_{3h} symmetry [55, 57]; that is, with a linear N-Al-N skeleton and trigonal bipyramidal configuration around the aluminium. The X-ray structure [56] confirms the linear skeleton, but there was too much disorder and thermal motion for the hydrogen positions to be determined. They were assumed to be in the plane of the aluminium and perpendicular to the N-Al-N axis. This hydrogen arrangement was confirmed in the X-ray study of NNN′N′-tetramethylethylenediaminealuminiumtrihydride which occurs as a chain structure, with *trans* ethylenediamine groups, and trigonal bipyramidal aluminium [59]:

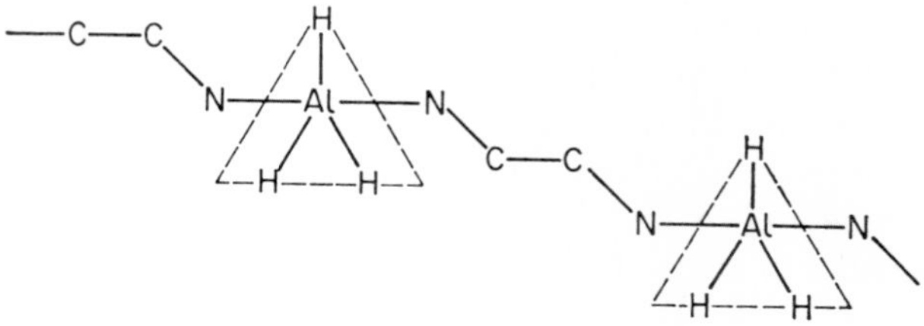

The Al-N distance is 2·195 Å, cf 2·18 Å found for the trimethylamine adduct [56] and the C-C and C-N distances were all approximately single bond distances. The preparation is given by [72]. Thus, the evidence from the infra-red and Raman spectra that the N-Al-N skeleton is linear can be taken as confirmed. In the diamine adduct, bands in the aluminium-hydrogen stretching region were found at lower frequencies, near 1720 cm^{-1}. The aluminium-hydrogen deformation modes, the N-Me stretches and deformations, and the N-Al-N skeletal modes were all shown by Beattie and Gilson [58] to be strongly coupled, so that this is a molecule where the approximation of 'characteristic modes' does not apply. In particular, no modes can be chosen as the skeletal modes, as any reasonable choice of force constants shows they strongly mix with the other modes mentioned. Beattie remarks that a mode in the region of 460 cm^{-1} is found in many trimethylamine adducts.

Comparative studies of the infra-red [73] and proton resonance [74] spectra of a number of alane adducts are reported. The reduction in frequency of the Al-H stretching modes on passing from the mono-adduct to the di-adduct is a common character, whether the donor molecule is an amine or an ether [73]. An analogous change is found in the proton resonance where the Al-H resonance was found at 1·83 to 1·88 ppm above the water signal for the adducts $AlH_3.DD'$ ($D = D' = Me_3N$,THF, and dioxane) while the resonance for $AlH_3.NMe_3$ was at 1·63 ppm, and that for AlH_3.THF was at 1·35 ppm (THF = tetrahydrofuran) [74].

Among reactions of these adducts must be noted those of trimethylamine alane with polyanions [75], with ethylamine and related compounds to give polymers containing one Al-H bond per unit [76], and the formation of the related dialane derivative [77]. This latter, $Al_2H_5.NMe_2$, is formulated with one Al-H-Al bridge like its boron counterpart:

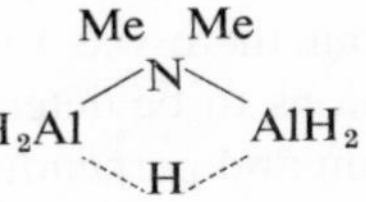

Me Me
N
H_2Al AlH_2
H

As aluminium hydride is not generally prepared as a pure substance, there is little in the way of useful physical data available. Its decomposition temperature varies with the sample's history, but, in all cases, decomposition starts below 200°C. Only one attempt to measure the heat of formation is reported [79], and this was on a sample containing ether. A value of −11·1 kcal/mole was found, with an uncertainty of 2·3 kcal, by measuring the heat of reaction with hydrochloric acid. The uncertainty reflects the uncertainties in correcting for the ether content of the sample; the hydride certainly has an exothermic–though fairly low–heat of formation at 25°C. The infra-red and nmr characteristics of the Al-H bond have been given above.

Wiberg and his co-workers claimed, in 1942, to have prepared digallane, Ga_2H_6, [80] and later reported the compounds $(GaH_3)_n$ and $GaH_3.OEt_2$ [81], all as relatively stable compounds. The ether adduct was stable to 35°C, and the hydrides to well above 100°C. This stability seems surprisingly high, and the existence of Ga_2H_6 when no aluminium analogue is known is anomalous. Recently, Wiberg's preparations were re-examined by Greenwood's group, and independently by Parry, and it was found that they could not be repeated

[82]. Further, an earlier study of the reaction of $GaBr_3$ with $LiAlH_4$ by conductimetric titration in diethyl ether [46] gave results which, though interpreted at the time in the light of Wiberg's papers, were in fact distinctly anomalous. The inflections on the titration curve would appear to indicate incomplete replacement of the bromine by hydrogen.

Greenwood, Parry, and their colleagues repeated Wiberg's syntheses and came to the conclusion that it was improbable that any uncoordinated form of gallium hydride had been prepared [82]. Furthermore, they isolated $Me_3N.GaH_3$ in the course of their studies [83, 84], and this was found to decompose slowly in a vacuum at room temperature. As $BH_3.NMe_3$ is stable to 125°C, while diborane decomposes at this temperature, the lower stability of the trimethylamine gallane makes it improbable that gallanes would be stable to 130°C as Wiberg reports. Similar comparisons between the stabilities of borohydrides, aluminohydrides and gallohydrides, MH_4^-, which decrease in that order, provide supporting evidence.

Further work [85] indicated that uncoordinated gallium hydride could be prepared by the reaction

$$Me_3NGaH_3 + BF_3 = GaH_{3(l)} + Me_3NBF_{3(g)}$$

The reaction was carried out at −15°C in the gas phase in an infra-red gas cell and the gallium hydride was deposited on the windows as an oil. The Ga-H stretch occurred at 1980 cm^{-1} (cf. Ge-H at 2000–2100 cm^{-1}) and the bending mode at 700 cm^{-1}. The gallium hydride had a melting point about −20°C and decomposed above −15°C. It was insoluble in non-coordinating solvents and probably polymeric. In the gas phase, as the reaction was occurring, a band appeared at 2000 cm^{-1} which might be due to the monomer.

These studies, from two independent schools, must be taken as disproving Wiberg's earlier work. The compounds he reported might possibly be etherates of halide-hydrides or alkyl-hydrides which would be more stable than the unsubstituted hydrides.

An uncoordinated compound, of higher stability, containing Ga-H, is dichlorogallane [86] prepared by the reaction

$$Me_3SiH + GaCl_3 = Me_3SiCl + HGaCl_2 \quad ,$$

carried out at −20°C. The dichlorogallane formed as colourless crystals which were soluble at low temperatures in benzene, cyclohexane or ether, and dimeric in benzene–probably through chlorine bridges. The compound decomposed slowly at room temperature and rapidly at the melting point of 29°C. Heating at 150°C gave H_2 and Ga_2Cl_4. The dichlorogallane showed a broad, intense, infra-red band at 2018 cm^{-1} but no nmr signal because of the high nuclear quadrupole moment of gallium. The dichlorogallane reacted with trimethylamine to give $HGaCl_2.NMe_3$, mpt 70°C, with an infra-red band at 1986 cm^{-1}.

Coordinated gallium hydride, especially the trimethylamine adduct, has been the subject of several recent investigations. Reports of the preparation [83, 84], vibrational spectrum [83, 87] and crystal structure have appeared [88]. The preparation is by the action of $LiGaH_4$ (prepared by the method of Finholt, Bond, and Schlesinger [59]) with trimethylamine hydrochloride. Me_3NGaH_3 is a volatile solid, mpt 70°C, which is soluble in ethers and hydrocarbons. A complete assignment of the spectrum in the gas phase shows that the compound is monomeric [83] and the crystal structure confirms this for the solid [84, 88]. In the presence of trimethylamine at temperatures in the range, -22 to -63°C the adduct is in equilibrium with the diamine adduct (dissociation pressure 1 mm at -63°C)

$$Me_3NGaH_3 + Me_3N \rightleftharpoons (Me_3N)_2GaH_3.$$

The heat of this reaction is reported as 11·54 kcal/mole [84] or as 10·35 kcal/mole [83], and the entropy as 41·1 eu [84] or 36·5 eu [83]. By displacing the trimethylamine with boron trifluoride in dimethylsulphide solution, the adduct $Me_2S.GaH_3$ was prepared [83]:

$$Me_3NGaH_3 + BF_3 \xrightarrow[-15°]{Me_2S} Me_3NBF_3\downarrow + Me_2SGaH_3 \quad .$$

The dimethylsulphide-gallane is much less stable than the trimethylamine adduct and completely decomposes to gallium, hydrogen and dimethylsulphide at room temperature.

The crystal structure of Me_3NGaH_3 shows a monomeric unit with normal C-H, C-N distances, and with Ga-N equal to 1·97 Å, compared with 1·94 Å in gallium nitride. The Ga-Ga distance is 5·91 Å, which is so long that any GaH_2Ga bridge is excluded. The Ga-H stretching modes occur at 1850 cm^{-1}, and the deformations at 760–715 cm^{-1}. The Ga-N mode is variously assigned at 480 cm^{-1} [83] in the infra-red, and at 370 cm^{-1} in the Raman spectrum [87]. This latter band was later ascribed to the symmetric trimethylamine deformation [89].

A number of related complexes were prepared in which one, two, or three of the hydrogens in Me_3NGaH_3 were replaced by chlorine, bromine or iodine [90]. The preparations were from the trihydride adduct by the action of anhydrous hydrogen halide, or of the trimethylammonium halide, or of the trimethylamine-trihalogallane, at low temperatures. The monohalides, Me_3NGaH_2X, were slightly volatile solids while the dihalides and trihalides were involatile. The monohalide reacted with BF_3 and borohydride to give GaH_2Cl, and $Me_3NGaH_2(BH_4)$ respectively, both unstable compounds decomposing at 0°C:

$$\begin{array}{l} Me_3NGaH_2Cl + BF_3 \rightarrow Me_3NBF_3 + GaH_2Cl \text{ (ir band in vapour at 2000 cm}^{-1}\text{)} \\ \quad\big\downarrow BH_4^- \\ Me_3NGaH_2(BH_4) + HCl. \end{array}$$

The infra-red spectra of all the mixed hydride-halide adducts, and the deuterium analogues, were recorded in benzene solution. The Ga-H stretching modes occurred in the region 1835–1970 cm^{-1}, the deformations at 710–745 cm^{-1}, and the GaH_x rock at 505–530 cm^{-1}. The Ga-H stretching frequency moves to higher frequency on halogen substitution, as do the corresponding Al-H [93] and B-H [94] frequencies in trimethylamine hydrogen-halogen adducts.

The phosphorus analogue of the amine-gallane has also been prepared [91]. Me_3PGaH_3 has approximately the same stability as the amine-gallane and is a monomer in the gas phase. The corresponding triphenylphosphine adduct is much less stable. There was no di-adduct with trimethylphosphine.

In the reaction

$$Me_3N + Me_3PGaH_3 \rightleftharpoons Me_3P + Me_3NGaH_3 \quad ,$$

almost equal amounts of each reactant were found to be present at equilibrium, with the trimethylamine adduct only slightly favoured. This is in contrast to the corresponding AlH_3 adducts, where the trimethylamine adduct is much more stable than the trimethylphosphine compound, and to the BH_3 adducts where the phosphine adduct is more stable than the amine one. This unusual order of stabilities has no proper explanation at present. It provides a further example of the 'third element effect' often remarked in Main Group chemistry where the elements in the period, gallium to bromine, do not behave like their congeners in the period above, and form compounds which are often more stable than expected.

The gallium proton resonance has been measured in Me_3PGaH_3 at $\tau = 5{\cdot}94$, and in Me_3NGaH_3 at $\tau = 5{\cdot}54$ [91]. This is similar to the value found for Me_3NAlH_3 of 6·09, and for Me_3NAlH_2Me of 6·04 [71] and the rather higher values found in the earlier study [74]. The infra-red spectrum showed stretching and deformation modes in the expected regions at 1846 cm^{-1} and 700–750 cm^{-1}.

In an interesting series of reactions, mixed hydrides of boron with aluminium or gallium have been studied (where the boron hydride starting material is decaborane, $B_{10}H_{14}$ [95]) using these trimethylamine adducts. If trimethylamineborane, Me_3NBH_3, is reacted with decaborane, the anions $B_{12}H_{12}^{2-}$ or $B_{11}H_{14}^{2-}$ can be made, under different reaction conditions. The reaction of $AlH_3.NMe_3$ in ether with decaborane was found to be

$$Me_3NAlH_3 + B_{10}H_{14} + n Et_2O = (Me_3NH)^+(B_{10}H_{12}AlH_2)^- n Et_2O + H_2$$

while the monochlorodihydroalane adduct reacted similarly, giving HCl instead of the hydrogen. This is the aluminium analogue of the B_{11} anion and its structure is thought to involve an AlH_2 unit bridging the 6,9 positions of $B_{10}H_{14}^{2-}$, with direct B-Al bonds. The reaction of the gallane adduct goes differently,

$$Me_3NGaH_3 + B_{10}H_{14} = (Me_3NH)^+(B_{10}GaH_{16})^-.$$

No hydrogen is evolved and the compound contains none of the ether used as solvent. The decaborogallium anion is surprisingly stable towards water and can be recovered unchanged from molar HCl solution. The structure is thought to be derived from that of the $B_{10}H_{16}^{2-}$ anion by bridging the 6,9 position with a GaH_2 unit, with direct Ga-B bonds [95].

Wiberg and his students [92, 96] have reported the formation of $LiInH_4$, InH_3 in solution, $(InH_3)_x$ insoluble polymer, InH, $LiInHBr_3.6Et_2O$, $LiInCl_3(BH_4)$, $LiInCl_3H$ and $In(BH_4)_3$. These compounds were prepared by standard methods, $LiInH_4$ from indium trihalides and ethereal lithium hydride, and the indium hydrides from the $LiInH_4$ solution in ether on standing. The reactions were carried out at −25°C and the stabilities reported were: $LiInH_4$ (dec. 0°C): InH_3 solution several days at −30°C or 6 hr at room temperature gives $(InH_3)_x$ as insoluble polymer: $(InH_3)_x$ overnight at room temperature gives InH: InH at 340°C gives In. Very similar thallium compounds were also prepared [97], all somewhat less stable.

While the properties of $LiInH_4$ and $LiTlH_4$ (dec 30°C), are not improbable, by extrapolation of the aluminium and gallium analogue properties, the hydrides (MH_3) and $(MH_3)_x$ seem to be too stable by comparison with the properties of gallium hydride, and its relatively unstable diethyl ether adduct. In view of the recent re-examination of Wiberg's gallium hydride results, these reports of indane and thallane must be treated with reserve. The monohydrides seem to be far too stable to be genuine (TlH decomposes at 270°C) and the indium monohydride seems to be out of line with the thallium compound when the known stabilities of the I and III states of these two elements are taken into account.

It would be most interesting to see more work in this area, and to try hydriding thallium dispersed in an alkali hydride medium to see if there were any TlH, analogous to the alkali hydrides.

4.6 The Hydrides of Silicon, Germanium, Tin and Lead

The silicon hydrides are the main content of two recent reviews of Group IV hydrides by Ebsworth [98] and by Stone [99]. In addition, MacDiarmid has written more specialized accounts of silanes and their derivatives [100, 101], and the organic side of silane chemistry is fully reviewed in all its aspects [102–5]. Recent reviews of organo-germanium chemistry include hydrides [106], while a recent account of organo-tin hydrides has appeared [107]. The germanium, tin and lead hydrides are discussed, with increasing brevity in that order, in [98] and [99]. As there is little to be said about lead hydride chemistry, and even tin hydrides are only sketchily explored, due to the instability of the metal-hydrogen bond in these cases, and as silicon-hydrogen chemistry is well-reviewed, our main attention here will be concentrated on the germanium hydrides – though first, a general review of the group is given.

Group IV elements all form tetrahydrides, MH_4, and the bond energies of all these hydrides are known, most from a number of independent determinations by different methods. The values, shown in Table 4.2, show a steady fall-off in the stability of the M-H bond as the Group is descended, and this is reflected in the stabilities of the hydrides, stannane SnH_4, decomposing at room temperature in vacuum and plumbane PbH_4, having only a transient existence at low temperatures. The metal-carbon strengths in alkyl compounds follow the same trend but are uniformly greater than the metal-hydrogen bond strengths, so that the properties of the simple alkyls of the Group give useful guidance to the expected properties of the hydrides. The metal-metal bond strengths also fall off with increasing atomic number. This is reflected in the occurrence of the hydrides shown in Table 1.2. Although the chain-forming properties analogous to those of carbon are less marked in its heavier congeners, silicon and germanium do form chains and these are of higher stability than is generally implied in the standard textbooks. Chain lengths up to M_{10} have been demonstrated for both elements and the lack of higher compounds is due more to the experimental difficulties than to their intrinsic instability. All the higher silanes and germanes are extremely sensitive to oxygen, silanes more than germanes, so that when the volatility becomes too low for the compounds to be handled in a vacuum system – at about a chain length of six metal atoms – handling problems become severe. The higher compounds have been identified only by vapour phase chromatography. Fractions up to pentagermane, Ge_5H_{12}, [108] and hexasilane, Si_6H_{14}, have been separated on the macro-scale from the alloy hydrolysis [109]. For the members of the series from four upwards, isomeric forms with branched chains are possible, and their existence has been demonstrated by chromatographic experiments for the higher silanes and germanes. In the case of the silanes, the two isomers of tetrasilane and the three of pentasilane are clearly distinguished [29] and there are a total of fourteen isomers of the hexasilanes and heptasilanes as expected. Their assignment is not unambiguous as the retention times for the more highly branched heptasilanes (on silicone) overlap with those of the less-branched hexasilanes. In a similar way, the identities of the hexagermanes, pentagermanes, and tetragermanes have been assigned [27], and it is established that hepta- octa- and nona-germanes were produced, although it again became impossible to fully distinguish isomers. On the macro-scale, *n*- and *iso*-tetrasilane have been separated and identified [110], and a mixed sample of tetragermanes shows an infra-red spectrum which can be assigned as a superposition of *n*- and *iso*-isomers, by comparison with the silicon ones [111]. It is clear, as far as work has progressed, that the polysilanes and polygermanes are accessible and show the expected isomerism, analogous to that of the paraffins. Tin hydrides are markedly less stable, but the preparation of distannane, Sn_2H_6, is reported [112, 113] and its properties established. It seems unlikely that higher stannanes beyond tristannane could exist long enough to be identified, and PbH_4 is so unstable that higher plumbanes are also improbable.

In addition to the homologous hydrides, mixed hydrides of various Group IV elements are known. Chains containing carbon and silicon, or carbon and germanium, are, of course, well known, but a variety of silicon-germanium hydrides have also been prepared. Silylgermane, SiH_3GeH_3, has been prepared on a macro-scale, by passing germane and silane through a discharge [30], and some of its chemical properties have been examined [114]. It behaves more like digermane than like disilane.

A variety of other silylgermanes have been isolated chromatographically [115] from the hydrolysis of germane-silane mixtures. Many more isomers are possible for the mixed hydrides (for example, 48 isomers for $(Si + Ge)_5H_{12}$ instead of the three for Si_5H_{12}) although it seems that not all possible isomers are actually formed. *Neo*-structures, and isomers with the link $Si(Ge)_nSi$ were not found. Fifteen different mixed isomers were separated and tentatively identified. Identification was aided by chromatographing the mixtures on tritolylphosphate and silicone columns, the former retarding germanes, and germanium-rich isomers, relative to silanes more than the latter: using higher temperatures on either column also retarded germanes relative to silanes. The alloy composition was also varied, and the germanium-silicon ratio was found by reacting the hydride with gold chloride and chromatographing the silicon tetrachloride and germanium tetrachloride formed. Structural isomers were further distinguished by their retention times – branched chain isomers being retained longer than straight chain ones – and by the action of molecular sieve [5A] which adsorbed the straight chain isomers much more strongly than the branched chain ones. Further analysis was performed by pyrolyzing the hydride and examining the products. In a search for other hydride systems it was found that no silicon-tin, germanium-tin, or silicon-boron, hydride could be formed by hydrolysis of mixed alloys, nor could a mixed hydride be formed by heating germanes and boranes. Pentaborane-9 appeared to assist the decomposition to the elements of germanes and silanes.

In a conference abstract, it is reported that the reaction

$$n\,GeH_3Na + Me_{(3-n)}\,SiCl_n \xrightarrow{10°C} (GeH_3)_nSiMe_{(3-n)} + n NaCl$$

goes in around fifty per cent yield [230]. The corresponding reaction with GeH_3Br or Me_3GeBr gave the digermane in less than ten per cent yield. This coupling reaction is important as it allows the formation of mixed hydrides of known structure – as opposed to the random mixture from discharges and pyrolyses. Unfortunately, yields are generally low, but the result above promises well for the controlled reaction.

Mixed hydrides of Group IV with Group V elements are also known. Silylamines will be discussed later and germylamines are not known. With phosphine and arsine, both germane and silane give rise to mixed hydrides in an electric discharge (31) and similar compounds are reported from mixed alloy hydrolysis [116]. The simplest members, SiH_3PH_2, GeH_3PH_2, SiH_3AsH_2 and

GeH_3AsH_2 have been isolated and characterized. Silylphosphine had been prepared earlier by pyrolysis of silane with phosphine [117] and its derivatives examined [222]. Infra-red [117, 31] and nmr [118] spectra of these four compounds are reported. More complex mixed hydrides were also indicated in these experiments [116, 31], and the two isomers of the formula Si_2PH_7 were later separated and identified [119]. These were shown to be disilylphosphine, $(SiH_3)_2PH$ and disilanylphosphine $(Si_2H_5)PH_2$, by physical and chemical properties.

These mixed hydrides have the simple structures expected, but the possibility of structural variation arises in trisilyl compounds, $(SiH_3)_3M'$, for $M' = N,P,As,Sb$, as there exists the possibility of $p_\pi \rightarrow d_\pi$ bonding [98]. The lone pair electrons on the Group V element may donate into vacant *d* orbitals on the silicon atoms, giving π bonding, and the shape of the molecule would change from pyramidal, as in trimethylamine, to planar. This effect is well known to occur in trisilylamine, $(SiH_3)_3N$, and it is of interest to see if it would occur in any other of the Group IV or Group V analogues. The way was opened by the discovery of Amberger [120] that trisilyl-phosphine, -arsine, and -stibine could be prepared by the reactions

$$3KM'H_2 + 3SiH_3Br \xrightarrow[Me_2O]{-100°C} (SiH_3)_3M' + 3KBr + 2M'H_3 \qquad (M' = P,As)$$

$$\text{or} \quad 3Li_3Sb + 3SiH_3Br \rightarrow (SiH_3)_3Sb + 3LiBr.$$

Ebsworth and Woodward have recently shown that the structure of trisilylphosphine is in all probability planar, or nearly so [121]. It must be noted that this evidence rests on a comparison of the infra-red and Raman spectra only, and so is not unambiguous. As the planar molecule has a centro-symmetric, D_{3h}, heavy atom skeleton, the skeletal stretching and bending modes should be mutually exclusive in the infra-red and Raman. The results for trisilylamine and trisilylphosphine are shown in Table 4.1. The operation of the exclusion rule is clear.

However, vibrational evidence for the structure of molecules must not be accepted uncritically. For example, the vibrational spectrum of $(SiH_3)_2O$ indicated a linear Si-O-Si skeleton [122] but structural studies show a bond angle around 150° [123].

In recent work, Ebsworth has found a new route to trisilyl compounds by a displacement reaction from trisilylamine [124]. A similar reaction gives trigermylphosphine,

$$3GeH_3X + (SiH_3)_3P \rightarrow (GeH_3)_3P + 3SiH_3X,$$

the first report of a germanium compound of this type. Trigermylamine cannot be prepared by the direct route from ammonia, and the displacement reaction gives a product which decomposes rapidly. Preliminary spectroscopic evidence suggests that trisilylarsine is planar, but that trisilylstibine and trigermylphosphine are non-planar [231].

Table 4.1. *The Infra-red and Raman Skeletal Modes of Trisilylamine*

If the SiH_3 groups are regarded as pseudo-atoms, then the trisilylamine molecule is planar with D_{3h} symmetry or else pyramidal with C_{3v} symmetry. In the D_{3h} case, the molecule is centro-symmetric and the Raman active modes are infra-red inactive and vice versa. In the C_{3v} case, all modes are infra-red and Raman active. The D_{3h} selection rules are given below:

symmetric stretch	ν_1	R (polarized)	—
asymmetric stretch	ν_3	R (depolarized)	IR
symmetric (out-of-plane) deformation	ν_2	—	IR
asymmetric (in-plane) deformation	ν_4	R (depolarized)	IR

The observed bands for trisilylamine [198] and trisilylphosphine [121], which can be assigned to skeletal modes as they do not shift on deuteration, are

$N(SiH_3)_3$		$P(SiH_3)_3$		Assignment (D_{3h})
496 R (pol)	—	414 R (pol)	—	ν_1
987 R (depol)	996 IR	455 R (depol)	456, 463 IR	ν_3
—	below range	—	below range	ν_2
204 R (depol)	below range	134 R (depol)	below range	ν_4

The infra-red spectra could only be measured down to 400 cm^{-1} so none of the deformation modes in the infra-red were observed. There were no Raman bands which could be assigned to ν_2, and there were no infra-red bands corresponding to the Raman bands at the ν_1 frequencies.

In addition to the parent hydrides, many derivatives of the Group IV hydrides are known. The compounds MH_3X, MH_2X_2 and MHX_3, where X is a halogen, pseudo-halogen or similar group, are well-known for M = Si or Ge [98, 99] and a number of the stannanes have also been prepared. Some properties are shown in the Tables at the end of this chapter. These compounds can be interconverted by passing the vapour over a heavy metal salt, usually silver or mercury, in the order

$$Te \rightarrow I \rightarrow Se \rightarrow S \rightarrow NCSe \rightarrow Br \rightarrow Cl \rightarrow CN \rightarrow NCS \rightarrow NCO \rightarrow O \rightarrow F$$

demonstrated by MacDiarmid for silanes [100]. This conversion series has also been shown to hold for a number of germyl compounds [125, 126]. The reactions of the type

$$MH_3X + AgX' = MH_3X' + AgX \quad (M = Si, Ge)$$

are by now quite fully studied. Disubstituted derivatives follow a similar sequence, but fewer examples are known, and decomposition occurs more readily. The iodide, which is the most useful starting material for use in this series, is readily made by the reaction

$$SiH_4 + HI/AlI_3 = SiH_3I + H_2$$
$$\text{or } GeH_4 + I_2 = GeH_3I + HI \text{ (the } AlI_3 \text{ reaction is unsatisfactory here.)}$$

The other halides may be made directly from the hydride by the aluminium trihalide catalysed reaction with the hydrogen halide, for both silicon and germanium compounds. Germyl bromide can also be made by direct reaction with bromine at low temperatures, and all the germyl halides may be made by passing germane over the heated silver salt [114]

$$GeH_4 + AgX = GeH_3X + \tfrac{1}{2}H_2 + Ag.$$

These heavy metal salt displacement series also hold, in approximately the same order, for organosilanes and organogermanes, for example, for Ph_3GeX. In addition, a displacement series for reactions of silyl compounds and hydrogen halides in the gas phase has been discussed [100]. This follows a slightly different order

$$H \rightarrow Se \rightarrow S \rightarrow I \rightarrow Br \rightarrow Cl \rightarrow F \rightarrow O \quad .$$

Only a few cases of the analogous germyl series have been examined.

Derivatives of stannane are very rare. The chloride, SnH_3Cl, has been prepared [232] by the action of HCl on stannane, but it starts to decompose at $-70°C$, compared with a decomposition temperature of $+50°C$ for GeH_3Cl. No derivative chemistry has therefore been explored, and organostannanes are made by reducing organo-tin halides, rather than by alkylation of stannyl compounds.

Organic derivatives of the types RMH_3, RMH_2X, $RMHX_2$, R_2MH_2, R_2MHX and R_3MH are all well-known and are discussed in the reviews. They are somewhat more stable thermally than the simple hydrides, so that the best known compound with a lead-hydrogen bond is Me_3PbH. This was prepared by the reaction of potassium borohydride on trimethyl-lead chloride in liquid ammonia [127]:

$$Me_3PbCl + KBH_4 \rightarrow Me_3PbBH_4 \rightarrow Me_3PbH + \text{"}H_3NBH_3\text{"} \quad .$$

The trimethylplumbane was distilled rapidly at $-5°C$, after the ammonia had been removed at $-78°C$. Trimethylplumbane is colourless, mpt $-100°C$, and it decomposes above $-100°C$ to a red solid and methane. Trimethylplumbane may also be prepared by reducing Me_3PbCl with lithium aluminium hydride in ether at $-78°C$. Similar reactions give Et_3PbH, Me_2PbH_2, and Et_2PbH_2 [170, 201]. Trimethylplumbane was shown to be more stable than the earlier reports indicated, when prepared in the absence of ammonia. The decomposition temperatures of 110°C for Me_4Pb, −37°C for Me_3PbH, and −50°C for Me_2PbH_2 support the observation of Kraus and Greer [171] that stannanes become more stable on increasing methylation. These values correspond with the reported decomposition of plumbane itself below −100°C. Nuclear magnetic resonance measurements show the Pb-H signal at 2·5 ppm to low field of stannane protons. This agrees with chemical evidence for an acidic proton, $Me_3Pb^{\delta-} - H^{\delta+}$, and the formation of Me_3PbNH_4.

The simple tetrahydrides form metal derivatives, MH_3M'', where M″ is an alkali metal. Germane and stannane also produce $MH_2M''_2$ [25, 128] when M″ is sodium. The reactions are

$$MH_4 + M'' \xrightarrow[-63^\circ C \text{ or } -45^\circ C]{\text{liquid } NH_3} \underset{\text{(in varying amounts)}}{MH_2M''_2 + MH_3M''} + xH_2$$

where the proportion of SnH_2Na_2 is higher than that of GeH_2Na_2 under similar conditions. The di-sodium derivatives react with further hydride

$$MH_2M''_2 + MH_4 = 2\,MH_3M'' \quad ,$$

giving an overall stoicheiometry

$$MH_4 + M'' = MH_3M'' + \tfrac{1}{2}H_2 \quad .$$

Silane cannot be reacted in ammonia as solvolysis is too rapid, but it reacts with potassium solution in methyl ether solvents to give SiH_3K [25, 129]. Disilane is cleaved to give silylpotassium in a similar solvent [129]. These alkali metal derivatives are conducting in liquid ammonia and may be formulated as ionic, e.g. $GeH_3^-Na^+$. The compounds of the lower alkali metals are stable only in the presence of solvent and rapidly decompose when ammonia is removed at −33°C. However, heavier alkali salts, such as $CsGeH_3$, are more stable and survive to room temperature [130]. Ring has shown that alkali salts of the higher silanes may be prepared by a displacement reaction in monoglyme [131],

$$SiH_3K + Si_2H_6 = Si_2H_5K + SiH_4 \quad .$$

Only about 10% of the expected amount of disilane was recovered on reaction with HCl so other reactions occur, and the higher silanes may only be by-products.

Until recently, no chemistry of the higher hydrides was known, apart from pyrolysis and degradation reactions. A series of studies by MacDiarmid and his students has now demonstrated that an extensive chemistry of disilane exists, and Si_2H_5X analogues of most silyl compounds SiH_3X exists. Preparation reactions are similar to those for the simple silanes and are shown in the chart. These disilanyl derivatives are relatively stable and volatile, and interconversion reactions readily occur [132–140]).

Preparations and Interconversions of the Disilane Derivatives. All reactions take place under mild conditions: usually within fifty degrees either side of room temperature, and in the gas phase.

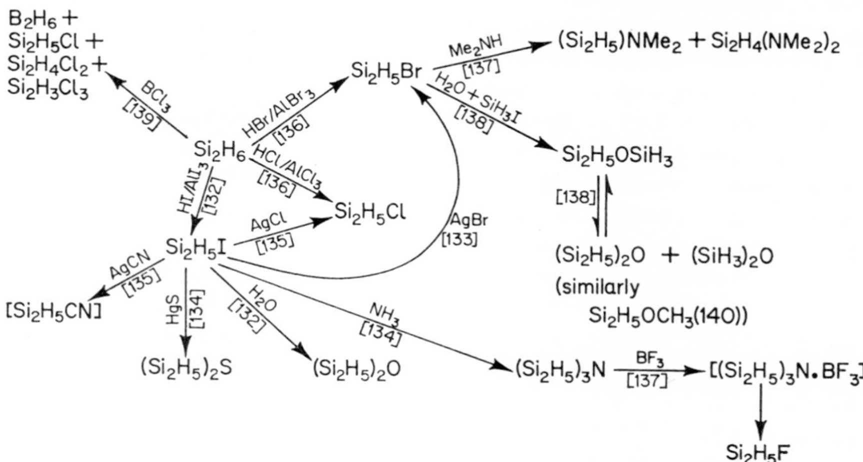

Preparations of Digermane Derivatives. Reactions carried out below room temperature, apart from those involving digermane and silver salts. All reactions from [114] except the iodide preparation [141].

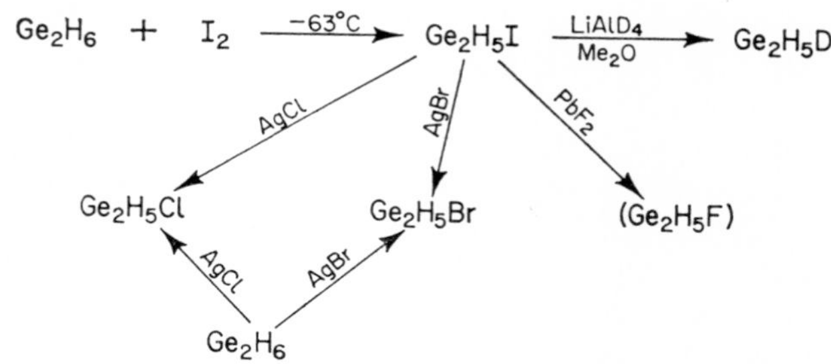

More recent work has shown that digermanyl halides may also be prepared, although stabilities are low [141, 114]. The best introductory reaction is the direct reaction between digermane and iodine at −63°C:

$$Ge_2H_6 + I_2 = Ge_2H_5I + HI \quad .$$

The HI recovery indicates that the reaction is almost quantitative but the recovery of digermanyl iodide is only about 50% as this compound decomposes at the distillation temperature of 0°C [141]. The other digermanyl halides were prepared by reaction with the silver salt on the iodide, *in situ*, at −63°C. An alternative route is by the direct reaction of digermane with silver bromide or chloride. This provides a good route to the chloride, but usually gives the bromide contaminated with GeH_2Br_2 which has a very similar volatility and is difficult to separate. The digermanyl halides increase in stability from the iodide to the chloride, the latter being moderately stable at room temperature. The fluoride has not yet been prepared pure, and could be less stable than the chloride. The nmr spectra of the disilanyl compounds [142], and of the digermanyl halides [143] have been studied. These show the expected quartet and triplet, with the MH_3 signal at higher field than the MH_2 resonance in the fluoride, chloride and bromide, but inverting in the iodide, for both silicon and germanium compounds.

A few substitution reactions of higher silanes are reported, [166, 167] and there is evidence for the existence of trigermanyl iodide, Ge_3H_7I [144]. The trigermanyl compounds are too unstable to allow recovery of any of the halides, but reaction *in situ* with $LiAlD_4$ in dimethyl ether yielded Ge_3H_7D. Substitution appears to be on the central germanium atom.

Apart from the trisilyl compounds of Group V elements, there are many examples of $p_\pi \rightarrow d_\pi$ bonding in silyl compounds. Thus, SiH_3X compounds for X = NCO, NCS, have a linear heavy atom skeleton, while the methyl analogues are bent at the nitrogen [145–8]. The cyanamide, $SiH_3NCNSiH_3$ has this carbodi-imide arrangement of heavy atoms while the methyl compound is $(CH_3)_2NCN$ [149]. Tetrasilylhydrazine [150] and disilyl ether [123] show bond angles indicating π bonding. Only the sulphide, $(SiH_3)_2S$ and the azide, SiH_3N_3, have angles similar to those in the methyl analogues [172, 173]. The possibility of $p_\pi \rightarrow d_\pi$ bonding in germyl derivatives has only recently been investigated. The germanium analogues of many of those silicon compounds which show structural effects of π bonding do not exist. However, recent studies indicate that π bonding is much less marked in germanium compounds. Thus, $(GeH_3)_2O$ shows a bond angle near the tetrahedral value [151], $(GeH_3)_3P$ is non-planar [231], and the instability of $(GeH_3)_3N$ indicates it does not resemble trisilylamine [154]. Preliminary spectroscopic studies on GeH_3NCO [152] and GeH_3NCS [153] show non-linear GeNCX skeletons. Thus, at present, germanium hydride derivatives show much less structural evidence for π bonding than do their silicon analogues.

In general chemistry, the evidence as to the extent to which germanium uses its 4*d* orbitals in π bonding is conflicting. In the classical discussion on the use of *d* orbitals, [155] 4*d* orbitals were not specifically considered, but it is implied that their more diffuse nature should not exclude at least weak π bonding. The energy gap between the 4*p* and 4*d* orbitals is somewhat less than that in the third quantum shell, which provides a compensating factor. In organometallic studies, it has been reported that π bonding between phenyl groups and germanium is less than that to silicon [168], or approximately equal [156, 157]. In Ph_3MOH, (M = Si, Ge, or Sn), it was concluded that π bonding to germanium was weaker than that between the oxygen and silicon, while the tin compound showed no evidence of Sn-O π bonding [169]. All the conclusions are indirect and based on postulated reaction mechanisms. A microwave study of silyl and germyl halides indicated that π bonding was less for Ge-X than for Si-X, but was still significant for Ge-F [224]. It is possible that π bonds will be favoured to elements in the same or neighbouring periods

– such as arsenic or phosphorus – where *d-p* character is possible in the donating orbitals. It is interesting in this respect that GeH_3AsH_2 is more stable than GeH_3PH_2 [31], although AsH_3 is much less stable than PH_3. However, there are differences of size, polarizability and electronegativity to be taken into account here, as well as π bonding.

In addition to the volatile hydrides, involatile, coloured, hydrogen-containing materials are commonly produced in the preparations of the volatile hydrides and as decomposition products. Similar compounds are reported in the decomposition of the Group V hydrides. This is an obscure field which would repay further study. For example, two solid germanium hydrides are reported, of compositions GeH and GeH_2 approximately (both polymers) [158, 159]. In addition, there are two quite different compounds, GeH_2. One was prepared, and reacts,

$$CaGe + HCl_{aq} = (GeH_2)_n \xrightarrow{heat} Ge + H_2$$

$$(GeH_2)_n \xrightarrow{Br_2} GeBr_4 + HBr$$

$$(GeH_2)_n \xrightarrow{HCl} Ge + GeH_4 + Ge_2H_6 + Ge_3H_8 + H_2$$

This was a yellow compound [159]. The other, a white solid unstable above $-33°C$, was prepared [160]

$$C_6H_5Br + GeH_3Na = C_6H_6 + NaBr + GeH_2 \quad .$$

This material was *soluble* in liquid ammonia, and stable in solution at $-33°C$, but when the ammonia was removed, it decomposed in 3–4 hr. at $-33°C$ to GeH_4 + 2GeH. Reaction of the dihydride in ammonia with one equivalent of sodium gave a deep red *solution*, with no hydrogen evolution, and this solution gave GeH_4 on addition of NH_4Br. GeH_3Na in ammonia is colourless or pale yellow but the action of 4:1 moles of sodium on trigermane in liquid ammonia also gives a red solution [25]. The monohydride, GeH, was yellow, orange or brown depending on its history, and decomposed to germanium and hydrogen on heating. The compositions of none of these hydrides is fully established and the formulae given are only rounded-off ones. As the 'monohydride' is now readily accessible [17], more work is to be expected.

Similar uncertainty attends the other lower hydrides. For example, silicon compounds of formulae SiH, $SiH_{1\cdot12}$ and $SiH_{1\cdot7}$ are reported [161, 162]. The monohydride was a yellow, brittle solid made by the reaction in ether, [161]

$$SiHBr_3 + Mg = SiH \quad .$$

This was relatively unreactive to dry air and neutral water but reacted with explosive violence with alkali to give silica and $2\frac{1}{2}H_2$. It was thought to be a cross-linked polymer.

The Group V solid hydrides may be included here, as the only critical and detailed study has been done in this field – on solid arsenic hydrides by Jolly and co-workers [18]. After repeating all the reported preparations, and critically examining the various formulae proposed for the solids – from AsH_2 to As_2H – they came to the conclusion that many of the reports referred only to finely-divided arsenic occluding hydrogen or arsine, but that the more hydrogen-rich products, with more than half a gram-atom hydrogen per arsenic, were difficult to explain in terms of adsorption alone. It was probable that a true 'subhydride', of variable composition existed. It was necessary to form this *via* arsine.

In this formation of lower hydrides of the Group IV and V elements, the hydride chemistry is paralleling the organic chemistry – where compounds such as PhGe and Ph_2Ge are reported – and also the halide chemistry to some extent. All the dihalides of germanium, for example, are known. Their structures are polymeric: a chain structure like that of SeO_2 is proposed for GeF_2 [163], while GeI_2 is well-known to have the cadmium iodide layer structure. The structures of the polymeric organic compounds are also slowly becoming established. Recent work includes studies of $(PhGe)_n$ and $(Ph_2Ge)_n$ [164], and of $(Me_2Sn)_m$ [165], where chains of up to twenty tin atoms were found, as well as a six-membered ring. These results suggest a similar complexity in the lower hydrides, which may have polymeric, cross-linked structures.

A further class of compounds of the Group IV hydrides has been reported recently, and is a field that is certain to grow rapidly. These are compounds with direct bonds from Group IV elements to transition metals. The corresponding carbon-metal (σ) bonds are well-known to be very unstable, except in the presence of ligands such as tertiary phosphines or cyclopentadiene. The silicon and germanium compounds $GeH_2\{Mn(CO)_5\}_2$ [176], and $SiH_3Co(CO)_4$ and $SiH_2\{Co(CO)_4\}_2$ [175], are much more stable than their carbon analogues. The preparations are simple: the germane was formed by reaction of $Mn(CO)_5H$ and GeH_4 in tetrahydrofuran at room temperature, and the silanes by reaction of SiH_3I with $Co(CO)_4^-$ in ether at low temperature. These compounds certainly involve π bonding between the germanium or silicon and the transition metal, and the existence of such $d_\pi - d_\pi$ bonding would account for the much greater stability relative to the carbon compounds.

The lower lead hydride, with a hydrogen to lead ratio of about 0·1, which has been mentioned [19], appears to be analogous to the transition metal hydrides. Atomic hydrogen was interacted with lead films at very low pressures and temperatures, giving a hydride $PbH_{0\cdot19}$. On heating to 140°C, only about a quarter of the hydrogen was lost. Hurd [21], lists a number of earlier reports of such hydride preparations.

4.7 Other Volatile Metal Hydrides

When titanium tetrachloride is mixed with hydrogen at low pressures and subjected to mercury photosensitization, a mass spectrum of the products shows the presence of TiH_4, TiH_3Cl, TiH_2Cl_2, and $TiHCl_3$ [176]. A total pressure of 4 mm gave the first two, while at 8 mm, the last two products were found. No titanium hydride formed at 30 mm. These compounds are the analogues of the titanium methyls [177] which are extremely unstable, especially $TiMe_4$. The hydrides are of even lower stability but their existence, even as transient species, is an interesting example of the hydrogen-methyl analogy in many hydrides and organometallics.

Of the hydrides of the Main Group V elements, there is little to add to earlier accounts [21]. The existence of P_3H_5 and As_3H_5 has been demonstrated by mass spectrometry [116]. These compounds, and P_2H_4 and As_2H_4, are so unstable that the existence of higher homologues seems extremely unlikely. Stibine, SbH_3, was shown to behave similarly to arsine, stannane, and germane in forming a derivative $SbHNa_2$, as well as SbH_2Na, with sodium in ammonia [25]. Bismuthine was too unstable for any definite proof of the existence of BiH_2Na to be obtained, despite the fact that the blue colour of sodium in ammonia is so intense that 10^{-4} moles could readily be detected by the reaction [178].

Attempts to prepare hydrides of the V state, MH_5 or R_3MH_2, which would be analogues of the pentaphenyls of the Group V elements, were not successful [179]. The only related compound reported is PH_3O which decomposes at $-115°$ to water and solid phosphorus hydride [67]. Jolly's account of solid arsenic hydrides [19] has been mentioned in the preceding section. $(PH)_x$ is discussed [68], and $(CF_3)P(H)F_4$ has been made [204].

The hydrides of the nitrogen, oxygen, and fluorine Groups continue the trends already observed in carbon Group hydrides, and the Main Group hydrides can be discussed as a block, with no obvious feature to act as a dividing line between metal and non-metal. The heavier elements form the less stable hydrides, so that mercury, thallium, lead, bismuth, and polonium hydrides – so far as they are known to exist at all – decompose below $-100°C$. Stability increases on ascending the Groups, and also increases towards Group IV from both sides so that stabilities go Ga $<$ Ge $>$ As $>$ Se, and Zn can be included too. Although this area, of covalent hydrides and their derivatives, includes systems such as the silicon and boron hydrides which have been long and fully studied, there is no sign of the field being 'worked-out'. Rather, the many recent innovations – mixed hydrides, study of the higher silanes and germanes, compounds with transition metals, the advances in boron hydride chemistry leading to the formation of mixed-atom skeletons, and new analytical and synthetic methods – indicate that a new resurgence of interest is taking place.

4.8 Some Remarks on the Reactions of the Covalent Hydrides

Apart from the interconversions of the hydrides and their derivatives discussed earlier in this chapter, and apart from obvious reactions such as oxidations and halogenations, the reactivity of the metal-hydrogen bond is of vital importance in one general reaction. This is

$$\text{M-H} + \text{C=C} \rightleftharpoons \text{M-C-C-H} \quad .$$

The addition occurs with all M-H bonds and with a wide variety of unsaturated linkages involving carbon, nitrogen and oxygen. In the cases of boron, aluminium, silicon, germanium, and tin, especially, the reaction has been widely explored and cannot be discussed in any detail here. The addition of B-H across unsaturated bonds is the 'hydroboration' reaction widely explored by H. C. Brown [180, 1]. This may be used as a route to organo-boron compounds, and also as a method of reacting double bonds by the sequence

$$R_2C{=}CR'_2 + {>}BH = R_2CHCR'_2B{<} \xrightarrow{H_2O_2} R_2CHCR'_2OH.$$

The boron goes to the least hindered carbon, and, of course, may be split off by a number of reagents.

The action of aluminium hydrides has been studied by Ziegler and his school [181, 182]. Here the emphasis has been on polymerization reactions, as the Al-C addition across double bonds occurs in a similar way to the Al-H reaction. Thus Al-H reacts with ethylene to give carbon chains of the order of twenty to thirty atoms long. The use of transition metal compounds along with aluminium hydrides led, of course, to the well-known Zeigler-Natta process for stereo-specific polymerization. Whereas B-H adds across any double bond, except extremely hindered ones, Al-H will commonly add only across terminal double bonds.

The reactions of the Group IV hydrides with unsaturated linkages are reviewed in the organometallic reviews quoted above [105], [106], [107], [177]. A discussion of the reactivity of the silicon-hydrogen bonds is given in a series of papers [228]. The reactivity of the germanium-hydrogen bond has been reviewed by Lesbré, of the Toulouse school which has done much work in this field [183]. Hydrostannation is reviewed by Neumann [205].

In addition to this general reaction, the M-H bond in a highly substituted organohydride, such as Ph_3MH, is relatively stable to air and water. Such compounds may be handled by normal organic techniques, and then the M-H group acts as a useful functional group, in much the same way as halogen. For example, the Grignard reaction on $GeCl_4$ can give a mixture of organogermanium chlorides, R_nGeCl_{4-n}, which it is impossible to separate by distillation. By reducing the mixture with $LiAlH_4$ to the corresponding hydrides, the separation is facilitated. The hydrides can then be readily converted to halides by treatment with halogen.

Table 4.2. *Heats of Formation and Bond Energies*

Compare also Table 1.3. These values are the results of recent determinations by mass spectra (MS) or combustion calorimetry under conditions designed to allow complete combustion (C). MS–[220], [221] : C–[218], [219], [225]

Heats of Formation at 25°C (kcal/mole)

CH_4	−17·9 [218]	NH_3	−11·0 [218]
SiH_4	7·3 [218]; 7·8 [220]	PH_3	1·3 [218]; 2·3 [222]
GeH_4	21·7 [218]; 20·8 [220]	AsH_3	15·9 [218]: 15·2 [220]
SnH_4	38·9 [218]; 35.0 [220]	SbH_3	34·7 [218]; 34·6 [220]
PbH_4	59·7 [220]	BiH_3	66·4 [220]
Si_2H_6	15·1 [220]; 17·1 [225]	Si_3H_8	25·9 [219]
Ge_2H_6	39·1 [220]; 38·8 [219]	Ge_3H_8	54·2 [219]; 48·4 [220]
Sn_2H_6	65·6 [220]	SiH_3PH_2	1·9 [229]
P_2H_4	(9·9)[220]; 5·0 [225]		
As_2H_4	35·2 [220]		
Sb_2H_4	57·2 [220]		

But note the very discrepant values found by normal combustion calorimetry for mono-di-, and tri-silane [226].

Bond Energies (kcal/mole)

	[218]	[220]
C-H	99·3	
Si-H	76·5	72·6
Ge-H	69·0	68·7
Sn-H	60·4	61·7
Pb-H		49·0
N-H	93·4	
P-H	78·6	80·5
As-H	66·8	73·1
Sb-H	60·9	61·3
Bi-H		46·9

Si-Si (Si_2H_6) 39·7 [220]; 46·4 [225]
(Si_3H_8) 46·9 [219]
Ge-Ge (Ge_2H_6) 33·2 [220] ; 38·2 [219]; 37·9 [225]
(Ge_3H_8) 27·9 [220]; 39·1 [219]
Sn-Sn (Sn_2H_6) 29·9 [220]
P-P = 43·7 [220]: 46·8 [225]
As-As = 44·7 [220]
Sb-Sb = 30·7 [220]

For the other hydrides, less quantitative indications of stability are available and these are listed below.

	Decomposition Temperature (°C)	References
$(BeH_2)_x$	190	[37]
$AlH_{1\cdot 02}$.nAl	0	[34]
$(AlH_3)_x$ (solvated)	below 200: heat of formation −11·1 ± 2·3 kcal/mole	[79]
$(GaH_3)_x$	−15	[85]
$(GaHCl_2)_2$	25	[86]
$(ZnH_2)_x$	25 (slow)	[35]
$(CdH_2)_x$ (solvate)	−20 (slow)	[48]
$(HgH_2)_x$ (solvate)	−125 (slow)	[44]

Table 4.3. *Infra-red Data and Sources*

This compilation is intended merely as a guide to recent published work and is not exhaustive.

	M-H stretching region (cm^{-1})	References
$(BeH_2)_x$	v. broad band, 1450–2060	[38]
$(MgH_2)_x$	v. broad 1100	
BH_2Be bridge	2180, 1450	[39]
BeH_2Be bridge	1300, 1100	[40]
$AlH_3.D$	1750–1800 (D = donor group)	[55, 73]
$AlH_3.2D$	1700–1750	[55, 57, 58, 73]
$(GaH_3)_x$ (uncoordinated)	1980–2000	[85]
GaH_2Cl	2000	[90]
$GaHCl_2$	2018	[86]
$GaH_3.D$	1840–1850	[83, 87, 91]
$GaH_xX_{3-x}.D$	1835–1970	[90]
Group IV Hydrides (see also [98, 99])		
Si-H $(SiH_3)_3$*SiH*	2210	[110]
SiH_2 and SiH_3	2100–2200	In hydrides [27 – S.&.M] [110] In silyl compounds [98–101, 119–23, 145–50, 172, 173, 184, 185, and 207] In disilanyl compounds [132–140] In mixed hydrides [119, 120] In organo-silanes [186–88; 105]
GeH	2180–2200 1950–2100	In GeH_2X_2 [195, 6] In hydrides [27 – D.&J.], [192, 194] In germyl compounds [151, 202, 203, 208, 217] In mixed hydrides [31] In organo-germanes (106 – Q. & B.) [193, 197, 199, 227]
Sn-H	1790–1910	[112, 128, 190, 191, 200, 206]
Pb-H	1709	[201]

The symmetrical deformation frequency in CH_3, SiH_3, and GeH_3 compounds is discussed by Jolly [189]: see also [31].

The Group V frequencies are found at 2300–2450 for P-H, 2050–2200 for As-H, and 1850–2000 for Sb-H stretching modes.

Table 4.4. *Nuclear Magnetic Resonance Sources*

This Table lists recent references to proton resonance measurements on the covalent hydrides.

AlH_3 adducts	[55, 74]
GaH_3 adducts	[91]
Group IV hydrides: see also [98, 99]	
Silicon hydrides	[110, 210]
Germanium hydrides	[27, 118, 144, 191]
Tin hydrides	[191, 209]
Pb-H in Me_3PbH	[127]
Mixed Hydrides of Group IV–V	
Silicon	[118, 119]
Germanium	[118]
Derivatives of Group IV hydrides: see also [98, 99]	
SiH_3 compounds	[138, 140, 210, 211, 213, 214]
Si_2H_5 compounds	[142]
GeH_3 compounds	[212]
Ge_2H_5 compounds	[114, 143]
organo- Si, Ge, Sn hydrides	[191, 209, 215, 216]

REFERENCES

[1] A. STOCK, *Hydrides of Boron and Silicon*, Cornell University Press, O.U.P. 1933; re-issued 1957.

[2] W. N. LIPSCOMB, *Advances in Inorganic Chemistry and Radiochemistry*, edited by H. J. Emeleus and J. S. Anderson, Interscience, 1959, **1**, 117.

[3] T. P. FEHLRER and W. C. KOSKI, *J. Amer. Chem. Soc.*, 1964, **86**, 2733.

[4] H. J. EMELEUS and J. S. ANDERSON, *Modern Aspects of Inorganic Chemistry*, Routledge and Kegan Paul, 3rd Edition, 1960, Chapter 11.

[5] R. P. BELL and H. C. LONGUET-HIGGINS, *Proc. Roy. Soc.*, 1945, **183A**, 357: W. P. PRICE, *J. Chem. Phys.*, 1947, **15**, 614.

[6] J. N. SCHOOLERY, *Discussions Faraday Soc.*, 1955, **19**, 219: R. A. OGG, *J. Chem. Phys.*, 1954, **22**, 1933.

[7] K. HEDBERG and V. SCHOMAKER, *J. Amer. Chem. Soc.*, 1951, **73**, 1482.

[8] D. SCHRIVER and W. JOLLY, *J. Amer. Chem. Soc.*, 1958, **80**, 6692.

[9] P. H. LEWIS and R. E. RUNDLE, *J. Chem. Phys.*, 1953, **21**, 986.

[10] H. C. LONGUET-HIGGINS and R. P. BELL, *J. Chem. Soc.*, 1943, 250.

[11] H. C. LONGUET-HIGGINS, Quart. Rev., 1957, **11**, 121: *J. Chim. phys.*, 1949, **46**, 275.

[12] A. I. SNOW and R. E. RUNDLE, *Acta Cryst.*, 1951, **4**, 348.

[13] A. STOCK and E. POHLAND, *Chem. Berichte*, 1926, **59**, 2215.

[14] R. I. WAGNER and A. B. BURG, *J. Amer. Chem. Soc.*, 1953, **75**, 3872.

[15] F. G. A. STONE and A. B. BURG. *J. Amer. Chem. Soc.*. 1954, **76**, 386.

[16] A. B. BURG and L. R. GRANT, *J. Amer. Chem. Soc.*, 1959, **81**, 1.

[17] W. L. JOLLY and J. E. DRAKE, *Inorganic Syntheses*, Volume VII, edited by J. Kleinberg. McGraw-Hill, 1963, 37.

[18] W. L. JOLLY, L. B. ANDERSON, and R. L. BELTRAMI, University of California, UCRL–4707, 1956, 'Solid Arsenic Hydrides'. *J. Amer. Chem. Soc.*, 1957, **79**, 2443.

[19] B. R. WELLS and M. W. ROBERTS, *Proc. Chem. Soc.*, 1964, 173.

[20] L. M. DENNIS, R. B. COREY, and R. W. MOORE, *J. Amer. Chem. Soc.*, 1924, **46**, 657.

[21] D. T. HURD, *The Chemistry of the Hydrides*, Wiley, 1952: F. PANETH and E. WINTERTY, *Chem. Berichte*, 1918, **51**, 1704, 1928.
[22] W. C. JOHNSON and A. PECHUKAS, *J. Amer. Chem. Soc.*, 1937, **59**, 2065.
[23] F. K. BLUMENBERG, U.S. Patent. 1,338,279.
[24] W. C. JOHNSON and T. R. HOGNESS, *J. Amer. Chem. Soc.*, 1934, **56**, 1252.
[25] H. J. EMELEUS and K. M. MACKAY, *J. Chem. Soc.*, 1961, 2676.
[26] T. S. PIPER and M. K. WILSON, *J. Inorg. Nucl. Chem.*, 1957, **4**, 22: E. D. MACKLIN, *J. Chem. Soc.*, 1959, 1989, 1984.
[27] J. E. DRAKE and W. L. JOLLY, *J. Chem. Soc.*, 1962, 2807; *Proc. Chem. Soc.* 1961, 379; UCRL–11078, 1963: E. J. SPANIER and A. G. MACDIARMID, *Inorg. Chem.*, 1962, **1**, 432: R. SCHWARZ and F. HEINRICH, *Zeit. an. Chem.*, 1935, **221**, 277: S. D. GOKHALE and W. L. JOLLY, *Inorg. Chem.*, 1964, **3**, 946.
[28] K. M. MACKAY and K. SUTTON, unpublished observations.
[29] C. S. G. PHILLIPS and P. L. TIMMS, *Analyt. Chem.*, 1963, **35**, 505.
[30] E. J. SPANIER and A. G. MACDIARMID, *Inorg. Chem.*, 1963, **2**, 215.
[31] J. E. DRAKE and W. L. JOLLY, *Chem. and Ind.*, 1962, 1470.
[32] G. E. COATES and F. GLOCKLING, *J. Chem. Soc.*, 1954, 22, 2526.
[33] G. CHIZINSKY, G. G. EVANS, T. R. P. GIBB, Jr., and M. J. RICE, Jr., *J. Amer. Chem. Soc.*, 1955, **77**, 3164.
[34] B. SIEGEL, *J. Amer. Chem. Soc.*, 1960, **82**, 1535.
[35] G. D. BARBARAS, C. DILLARD, A. E. FINHOLT, T. WARTIK, K. E. WILZBACH, and H. I. SCHLESINGER, *J. Amer. Chem. Soc.*, 1951, **73**, 4585.
[36] E. WIBERG and R. BAUER, *Zeit. Naturf.*, 1951, **6b**, 171.
[37] E. C. HEAD, C. E. HOLLEY, Jr., and S. W. RABIDEAU, *J. Amer. Chem. Soc.*, 1957, **79**, 3687.
[38] L. BANFORD and G. E. COATES, *J. Chem. Soc.*, 1964, 5591.
[39] W. C. PRICE, *J. Chem. Phys.*, 1949, **17**, 1044.
[40] N. A. BELL and G. E. COATES, *J. Chem. Soc.*, 1965, 692.
[41] N. A. BELL and G. E. COATES, *Proc. Chem. Soc.*, 1964, 59.
[42] K. NAKAMOTO, *Infra-red Spectra of Inorganic and Coordination Compounds*, Wiley, 1963.
[43] G. W. ADAMSON and H. M. M. SHEARER, *Chem. Comm.*, 1965, 240.
[44] E. WIBERG and W. HENLE, *Zeit. Naturf.*, 1951, **6b**, 461.
[45] E. WIBERG, W. HENLE, and R. BAUER, *Zeit. Naturf.*, 1951, **6b**, 393; E. WIBERG and W. HENLE, *ibid.* 1952, **7b**, 249.
[46] G. JANDER and K. KRAFFCZYK, *Zeit. anorg. Chem.*, 1956, **283**, 217.
[47] P. KOBETZ and W. E. BECKER, *Inorg. Chem.*, 1963, **2**, 859.
[48] E. WIBERG and W. HENLE, *Zeit. Naturf.*, 1951, **6b**, 461.
[49] G. W. BETHKE and M. K. WILSON, *J. Chem. Phys.*, 1957, **26**, 1107.
[50] P. BREISACHER and B. SIEGAL, *J. Amer. Chem. Soc.*, 1964, **86**, 5053.
[51] O. STECHER and E. WIBERG, *Chem. Berichte*, 1942, **75B**, 2003; *Angew. Chem.*, 1939, **52**, 372.
[52] A. E. FINHOLT, A. C. BOND, and H. I. SCHLESINGER, *J. Amer. Chem. Soc.*, 1947, **69** 1199.
[53] J. R. SURTEES, *Chem. and Ind.*, 1964, 1260.
[54] F. M. PETERS, *Canad. J. Chem.*, 1964, **42**, 1755.
[55] G. W. FRASER, N. N. GREENWOOD, and B. P. STRAUGHAN, *J. Chem. Soc.*, 1963, 3742.
[56] C. W. HEITSCH, C. E. NORDMANN, and R. W. PARRY, *Inorg. Chem.*, 1963, **2**, 508.
[57] C. W. HEITSCH and R. N. KNISELY, *Spect. Acta.* 1963, **19**, 1386.
[58] I. R. BEATTIE and T. GILSON, *J. Chem. Soc.*, 1964, 3528.
[59] G. L. PALINEK, *Acta Cryst.*, 1964, **17**, 1573.
[60] E. WIBERG, *Angew. Chemie*, 1953, **65**, 16 (Review).
[61] E. C. ASHBY, *J. Amer. Chem. Soc.*, 1964, **86**, 1882.

[62] M. J. JORGENSON, *Tetrahedron Letters*, 1962, 558.
[63] E. WIBERG and A. JAHN, *Zeit. Naturf.*, 1952, **7b**, 580: E. L. ELIEL and M. N. RERICK, *J. Amer. Chem. Soc.*, 1960, **82**, 1367.
[64] E. L. ELIEL, *Rec. Chem. Progress*, 1961, **22**, No. 3: M. N. RERICK, *The Mixed Hydrides*, Metal Hydrides Inc., Beverly, Mass.
[65] Brit. Pat. 860,377 (1961).
[66] M. J. RICE, T. R. P. GIBB, Jr., E. G. MELORIE, U.S. Atomic Energy Commission, NYO–7542 (1955).
[67] E. WIBERG and G. MULLER-SCHIEDMAYER, *Zeit. anorg. Chem.*, 1961, **308**, 352.
[68] Idem., *Chem. Berichte*. 1959, **92**, 2372.
[69] See (51); also E. WIBERG, H. GRAF, and R. U. LACAL, *Zeit. anorg. Chem.*, 1953, **272**, 221; *Zeit. Naturf.* 1952, **7b**, 578.
[70] E. WIBERG, H. NOTH, and R. U. LACAL, *Zeit. Naturf.*, 1956, **11b**, 487.
[71] F. M. PETERS, B. BARTOCHA, and A. J. BILBO, *Canad. J. Chem.*, 1963, **41**, 1051.
[72] J. M. DAVIDSON and T. WARTIK, *J. Amer. Chem. Soc.*, 1960, **82**, 5506.
[73] R. EHRLICH, A. R. YOUNG II, B. M. LICHSTEIN, and D. D. PERRY, *Inorg. Chem.*, 1963, **2**, 650.
[74] R. DAUTEL and W. ZEIL, *Zeit. Elektrochem.*, 1958, **62**, 1139.
[75] N. R. FETTER, and D. W. MOORE, *Canad. J. Chem.*, 1964, **42**, 885.
[76] R. EHRLICH, A. R. YOUNG II, B. M. LICHSTEIN, and D. D. PERRY, *Inorg. Chem.*, 1964, **3**, 628.
[77] A. R. YOUNG II and R. EHRLICH, *J. Amer. Chem. Soc.*, 1964, **86**, 5359.
[78] E. C. ASHBY and W. E. FOSTER, *J. Amer. Chem. Soc.*, 1962, **84**, 3407.
[79] C. E. MESSER, U.S. Atomic Energy Commission, NYO–8028 (1960).
[80] E. WIBERG and T. JOHANNSEN, *Naturwiss*, 1941, **29**, 320; *Angew. Chem.*, 1942, **55**, 38.
[81] E. WIBERG and M. SCHMIDT, *Zeit. Naturf.*, 1952, **7b**, 577; 1951, **6b**, 172.
[82] D. F. SHRIVER, R. W. PARRY, N. N. GREENWOOD, A. STORR, and M. G. H. WALLBRIDGE, *Inorg. Chem.*, 1963, **2**, 867.
[83] N. N. GREENWOOD, A. STORR, and M. G. H. WALLBRIDGE, *Inorg., Chem.*, 1963, **2**, 1036.
[84] D. F. SHRIVER and R. W. PARRY, *Inorg. Chem.*, 1963, **2**, 1039.
[85] N. N. GREENWOOD and M. G. H. WALLBRIDGE, *J. Chem. Soc.*, 1963. 3912.
[86] H. SCHMIDBAUER, W. FINDEISS, and E. GAST, *Angew. Chem.* (*Inter.*), 1965, **4**, 152.
[87] D. F. SHRIVER, R. AMSTER, and R. C. TAYLOR, *J. Amer. Chem. Soc.*, 1962, **84**, 1321.
[88] D. F. SHRIVER and C. E. NORDMAN, *Inorg. Chem.*, 1963, **2**, 1298.
[89] R. C. TAYLOR, Private communication reported in [83].
[90] N. N. GREENWOOD and A. STORR, *J. Chem. Soc.*, 1965, 3426.
[91] N. N. GREENWOOD, E. F. J. ROSS, and A. STORR, *J. Chem. Soc.*, 1965, 1400.
[92] E. WIBERG and M. SCHMIDT, *Zeit. Naturf.*. 1957, **12b**, 54.
[93] E. G. HOFFMANN and G. SCHOMBURG, *Zeit. Elektrochem.*, 1957, **61**, 110.
[94] J. H. MORRIS, Unpublished observations.
[95] N. N. GREENWOOD and J. A. MCGINNETY, *Chem. Comm.*, 1965, 331.
[96] E. WIBERG, O. DILLMANN, H. NOTH, and M. SCHMIDT, *Zeit. Naturf.*, 1957, **12b**, 56, 59.
[97] E. WIBERG, O. DILLMANN, and M. SCHMIDT, *Zeit. Naturf.*, 1957, **12b**, 60.
[98] E. A. V. EBSWORTH, *Volatile Silicon Compounds*, Pergamon Press, 1963.
[99] F. G. A. STONE, *Hydrogen Compounds of the Group IV Elements*, Prentice-Hall, 1962.
[100] A. G. MACDIARMID, *Quart. Rev.*, 1956, **10**, 208; see also his article on preparations of silyl compounds in *Preparative Inorganic Reactions* (edited by W. L. Jolly. Interscience, 1964, **1**, 165.
[101] A. G. MACDIARMID, Silanes and their Derivatives, *Advances in Inorganic Chemistry and Radiochemistry*, edited by H. J. Emeleus and A. G. Sharpe. Academic Press, 1961, **3**, 207.

[102] U. WANNAGAT, *ibid*, 1964, **6**, 225, *Silicon-Nitrogen Compounds*.
[103] J. J. ZUCKERMAN, *ibid*, 1964, **6**, 383, *Direct synthesis of Organo-silicon Compounds*.
[104] H. GILMAN and G. L. SCHWEIBE, *Advances in Organometallic Chemistry*, edited by F. G. A. Stone and R. West, Academic Press, 1964, **1**, 47.
[105] C. EABORN, *Organosilicon Compounds*. Butterworth, 1960.
[106] D. QUANE and R. S. BOTTEI, *Chem. Rev.*, 1963, **63**, 403: F. RIJKENS and G. J. M. VAN DER KERK, (Germanium Research Committee), 1964 and F. RIJKENS, (Germanium Research Committee) 1960–both from the Institute for Organic Chemistry, T.N.O., Utrecht: O. H. JOHNSON, *Chem. Rev.*, 1951, **48**, 259.
[107] H. G. KUIVILA, *Advances in Organometallic Chemistry*, edited by F. G. A. Stone and R. West. Academic Press, 1964, **1**, 47.
[108] E. AMBERGER, *Angew. Chem.*, 1959, **71**, 372;
[109] Chapter 2 in Reference [1].
[110] S. D. GOKHALE and W. L. JOLLY, *Inorg. Chem.*, 1964, **3**, 946.
[111] K. M. MACKAY, P. ROBINSON and K. SUTTON, Unpublished Observations.
[112] W. L. JOLLY, *Angew. Chem.*, 1960, **72**, 268.
[113] See reference [17] p. 40.
[114] E. J. SPANIER, A. G. MACDIARMID, K. M. MACKAY and P. ROBINSON, *J. Inorg. Nucl. Chem.*, 1966, in press.
[115] P. L. TIMMS, C. C. SIMPSON, and C. S. G. PHILLIPS, *J. Chem. Soc.*, 1964, 1467; also ref. [29].
[116] P. ROYEN, C. ROCKTASCHEL, and W. MOSCH, *Angew. Chem.* (*Inter.*), 1964, **3**, 703.
[117] G. FRITZ, *Zeit. anorg. Chem.*, 1955, **280**, 332.
[118] J. E. DRAKE and W. L. JOLLY, *J. Chem. Phys.*, 1963, **38**, 1033: also the report UCRL 10422, University of California, 1962.
[119] S. D. GOKHALE and W. L. JOLLY, *Inorg. Chem.*, 1965, **4**, 596; 1964, **3**, 1141.
[120] E. AMBERGER and H. D. BOETERS, *Chem. Berichte*, 1964, **97**, 1999.
[121] G. DAVIDSON, E. A. V. EBSWORTH, G. M. SHELDRICK and L. A. WOODWARD, *Chem. Comm.*, 1965, 122.
[122] R. C. LORD, D. W. ROBINSON and W. SCHUMB, *J. Amer. Chem. Soc.*, 1956, **78**, 1327.
[123] J. R. ARONSON, R. C. LORD and D. W. ROBINSON, *J. Chem. Phys.*, 1960, **33**, 1004: D. C. MCKEAN, *Spect. Acta.*, 1958, **13**, 38; with R. TAYLOR and L. A. WOODWARD, *Proc. Chem. Soc.*, 1959, 321.
[124] E. A. V. EBSWORTH, S. C. CRADOCK. Private Communication, 1965.
[125] T. N. SRIVASTAVA, J. E. GRIFFITHS, and M. ONYSZCHUK, *Canad. J. Chem.*, 1962, **40**, 739.
[126] A number of undergraduate students at Nottingham (1964–5) have shown that GeH_3I gives GeH_3X (X = Br, CN, CNO, CNS, with AgX) and (X = Cl, O, Se with HgX_2) and (X = F, O with PbF_2 or PbO). GeH_3Br gives GeH_3Cl and GeH_3Cl gives GeH_3F.
[127] R. DUFFY and A. K. HOLLIDAY, *J. Chem. Soc.*, 1961, 1679; *Proc. Chem. Soc.*, 1959, 124: R. DUFFY, J. FEENEY and A. K. HOLLIDAY, *J. Chem. Soc.*, 1962, 1144.
[128] H. J. EMELEUS and S. F. A. KETTLE, *J. Chem. Soc.*, 1958, 2444.
[129] M. A. RING and D. M. RITTER, *J. Amer. Chem. Soc.*, 1961, **83**, 802: *J. Chem. Phys.*, 1961, **65**, 182.
[130] E. A. V. EBSWORTH. Private Communication, 1964.
[131] M. A. RING, L. P. FREEMAN, and A. P. FOX, *Inorg. Chem.*, 1964, **3**, 1200.
[132] L. G. L. WARD and A. G. MACDIARMID, *J. Amer. Chem. Soc.*, 1960, **82**, 2151.
[133] idem, *J. Inorg. Nucl. Chem.*, 1961, **20**, 345.
[134] idem, *ibid*, 1961, **21**, 287.
[135] A. D. CRAIG, J. V. URENOVITCH, and A. G. MACDIARMID, *J. Chem. Soc.*, 1962, 548.
[136] M. ABEDINI, C. H. VAN DYKE, and A. G. MACDIARMID, *J. Inorg., Nucl. Chem.*, 1963, **25**, 307.

[137] M. ABEDINI and A. G. MACDIARMID, *Inorg. Chem.*, 1963, **2**, 608.
[138] C. H. VAN DYKE and A. G. MACDIARMID, *Inorg. Chem.*, 1964, **3**, 747.
[139] idem, *J. Inorg. Nucl. Chem.*, 1963, **25**, 1503.
[140] C. H. VAN DYKE, Ph.D. Dissertation, University of Pennsylvania, 1964.
[141] K. M. MACKAY and P. J. ROEBUCK, *J. Chem. Soc.*, 1964, 1195.
[142] C. H. VAN DYKE and A. G. MACDIARMID, *Inorg. Chem.*, 1964, **3**, 1071.
[143] A. G. MACDIARMID, Unpublished observations: see also [114].
[144] K. M. MACKAY and P. ROBINSON, *J. Chem. Soc.*, 1965 (Sept).
[145] E. A. V. EBSWORTH and M. J. MAYS, *J. Chem. Soc.*, 1962, 4844.
[146] E. A. V. EBSWORTH, R. MOULD, R. TAYLOR, G. R. WILKINSON, and L. A. WOODWARD, *Trans. Faraday Soc.*, 1962, **58**, 1069.
[147] C. I. BEARD and B. P. DAILEY, *J. Amer. Chem. Soc.*, 1949, **71**, 929.
[148] E. A. V. EBSWORTH and M. J. MAYS, *J. Chem. Soc.*, 1963, 3893.
[149] E. A. V. EBSWORTH and M. J. MAYS, *Spect. Acta.*, 1963, **19**, 1127; *J. Chem. Soc.*, 1961, 4879.
[150] B. J. AYLETT, J. R. HALL, D. C. MCKEAN, R. TAYLOR and L. A. WOODWARD, *Spect. Acta.* 1960, **16**, 747.
[151] T. D. GOLDFARB and S. SUJISHI, *J. Amer. Chem. Soc.*, 1964, **86**, 1679.
[152] J. E. GRIFFITHS and A. L. BEACH, *Chem. Comm.*, 1965, 437.
[153] K. M. MACKAY and P. ROBINSON, Unpublished observations.
[154] E. A. V. EBSWORTH, private communication.
[155] D. P. CRAIG, A. MACCOLL, R. S. NYHOLM, L. E. ORGEL, and L. E. SUTTON, *J. Chem. Soc.*, 1954, 332; 354.
[156] R. A. BENKESER, C. E. DEBOER, R. H. ROBINSON, and D. M. SAUVE, *J. Amer. Chem. Soc.*, 1956, **78**, 682.
[157] J. CHATT and A. A. WILLIAMS, *J. Chem. Soc.*, 1954, 4403.
[158] C. A. KRAUS and E. S. CARNEY, *J. Amer. Chem. Soc.*, 1934, **56**, 765.
[159] P. ROYEN and R. SCHWARZ, *Zeit. anorg. Chem.*, 1933, **215**, 288, 95; 1933, **211**, 412.
[160] S. N. GLARUM and C. A. KRAUS, *J. Amer. Chem. Soc.*, 1950, **72**, 5398.
[161] G. SCHOTT, W. HERMANN, and E. HIRSCHMANN, *Angew. Chem.*, 1956, **68**, 213.
[162] A. STOCK and K. SOMIESKI, *Chem. Berichte*, 1923, **56**, 251, 1701.
[163] N. BARTLETT, private commuhication; with K. C. YU, *Canad. J. Chem.*, 1961, **39**, 80.
[164] K. A. HOOTON and F. GLOCKLING. *J. Chem. Soc.*, 1963, 1849.
[165] T. L. BROWN and G. L. MORGAN, *Inorg. Chem.* 1963, **2**, 736.
[166] A. STOCK and P. STIEBELER, *Chem. Berichte.*, 1923, **56B**, 1087.
[167] H. J. EMELEUS and A. G. MADDOCK, *J. Chem. Soc.*, 1946, 1131.
[168] J. A. BEDFORD, J. R. BOLTON, A. CARRINGTON, and R. H. PRINCE, *Trans. Faraday Soc.*, 1963, **59**, 53.
[169] R. WEST, R. H. BANEY and D. L. POWELL, *J. Amer. Chem. Soc.*, 1960, **82**, 6269.
[170] W. E. BECKER and S. E. COOK, *J. Amer. Chem. Soc.*, 1960, **82**, 6264.
[171] C. A. KRAUS and W. M. GREER, *J. Amer. Chem. Soc.*, 1922, **44**, 2629.
[172] E. A. V. EBSWORTH, R. TAYLOR and L. A. WOODWARD, *Trans. Faraday Soc.*, 1959, **55**, 211.
[173] E. A. V. EBSWORTH, D. R. JENKINS, M. J. MAYS and T. M. SUGDEN, *Proc. Chem. Soc.*, 1963, 21.
[174] A. G. MASSEY, A. J. PARK, and F. G. A. STONE, *J. Amer. Chem. Soc.*, 1963, **85**, 2021.
[175] B. J. AYLETT and J. M. CAMPBELL, *Chem. Comm.*, 1965, 217.
[176] P. BREISACHER and B. SIEGEL, *J. Amer. Chem. Soc.*, 1963, **85**, 1705.
[177] G. E. COATES, *Organometallic Compounds*, Methuen, second edition, 1960.
[178] K. M. MACKAY, Ph.D. Thesis, University of Cambridge, 1960.
[179] E. WIBERG and K. MODRITZER, *Zeit. Naturf.*, 1956, **11b**, 747.
[180] H. C. BROWN and B. C. SUBBA RAO, *J. Org. Chem.*, 1957, **22**, 1137.

[181] *Organometallic Chemistry*, edited by H. Zeiss, ACS Monograph 147, Reinhold, 1960: includes 'Organoboranes' by H. C. BROWN, 'Organo-Aluminium Compounds' by K. ZIEGLER.

[182] *Perspectives in Organic Chemistry*, edited by Sir A. Todd, Interscience, 1956: 'Neue Entwicklungen der metallorganischen Synthese' – chapter by K. ZIEGLER. See also [177].

[183] M. LESBRÉ, *Chem. Weekblad*. 1962, **58**, 351.

[184] D. F. BALL, M. J. BUTTLER, and D. C. MCKEAN, *Spect. Acta*. 1965, **21**, 451.

[185] M. J. BUTTLER and D. C. MCKEAN, *Spect. Acta*. 1965, **21**, 485.

[186] D. F. BALL and D. C. MCKEAN, *ibid*, p. 204.

[187] D. F. BALL, T. CARTER, D. C. MCKEAN, and L. A. WOODWARD, *ibid*, 1964, **20**, 1721.

[188] D. F. BALL, P. L. COGGIN, D. C. MCKEAN, and L. A. WOODWARD, *ibid*, 1960, **16**, 1358: (and references therein).

[189] W. A. JOLLY, *J. Amer. Chem. Soc*., 1963, **85**, 3083.

[190] S. F. A. KETTLE, *J. Chem. Soc*., 1959, 2936.

[191] P. E. POTTER, L. PRATT, and G. WILKINSON, *J. Chem. Soc*., 1964, 524.

[192] J. E. GRIFFITHS and G. E. WALRAFEN, *J. Chem. Phys*., 1964, **40**, 321.

[193] J. E. GRIFFITHS, *ibid*. 1963, **38**, 2879.

[194] V. A. CRAWFORD, K. H. RHEE, and M. K. WILSON, *ibid*, 1962, **37**, 2377.

[195] J. E. GRIFFITHS, T. N. SRIVASTAVA, and M. ONYSZCHUK, *Canad. J. Chem*., 1963, **41**, 2101.

[196] E. A. V. EBSWORTH and A. G. ROBIETTE, *Spect. Acta*, 1964, **20**, 1639.

[197] J. SATGÉ, *Annales de Chimie*, 1961, **6**, 519.

[198] E. A. V. EBSWORTH, J. R. HALL, M. J. MACKILLOP, D. C. MCKEAN, N. SHEPPARD, and L. A. WOODWARD, *Spect. Acta*., 1958, **13**, 202.

[199] N. A. CHUMAEVSKII, *Optics and Spectroscopy* (*Optika i Spekt*.), 1962, **13**, 37.

[200] A. K. SAWYER and H. G. KUIVILA, *J. Amer. Chem. Soc*., 1963, **85**, 1010.

[201] E. AMBERGER, *Angew. Chem*., 1960, **72**, 494.

[202] D. E. FREEMAN, K. H. RHEE, and M. K. WILSON, *J. Chem. Phys*., 1963, **39**, 2908.

[203] J. E. GRIFFITHS, T. N. SRIVASTAVA, and M. ONYSZCHUK, *Canad. J. Chem*., 1962, **40**, 579.

[204] R. G. CAVELL and J. F. NIXON, *Proc. Chem. Soc*., 1964, 229.

[205] W. P. NEUMANN, *Angew. Chem*., 1964, **76**, 849.

[206] L. MAY and C. R. DILLARD, *J. Chem. Phys*., 1961, **34**, 694: *J. Mol. Spect*., 1964, **14**, 250.

[207] R. B. REEVES and D. W. ROBINSON, *J. Chem. Phys*., 1964, **41**, 1699.

[208] T. D. GOLDFARB, *J. Chem. Phys*., 1962, **37**, 642: (also, with B. P. ZAFONTE, 1964, **41**, 3653).

[209] N. FLITCROFT and H. D. KAESZ, *J. Amer. Chem. Soc*., 1963, **85**, 1377.

[210] E. A. V. EBSWORTH and J. J. TURNER, *Trans. Faraday Soc*., 1964, **60**, 256; and references therein.

[211] idem, *J. Phys. Chem*., 163, **67**, 805.

[212] E. A. V. EBSWORTH, S. C. FRANKISS, and A. G. ROBIETTE, *Proton Resonance Spectra in Some Derivatives of Monogermane*, to be published (*Spect. Acta*).

[213] E. A. V. EBSWORTH and N. SHEPPARD, *J. Inorg. Nucl. Chem*., 1959, **9**, 95.

[214] E. A. V. EBSWORTH, H. J. EMELEUS, and N. WELCMAN, *J. Chem. Soc*., 1962, 2290.

[215] E. A. V. EBSWORTH and S. G. FRANKISS, *Trans. Faraday Soc*., 1963, **59**, 1518.

[216] G. P. VAN DER KELEN, L. VERDONCK, and D. VAN DE VONDEL, *Bull. Soc. Chim. Belg*., 1964, **73**, 733.

[217] M. G. KRISHNA PILAI and A. PERUMAL, *Bull. Soc. Chim. Belg*., 1964, **73**, 29.

[218] S. R. GUNN, *J. Phys. Chem*., 1964, **68**, 949.

[219] S. R. GUNN and L. G. GREEN, *J. Phys. Chem*., 1964, **68**, 946.

[220] F. E. SAALFELD and H. J. SVEC, *Inorg. Chem*., 1963, **2**, 46, 50.

[221] idem, *J. Inorg. Nucl. Chem.*, 1961, **18**, 98.

[222] G. FRITZ and G. POPPENBURG, *Naturwiss.*, 1962, **49**, 449; *Angew. Chem.*, 1960, **72**, 208: with M. G. ROCHOLL, *Naturwiss.*, 1962, **49**, 255.

[223] E. A. V. EBSWORTH and S. G. FRANKISS, *J. Amer. Chem. Soc.*, 1963, **85**, 3516.

[224] J. E. GRIFFITHS and K. B. MCAFEE, Jr., *Proc. Chem. Soc.*, 1961, 456.

[225] S. R. GUNN and L. G. GREEN, *J. Phys. Chem.*, 1961, **65**, 779.

[226] F. FEHER, G. JANSEN, and H. ROHMER, *Angew. Chem.*, 1963, **75**, 859.

[227] D. F. VAN DE VONDEL, *J. Organomet. Chem.*, 1965, **3**, 400.

[228] M. R. STOBER, M. S. MUSOLF, and J. SPEIR, *J. Org. Chem.*, 1965, **30**, 1651; (and earlier papers of this series).

[229] F. E. SAALFELD and H. J. SVEC, *Inorg. Chem.*, 1964, **3**, 1442.

[230] W. A. DUTTON and M. ONYSZCHUCK, *Abstr. 147th A.C.S. Meeting*, April 1964, 33L.

[231] E. A. V. EBSWORTH, L. A. WOODWARD, S. C. CRADOCK, and G. DAVIDSON, unpublished observations.

[232] E. AMBERGER, *Angew. Chem.*, 1960, **72**, 78.

[233] G. URRY, *Inorg. Chem.*, 1963, **2**, 432.

CHAPTER 5

Complex Hydrides of the Transition Metals

In addition to the solid, metallic, hydrides of the transition elements, it has become clear in the last ten years that a wide variety of complexes, containing hydrogen as a ligand, may be formed by these elements. Although the first representatives of this type to be prepared, such as $HCo(CO)_4$, were very unstable, conditions for preparing stable hydride complexes are now understood. Compounds of all the transition elements except the titanium Group, with hydrogen, are known. In this Chapter, it is our object to introduce these compounds by a brief review of the compound types and a discussion of their properties. An exhaustive treatment is not possible in the space available. The hydrides have been reviewed by Green [8] and by Chatt [33]. Before turning to the complexes where other ligands are present, we first note the three or four cases where only hydrogen is attached to the transition element.

5.1 Complex Ions Containing Only Hydrogen

It is now established that rhenium [1], and technetium [3] form hydride ions in the VII state, K_2MH_9. The early studies of this system, by Lundell and Knowles [4a], showed that the action of zinc on acid perrhenate solutions gave a reducing species which was identified as 'rhenide', Re^-. More recently, a species $KRe.4H_2O$ was claimed from reduction of perrhenate by potassium in aqueous ethylenediamine, and identified with the earlier 'rhenide' [5]. Further studies of this 'potassium rhenide' led to the realization that the species contained Re-H bonds, and the formula was revised, through $KReH_4.2H_2O$ and K_2ReH_8 to the final one, K_2ReH_9 [1], which has been confirmed by neutron diffraction studies [2]. A re-investigation of the products of the zinc and potassium reductions showed that the zinc reaction gave a different compound of rhenium; although Lundell and Knowles' compound may also be a rhenium-hydrogen compound [4b]. K_2ReH_9 is one product of the action of K/NH_3 on K_2ReBr_6 [7].

The structure of K_2ReH_9 is hexagonal with the unit cell containing three formula units. The nine hydrogen atoms surround the rhenium, six at the corners of a trigonal prism, and three beyond the centres of the rectangular faces. The average Re-H distance is 1·68 Å and the H-Re-H angle in a vertical mirror plane of the prism is 94°. This ReH_9^{2-} trigonal prism fits inside another formed by nine potassium ions around the central rhenium, with the potassiums shared between two rhenium atoms [1, 2]. The corresponding technetium compound, K_2TcH_9, is prepared in the same way and is isomorphous with the rhenium compound. As the infra-red spectra of the two compounds are very similar, the structure of the technetium compound can be taken to be the same as that of the rhenium hydride [3].

These compounds are relatively stable, an alkaline solution of the rhenium compound being stable at room temperature for several weeks. They evolve hydrogen slowly with water–indeed, TcH_9^{2-} has to be prepared in anhydrous conditions–and quantitatively with acid. The problems encountered in determining the formula arose mainly because hydrogen contributes so little to the molecular weight (1 H $= 0{\cdot}37\%$ in the rhenium compound) and the compound is commonly contaminated by small amounts of perrhenate, and possibly with carbonate. K_2TcH_9 is more reactive than the rhenium compound.

The infra-red spectra show metal-hydrogen stretching modes at 1869, 1795, 1779 cm^{-1} for the technetium hydride and 1931, 1846, 1814 cm^{-1} for the rhenium compound–indicating stronger M-H bonds in the latter. In the bending region, the absorptions are at 689 cm^{-1} and 735 cm^{-1} respectively. These absorptions are in the normal regions for metal-hydrogen bonds. The nmr spectra show proton resonances at the very high field associated with hydrogen bonded to a transition metal; at τ-values of 18·4 ppm for the technetium hydride and 19·1 ppm for the rhenium compound. The line for $(ReH_9)^{2-}$ is sharp, but the technetium hydrogen absorption is a broad line, attributed to the partial resolution of the ten line multiplet arising from coupling with Tc^{99} with a spin of 9/2. The nuclear quadrupole moment of Tc^{99} is very low, $0{\cdot}3 \times 10^{-24}$ cm^2, allowing the partial formation of the multiplet without excessively fast quadrupole relaxation.

The nmr results show that all the hydrogens in the ReH_9^- ion are equivalent [2] and this is also shown by exchange reactions in D_2O [1]. All the Re-H distances are equal within 5%, and it is shown [2] that one of the E' deformation modes takes three of the hydrogens at the apices of the prism into equatorial positions, and vice versa. In the optical spectrum a single absorption is observed at 46,080 cm^{-1} with extinction coefficient $1{\cdot}8 \times 10^3$. This indicates a large splitting between bonding and anti-bonding orbitals in accord with other evidence for a high ligand-field strength of H^- which is discussed in the next section.

The formation of a complex containing only hydrogen, of this stoicheiometry, seems at first sight surprising in view of the general instability of metal-hydrogen bonds in the absence of strong π-bonding ligands (section 5.3). This general instability is ascribed, on a simple view, not to any intrinsic weakness of the metal-hydrogen bond, but to the fact that the dissociation

$$\text{M-H} \rightarrow \text{M.} + \text{H. or } M^+ + H^-$$

is irreversible (a similar argument applies to an ionic dissociation) as the hydrogen atom or ion will readily be removed as H_2. Contrast this with the reversible dissociation possible for the majority of complexes where ligand molecules or ions are stable species, with a sufficiently long lifetime to allow the complex to re-form. (σ-bonded carbon in alkyl and aryl groups resembles H in this respect, and such transition metal compounds are equally unstable.) This dissociation may be regarded as depending on the strength of the M-H bond, and this in turn depends on the electron population of the anti-bonding orbitals. In the average complex, with non-bonding *d* orbitals–for example the t_{2g} orbitals of an octahedral complex–the highest energy electrons will be in these orbitals, so that the stability of the hydride will depend on the non-bonding to anti-bonding energy gap (ΔE). In the MH_9^{2-} case, however, all the valency orbitals on the technetium or rhenium–that is, the 5*d*, 6*s* and 6*p* orbitals on rhenium and the 4*d*, 5*s*, and 5*p* technetium orbitals–nine in all, are involved with the nine hydrogen orbitals in forming the nine bonding and

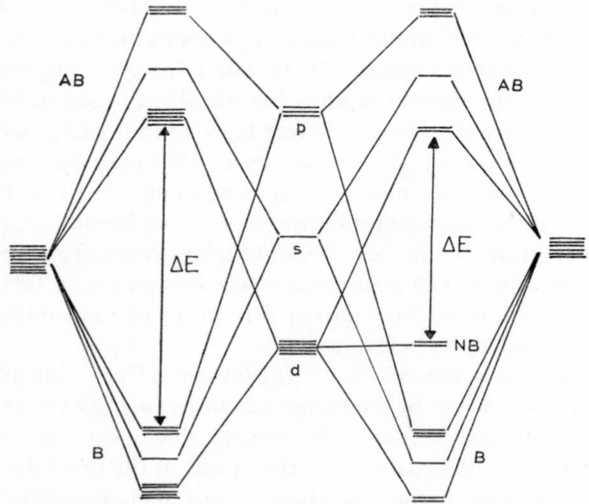

Figure 3. Diagrammatic representation of the energy levels of complexes:

(*a*) Any MH_9 species where all the metal valence shell *d*, *s* and *p* orbitals are used forming the nine bonding (B) and nine antibonding (AB) orbitals of the complex.

(*b*) An octahedral complex MX_6. Here two *d* orbitals, with the *s* and three *p* orbitals, form the six bonding (B) and six anti-bonding (AB) orbitals of the complex, leaving three nonbonding (NB) *d* orbitals.

ΔE is the energy difference between the highest filled orbitals and the lowest antibonding orbitals. It is larger in case (*a*) than in case (*b*) as there are no nonbonding levels in (*a*).

nine anti-bonding orbitals in the complex ion. The position is shown diagrammatically in Figure 3a. There are therefore no intermediate energy, non-bonding, orbitals in the nine-co-ordinate complex, as there are, for example, in the six-co-ordinate complex of Figure 3b, to allow a relatively easy excitation promotion of an electron into an anti-bonding orbital. Hence these hydrides should be of the same order of stability as a Main Group element hydride where a similar situation holds. The main requirement then, is that the polarity of the metal-hydrogen bond in either sense (M^+–H^- or M^-–H^+) is not so extreme that rapid interaction with the environment occurs. Here, as the compound is stable in alkali, the hydrogen is clearly hydridic.

If this simple picture has any substance, and it gives at least a qualitative guide to the stability of hydride complexes, then it may be predicted that other MH_9 species may also be found to be relatively stable. Presumably a relatively high, but not too oxidizing state of the central metal is required. The possible existence of WH_9^{3-} (or even OsH_9^-) does not seem beyond the bounds of reason.

Only one other species occurs in the literature which might be a hydrido-complex of a transition metal, and this is the rhodium compound, or compounds, mentioned in Chapter 3. The action of lithium hydride on rhodium gives Li_4RhH_4, which reacts with hydrogen to give Li_4RhH_5, both black species, melting above 560°C [6]. This is over 100° below the melting point of LiH and the species was found to be free of the obvious impurities, Li, LiH, Rh, LiRh, Li_2O and LiOH. This system would surely repay further study. It either represents a new type of hydrido-complex, of rhodium in some low oxidation state, or else a unique type of metallic hydride system involving rhodium.

5.2 The Complex Hydrides Containing Other Ligands

It is now recognized that hydride complexes of the transition elements are of wide occurrence. The Tables give examples of the main types. In general, reduction of a transition metal in presence of a π-bonding ligand is liable to give a hydride. In the earlier literature, many of these compounds were thought to involve low oxidation states of the metals and the presence of hydrogen was not suspected. It is now clear that hydrogen bound to a transition element is characterized by an infra-red absorption, due to the M-H stretch, in the region 1600–2200 cm^{-1}, and, especially, by a proton resonance signal at very high field with τ values above 10. Values are in the range 15–50τ, whereas all common hydrides, such as organic compounds, water, ammonia, hydrides of the Main Group metals and the like, have τ values from 0 to 10 ppm. Other data, such as magnetic susceptibilities and dipole moments, may help to confirm the presence of hydride, but the nmr measurement is the most certain, as long as the compound is sufficiently soluble to allow its detection. The infra-red absorption, especially if it is confirmed by deuteration, is also useful evidence for the presence of hydrogen, as the bands are often strong and occur in a region which is fairly free from other absorptions. The carbonyl and cyanide stretches, and the bending modes of O-H, N-H and C-H groups, overlap near the ends of the range.

Apart from the obvious use of hydriding agents such as $LiAlH_4$ or $NaBH_4$, the metal hydrides are often produced by the action of alcoholic KOH, hydrazine, hypophosphorous acid, or even by direct hydrogenation under pressure. The most secure method is to use the anhydrous halide and react this with a complex hydride in an anhydrous solvent such as an ether. For example,

$$(C_5H_5)Fe(CO)_2Cl \xrightarrow[THF]{NaBH_4} (C_5H_5)Fe(CO)_2H \quad [8]$$

$$\text{or } trans\text{-}Pt(Cl)_2(PR_3)_2 \xrightarrow[THF]{LiAlH_4} trans\text{-}Pt(H)Cl(PR_3)_2 \quad [8]$$

Some hydrogenations occur under surprisingly mild conditions,

$$Ir(CO)Cl(PPh_3)_2 \xrightarrow[benzene]{H_2,\ 25°C} Ir(CO)(H)_2Cl(PPh_3)_2 \quad [9]$$

(note this involves an oxidation of Ir(I) to Ir(III)).

Work by Vaska, over a number of years, [10], has demonstrated the formation of hydrides [11] and of carbonyl hydrides [10] when anhydrous halides are treated with triphenylphosphine or triphenylarsine in alcohol. The reaction works for a variety of alcohols under mild conditions, such as reaction at room temperature for a number of days, or by heating to 150–200°C for an hour or two. Thus the compounds $HOs(X)(CO)L_3$, (X = Cl, Br; L = Ph_3P, Ph_3As) were prepared under conditions of which the following is typical

$$(NH_4)_2(OsCl_6) \xrightarrow[4\frac{1}{2}\ hr.\ 165°C]{DEGME/H_2O;\ xs\ PPh_3} HOsCl(CO)(PPh_3)_3$$

(DEGME = diethyleneglycol monomethylether).

The use of a variety of alcohols, such as methanol, ethanol, glycerol, as well as various polyglycols and partially etherated polyglycols, all allow similar reactions. Studies with deuterated alcohols and samples containing radio-carbon demonstrated that the H, and the CO, of the complex arise from the alcohol. Similar reactions with alcohols are reported by other groups [12].

At present, so many preparative methods have led to hydrides instead of low oxidation state complexes, that the tendency is to suspect a hydride until its existence has been disproved: a complete reversal of the position of only a few years ago. Of course, hydrido-complexes are not always formed and the complexes $Pt(PPh_3)_4$ [13] and $Os(NH_3)_5$ [14], for example, have both been shown recently to be true zero-valent compounds and not hydrides. Even relatively small changes in reaction conditions may affect hydride formation, vis-a-vis the formation of the low oxidation state complex. For example, [15]

$$K_2PtCl_4 \xrightarrow[R_2PCH_2CH_2PR_2]{NaBH_4\ \text{or}\ NaC_{10}H_8} Pt^0(R_2PCH_2CH_2PR_2)_2$$

$$K_2PtCl_4 \xrightarrow[EtOH/KOH]{Ph_3P} PtH_2(PPh_3)_2$$

Reactions. Reactions of the complex hydrides have not been studied in great detail as yet. Apart from the obvious reactions, such as formation of the corresponding halogen complex by reaction with halogens,

$$R_nMH \xrightarrow{X_2} R_n\,MX + HX,$$

the number of reactions general to all the hydrido-complexes is limited. One common reaction is that with carbon tetrachloride, [43, 17]

$$R_nMH + CCl_4 = R_nMCl + CHCl_3,$$

where the formation of chloroform is a useful diagnostic test for the existence of the hydride. However, it may be misleading on occasion [13, 15]. The other common reaction is the formation of alkyl compounds from the hydride,

$$R_nMH + CH_2N_2 = R_nMCH_3$$

$$R_nMH + C_2H_4 = R_nM(C_2H_5).$$

These reactions occur with a variety of suitable unsaturated reactants. The reaction with olefins may often be reversed by heating [17]

$$trans\text{-}PtHX(PR_3)_2 \underset{180^\circ \text{ under nitrogen}}{\overset{+\ C_2H_4,\ 95^\circ,\ 40 \text{ atm.}}{\rightleftarrows}} trans\text{-}Pt(C_2H_5)X(PR_3)_2.$$

With fluoro-olefins, or olefins with activated double bonds, the addition occurs more readily

$$ReH(CO)_5 + CF_2{=}CF_2 \xrightarrow[\text{1 atm. sealed tube}]{15^\circ,\ 3 \text{ days}} (CO)_5ReCF_2CF_2H \qquad [88]$$

$$[Co(CN)_5H]^{-3} + C_4H_6 \xrightarrow[\text{1 atm}]{\text{cold aq. soln}} [Co(CN)_5(C_4H_7)]^{3-} \qquad [89].$$

Similar reactions with $HMn(CO)_5$, $(C_5H_5)Mo(CO)_3H$, and related compounds with fluoro-olefins are also reported [90]. In the case of $CFCl{=}CF_2$, the hydrogen goes entirely on the CFCl end of the molecule with the rhenium carbonyl hydride, but equally on either carbon when $HMn(CO)_5$ is the reagent. With other mixed halo-olefins, the hydrogen goes on to the least electronegative carbon, [88]. The reaction with $HCo(CN)_5^-$ is of interest, as this is a type system for the reduced vitamin B_{12} reaction [54, 55, 90b]. When B_{12} is reduced, it passes through a well-established stage termed B_{12r}, which contains cobalt (II), to a product, vitamin B_{12s}. The latter is variously thought to be a cobalt I species free of hydrogen [55], or a cobalt III hydride [54]. A third postulate, of a cobalt I species with acidic hydrogen, is also put forward instead of, or in equilibrium with, the other two species. Vitamin B_{12s} reacts with diazomethane, and olefins, to give alkyl cobalt compounds, and it is hoped that the study of the simpler cyanide hydride reaction will throw more light on the B_{12} reaction. From this point of view, it is unfortunate that $Co(CN)_5H^{3-}$ and $CO(CN)_5^{3-}$ co-exist in reduced cobalt cyanide systems.

Further interest in the olefin addition reaction is more general, and stems from the use of transition metal catalyst systems as hydrogenating and polymerizing reagents. An intermediate in such reactions is often postulated to be the M-H bond on the metal surface, to which the transition metal hydride complex offers a useful analogue. A further step in this type of study is provided in a recent note by Shaw [46] who notes that an intermediate containing both M-H and M-olefin bonded on the metal surface is often postulated. He prepared a type complex, $[IrHCl_2(C_8H_{12})]_2$, (C_8H_{12} = *cyclo*-octa-1,5-diene), and studied its reactions.

The hydrogen which attaches to the metal in the reverse reaction, the pyrolysis of an alkyl compound, has been shown to come from the β-carbon. The reaction with olefins is similar to that observed with the Main Group hydrides, and of similar importance.

A number of more specific reactions of particular transition metal hydrides are reported – although some of these may turn out to be general reactions on fuller investigation.

In their reactions with acids and bases, the hydrides fall into two classes: those where the hydrogen is acidic, and those where it is basic. The first class is the smaller, and consists of the carbonyl hydrides. These are formed by acidification of the carbonyl anions, and readily form metal salts and the like ([91], and all the references to carbonyl hydrides and their ions in the Tables at the end of the Chapter):

$$\text{e.g. } Mn(CO)_5Na \underset{Na/NH_3}{\overset{H^+}{\rightleftharpoons}} Mn(CO)_5H.$$

The carbonyl hydrides were the first transition metal hydrides to be discovered. They are volatile species of low stability and differ from the majority of the hydride complexes in other ways. For example, the stability decreases with the heavier metals in the Group, so that $HRe(CO)_5$ is less stable than $HMn(CO)_5$. The M-H stretching frequency is also generally weak, and often difficult to find among the carbonyl bands – giving rise to early theories of the structures of the carbonyl hydrides where the hydrogen was not thought to form a bond to the metal.

In all other classes of hydride, the hydrogen is basic, and preparations in alkaline media are common: either with alcoholic KOH, or slightly alkaline borohydride. The hydrogen usually reacts with acid, for example with hydrogen halides to reverse the preparation reaction, [37]

$$RuHX(diphos)_2 \underset{LiAlH_4}{\overset{HCl}{\rightleftharpoons}} (\text{equivalent to } H^-)\ RuClX(diphos)_2.$$

Sometimes, however, HCl can add to the complex [17]

$$PtHX(PR_3)_2 \underset{warm}{\overset{HCl}{\rightleftharpoons}} PtH_2Cl_2(PR_3)_2.$$

In this case, an unstable platinum IV complex is formed which easily loses HCl. The cyclopentadienyl hydrides, and related compounds, are sufficiently basic to acquire further hydrogen from strongly acid media, such as boron trifluoride water mixtures, to form cations,

$$Mo(\text{or } W)H_2(C_5H_5)_2 = MoH_3(C_5H_5)_2^+\ (\text{in } CF_3COOH) \qquad [42].$$

Similarly, $ReH_2(C_5H_5)_2^+$ and $CrH(CO)_3(C_6H_6)^+$ are formed in BF_3/CF_3COOH media. Other cyclopentadienyl carbonyls form binuclear complexes in strongly acidic media which contain a hydrogen associated with two metal atoms [61], $[W(C_5H_5)(CO)_3]_2H^+$. These are discussed later. All the basic hydrides are more stable than the acidic carbonyl hydrides mentioned above. Least stable are the cyanide hydrides, such as $Co(CN)_5H^{3-}$, which decompose at or just above room temperature. The cyclopentadienyl hydrides, and cyclopentadienyl carbonyl hydrides are much more stable, as are the hydrides containing tertiary phosphines and related ligands. Some of these are stable thermally up to about 300°C (see Tables) and the more stable compounds can be handled in air at room temperature.

In all the metal hydride complexes, except the carbonyl hydrides, stability–both thermal and to replacement–increases down the Group. For example, for *trans*-$MHX(C_2H_4(PEt_2)_2)_2$ complexes (in °C) Chatt and Hayter quote the following figures [35],

		M = Fe	Ru	Os
X = Cl	mpt	155	175	171
	decompn.	155	310	315
X = H	mpt	—	150	150
	decompn.	—	280	295

This is the same order as the increase in stability of σ-bonded alkyls and aryls, and the opposite order of stability to that found for hydrides and organic derivatives of the Main Group elements.

There are one or two interesting examples of replacement reactions of hydrogen in complexes. One is Nyholm's formation of a Rh-Hg bond by the reaction

$$cis\text{-}Cl_2RhH(AsR_3)_3 + HgX_2 \xrightarrow[\text{alcohol}]{\text{warm}} Cl_2Rh(HgX)(AsR_3)_3 \qquad [29]$$

where X = F, Cl, Br, I, or OAc. Another is the formation of metal-sulphur compounds by reaction with alkyl disulphides [92]

$$(C_5H_5)M(CO)_3H + RS_2 = [(C_5H_5)M(CO)_3SR]_2 \text{ (M = Mo,W).}$$

On the other hand, replacement reactions may be carried out on other ligands in hydride complexes,

$$PtXH(PR_3)_2 + \text{amine} = Pt(\text{amine})H(PR_3)_2 \qquad [17].$$

These reactions were carried out on *trans* compounds and this, and much other evidence, shows that hydrogen has a strong *trans* effect in labilizing ligands opposite to itself. A different type of replacement was found in the reaction of butyl-lithium with cyclopentadiene hydrides of Re and W. Here, the M-H bond remained intact and H-Li exchange took place in the cyclopentadienyl rings which could then be reacted to give C_5H_4X compounds where X = D, HgCl, Me etc. [39].

$$(C_5H_5)_2ReH + BuLi = (C_5H_4Li)_2ReH = (C_5H_4X)_2ReH.$$

Sarry [64] has reported the compound, $\{HW(C_6H_5Li)_2\}_n$, where n is greater than one, which may be similar.

5.3 Physical Properties of Hydrogen in Complexes

The typical properties of hydrogen in complexes, by which these are most often identified, are the proton magnetic resonance and the infra-red absorptions. In addition, as hydride complexes are usually formed only by π-bonding ligands of high ligand field, the hydrides are usually diamagnetic, with all the electrons paired. The hydrogen is definitely bonded to the metal (the case of polynuclear complexes is treated later) and this is verified by the few crystal structures which have been reported, by the existence of infra-red bands which shift on deuteration, and by the observation of coupling in the proton resonance spectrum. Earlier theories of non-bonded hydrogen are now discounted.

The Proton Resonance Spectrum. The Tables show the τ values of the hydrogen bonded to transition elements. These values are markedly higher than those of any other observed hydrogen compounds, except for cases where there are abnormally large ring currents. As the hydrogens in ligands, such as cyclopentadiene or organophosphines, resonate at much lower fields, $\tau = 1$–10, it is easy to distinguish the presence of M-H bond. This often provides the only means of showing the presence of the hydride for unstable species which occur only in solution. The presence of a proton resonance signal at high fields is unambiguous proof of the existence of the metal hydride. Unfortunately, such high resolution spectra can only be measured on fairly concentrated solutions, so the test cannot be applied to poorly soluble materials. (Though recent developments in detecting high resolution signals on solid samples subject to very fast rotation may improve this state of affairs in the future [93].)

The proton resonance spectrum may be used to give structural information. For example, the metal proton will couple with the spins of other magnetic nuclei attached to the metal, such as phosphorus with a spin of $\frac{1}{2}$. Thus, in *trans*-$Ru(C_6H_5)H(diphos)_2$ (diphos = $Me_2PCH_2CH_2PMe_2$), the proton couples to the four phosphorus atoms, which are equivalent and *cis* to the hydrogen, so that the signal at $\tau = 23{\cdot}3$ is a 1:4:6:4:1 quintet with a P-H coupling of 23·5 c/s. This, itself, is sufficient to prove the *trans* configuration of the H and the phenyl group. On the other hand, in *cis*-$RuMeH(diphos)_2$, where the hydrogen is also *cis* to three phosphorus atoms and *trans* to one, the metal-hydrogen signal at $\tau = 18{\cdot}2$ shows two different couplings, the *trans* one, $J_{PH} = 76$ c/s, and the *cis* one $J_{PH} = 19$ c/s, and the signal is a double quartet: that is, a quartet from the coupling with the three *cis* phosphorus atoms split into two by the coupling with the *trans* phosphorus. Similar studies have often proved useful in structural determinations, especially of isomers. The above example illustrates the general case that *trans* couplings are larger than *cis* ones.

Of course, if the transition metal itself is magnetic, the main coupling will be to its spin, and these direct M-H couplings can be very large. Compare the values for the platinum complexes in the Table of over 1000 c/s. On the other hand, the coupling to Rh^{103} in the amine hydrides is only 27 c/s.

This unusually high shielding in the transition metal hydrides was originally ascribed, [23, 24] to the hydrogen's being 'buried' in the metal orbitals. However, Lipscomb has shown [87] that the high field shift of the proton in $HMn(CO)_5$ and other carbonyl hydrides can be predicted without the necessity of assuming unduly short M-H bonds. A more complete treatment by Buckingham [86], has confirmed this point. Buckingham shows that, by applying the standard Ramsey treatment, and evaluating both the diamagnetic and paramagnetic contributions to the shielding (Lipscomb used only the diamagnetic component), reasonably good predictions of the shielding can be made for square planar, octahedral, and other complexes derived from octahedral symmetry. The paramagnetic contribution is the major one, in general, although it is apparently sufficiently low in the carbonyl hydrides to allow Lipscomb's treatment to give reasonable agreement with the observed values. The shift depends on the M-H distance, the energy difference between the ground state and the first excited state (taken as the octahedral ligand field splitting), and on Slater's k function. The dependence on the M-H distance is not too critical (Buckingham changes from 2 a.u. (ca 1·1 Å) to 3 a.u. between the two papers), although more certain values for the other parameters would highlight this factor. The main uncertainty arises from the possibility of distortions from regular shapes (see the structures below) as the calculated values are very sensitive to this anisotropy. The agreement between observed and calculated values in these recent Lipscomb and Buckingham papers [86, 87] is sufficiently close to show that the basic cause of the high field shift has been found. It now remains for the structural parameters, which are becoming available, to be inserted into the calculations in order to improve the calculated values. The major effect in the high field shift is the paramagnetic shielding due to partly-filled d orbitals, and this is present in all the very high field shifts shown in the Tables. It is noticeable that the hydrides where the metal d shell is full, including ReH_9^{2-}, show lower shifts with τ values between 10 and 20 ppm.

One structural study has been carried out using broad line magnetic resonance techniques [21], on $FeH_2(CO)_4$. From the measured relaxation time the authors calculated an Fe-H distance of about 1·1 Å. However, this was based on the assumption that only the intra-molecular H-H interaction had to be taken into account, and later structural work on $MnH(CO)_5$ [94] makes this a risky assumption.

Crystal Structure Determinations. Two cases exist where the M-H bond distance has been determined in a transition metal hydride, though a number of neutron diffraction studies are reported to be under way at present (see [94], for example). The case of ReH_9^{2-} has been discussed: here, neutron diffraction shows an average M-H distance of 1·68 Å [2]. The other case is unusual in that a reasonably reliable M-H distance is reported from an X-ray diffraction study on the five-co-ordinated rhodium hydride, $(CO)RhH(PPh_3)_3$ [20]. In this case, a number of factors combine to allow the hydrogen to be located with reasonable certainty by X-ray analysis, especially because the phenyl rings on the phosphorus atoms interlock so that there is little thermal motion. The structure is a trigonal bipyramid with the three phosphine groups forming the equatorial plane and the CO and H on the axis. The rhodium is raised 0·36 Å above the P_3 plane towards the C of the carbonyl. (Alternatively, the phosphorus bonds are bent towards the hydrogen.) This is the direction of distortion expected on steric grounds. The Rh-H distance is 1·60 ± 0·12 Å and the H-Rh-CO angle is 170 ± 5°. These distortions towards the hydrogen are important because of their effect on the calculations of the proton shift in the nmr spectrum.

X-ray structural determinations have been carried out on a number of other hydride complexes, but only the heavy atom positions were determined. However, the structures found make the probable position of the hydrogen very clear. The first case reported was the determination of the structure of *trans*-$PtHBr(PEt_3)_2$ [95]. Here, the Br and the two P atoms form three corners of a square around the platinum, so that the H almost certainly completes the expected square-planar arrangement. The P-Pt-Br angles are 94°; that is, the Pt-P bonds are bent towards the probable hydrogen position. The Pt-P distances are normal for a π-bonded system, but the Pt-Br distance is unusually long. This is reflected in the lability of the bromine, and can be ascribed to the strong *trans* effect of the hydrogen. Although it was not located, the hydrogen was placed at 1·62 Å from the platinum. This determination was of only moderate accuracy as the compound is unstable to X-rays, but a recent study of the stable, related, complex, *trans*-$PtHCl(PPh_2Et)_2$, [101], fully confirms the earlier results. Again, the hydrogen was not found, but the Cl and the two P atoms form three corners of a square. The Pt-Cl bond is lengthened, and the Cl-Pt-P angles are about 94°. It was also found that the Pt, Cl, and two P atoms are not quite coplanar.

A preliminary announcement of the structure of $OsH(CO)Br(PPh_3)_3$ gives an octahedral structure. The CO and Br are *trans*, while the bond to that phosphorus atom *trans* to the sixth position, probably occupied by H, is longer than the other two Os-P bonds (2·56 Å against 2·34 Å: compare 2·26 Å in the platinum compound). Again, there is a displacement of groups towards the hydrogen, so that the P-Os-P angles in the P_3OsH plane are 99° and 103°, while the Br-Os-P angle in the BrPOs(CO)H plane is 98°. The other compounds $MHX(CO)L_3$, M = Ru, Os; X = Cl, Br; L = PPh_3, $AsPh_3$, are said to be isostructural [96].

An interesting example is the case of $Mn(CO)_5H$ [94]. This is the most manageable of the carbonyl hydrides, and it was important to see if these unstable, acidic, hydrides differed from the more stable examples discussed above. The crystal structure shows that the $Mn(CO)_5$ unit is a square pyramid, similar to the configuration in $Mn_2(CO)_{10}$. The manganese is raised slightly above the basal plane so that the angles C_{apical}-Mn-C_{basal} are about 97°. There is thus a displacement towards the probable hydrogen position once again. Of particular importance is the packing of the molecules in the crystal. The square-pyramidal $Mn(CO)_5$ units are arranged so that their bases are towards each other in pairs, and tilted so that the angle between the OCMn four-fold axes is about 135°. This brings the hydrogen atoms of two neighbouring molecules very close to each other–to within the normal van der Waals contact distance of 2·2 to 2·4 Å, assuming the hydrogens are on the four-fold axis of the $Mn(CO)_5$ pyramid. This would give a Mn-H distance of 1·5 to 1·6 Å. More important, it means that there is appreciable molecular interaction between hydrogens in neighbouring molecules, so that the assumption of no intermolecular interaction in the broad line study of $H_2Fe(CO)_4$ is on uncertain ground. A neutron diffraction study of $HMn(CO)_5$ is promised.

The 'Wedge-shaped' Compounds, $(C_5H_5)_2MH_n$. The dicyclopentadienyl compounds of molybdenum, tantalum, tungsten, and rhenium all form hydrides by reactions of the type

$$MCl_5\ (WCl_6) + NaC_5H_5 + NaBH_4 \xrightarrow{THF} (C_5H_5)_2MH_n \qquad [42, 43]$$

where $n = 3$ for Ta; 2 for Mo,W; and 1 for Re. Balhausen and Dahl proposed that these hydrides, and cations derived from them, should have a structure in which the cyclopentadiene rings are inclined at an angle to each other, as opposed to the parallel structure of ferrocene [41]. They calculated that as long as the maximum ring–ring angle lay between 0 and 45°, the metal–ring overlap should not be appreciably weakened. With this ring–metal–ring structure, there remained three orbitals on the metal, all in the medial plane of the molecule and pointing away from the rings, which could either hold electron pairs or be used in bonding: see sketch.

In the compounds $(C_5H_5)_2M$, there are respectively 3, 4 or 5 electrons for Ta, Mo(W) or Re, which are not used in ring bonding. If these electrons are placed in the three orbitals ψ_x, $\psi_{\pm y}$, then $(C_5H_5)_2$ TaH_3, $(C_5H_5)_2$ $Mo(W)H_2$, and $(C_5H_5)_2ReH$ would correspond to filled orbitals. Further, the electron pair in $(C_5H_5)_2MoH_2$ (or W) and the two pairs in the rhenium compound are poten-

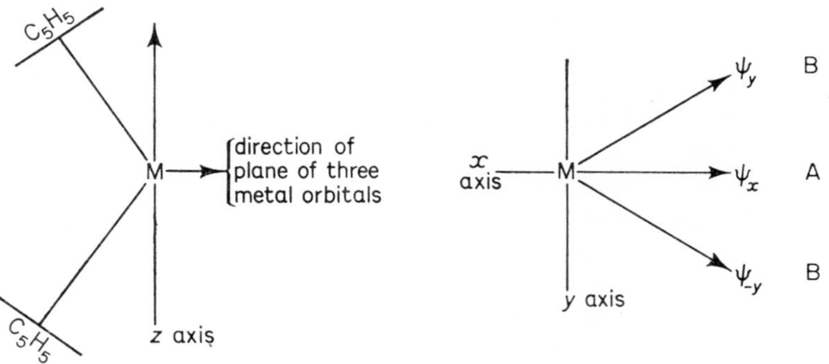

tial donors to Lewis acids. It was indeed found that $(C_5H_5)_2Mo(W)H_3^+$ and the corresponding $(C_5H_5)_2ReH_2^+$ compounds could be made, as could $Fe(C_5H_5)_2H^+$. (See Tables at the end.) Furthermore, although the two orbitals ψ_y and ψ_{-y} are equivalent (we shall term these B), they are not equivalent to ψ_x (A). It was found, in agreement with this, that $(C_5H_5)_2TaH_3$ showed two high field lines in the proton spectrum, in the ratio 2:1, corresponding to the B_2A protons. The tungsten ion, $(C_5H_5)_2WH_3^+$ showed a similar B_2A spectrum, but the corresponding Mo ion gave only a broader, unresolved high field proton spectrum.

This structural calculation, and the evidence from the nmr spectra, has recently been confirmed by a structural determination of the compound, $(C_5H_5)_2MoH_2$. This is indeed wedge-shaped with a ring–ring angle of $34 \pm 1°$ [40]. The Mo-H distance is $1{\cdot}2 \pm 0{\cdot}3$ Å, with a large uncertainty, and the neutron diffraction study is under way.

In further vindication of this analysis, it has also been shown by Shriver [60], that BF_3 is coordinated by the tungsten hydride to give $(C_5H_5)_2WH_2.BF_3$. The BF_3 is coordinated to the third of the AB_2 orbitals – presumably the unique A orbital. This is the first example of coordination by an acid other than H^+.

Complexes Where the Hydrogen is Associated with Two Metal Atoms. The Tables list a number of binuclear compounds with one hydrogen, MM′H, which have been prepared by Hayter and others [65, 69, 79] and by Wilkinson [61]. Examples include $Mo_2H(C_5H_5)_2(CO)_4(PMe_2)$(I) and $Fe_2H(C_5H_5)_2(CO)_4^+$ (II). The nuclear magnetic resonance spectra of these compounds show a signal at high field, so the hydrogen is clearly associated with the metal atom. Further analysis of the nmr spectra suggests that the hydrogen associates equally with both metal atoms, and Hayter proposes either a three-centre bond or a rapid exchange process. The crystal structure of I has been reported [97]. This is very similar to those of other dimeric molecules such as $[(C_5H_5)Mo(CO)_3]_2$. There is a bridging PMe_2 group between two completely symmetrical $(C_5H_5)Mo(CO)_2$ halves. This shows that the hydrogen atom must be equally associated with the two Mo atoms, or the environments of the two would not be symmetrical. The Mo-P-Mo angle is 85° and the Mo-P distance is 2·42 Å, which is 0·3 Å less than the single bond radii sum, showing some Mo-P π-bonding. The Mo-Mo distance is 3·26 Å, which is reasonable if there is a metal-metal bond, but the authors prefer to interpret the structure in terms of a bent Mo-H-Mo three-centre bond holding two electrons (analogous to the B-H-B bond in diborane). This would complete a coordination of one cyclopentadienyl ring, two carbonyls, the phosphorus and the hydrogen around each molybdenum which would be almost identical to the arrangement of the cyclopentadiene and four carbonyls in $(C_5H_5)Nb(CO)_4$ and of the ring, three carbonyls and the second Mo in the dimer $[(C_5H_5)Mo(CO)_3]_2$. The resulting Mo-H distance would be 1·8 Å which, as Mo is 0·1 Å bigger than Re, matches well with the 1·68 Å of the ReH_9^{2-} ion. A neutron diffraction study is hoped for.

Similar structure for the other phosphine-bridged structures in the Tables are reasonably postulated, and the non-phosphine dimers like II could be formulated with a metal–metal bond and a bridging hydrogen, though this is more speculative.

The probable existence of a three-centred MoHMo bond in this compound gives support to the suggestion that the trimeric rhenium hydride $\{ReH(CO)_4\}_3$ [57] may also have bridging hydrogens. The structure suggested for this compound, like that found for the $Os_3(CO)_{12}$ molecule, is of a triangle of Re atoms, each with four terminal CO groups. The hydrogens are then possibly in bridging positions along the edges of the Re_3 triangle.

The Infra-red Spectra of Hydride Complexes. The metal-hydrogen stretching mode in hydride complexes is found in the region from 1600–2200 cm^{-1} while bending modes occur at 600–900 cm^{-1}. In compounds with a number of hydrogen atoms, a rocking mode may occur around 400 cm^{-1}. The stretching mode is usually the easiest to find and serves as a useful diagnostic test for the presence of hydrogen, especially in solids where the nmr signal may not be found. The intensity of the band varies considerably, but the mode has now been found in practically all solid hydrides and in most solutions where the species is in reasonable concentration. The biggest difficulty comes with hydride complexes containing the carbonyl or cyanide groups as these also absorb in the M-H region. Often the assignment can be made by seeing which bands shift on deuteration, although there are cases where deuteration also affects the carbonyl modes. Such coupling is, however, generally weak as the hydrogen mass differs so much from that of the other species present. For this reason, also, the mass of the particular metal to which the hydrogen is attached has little effect on the frequency of the stretching mode so that this, to a first approximation, may be taken to reflect the strength of the M-H bond. This generalisation is fairly safe if series of similar compounds are compared. The values given in the Tables support this: in the *trans*-$MHX(diphos)_2$ compounds of Fe, Ru, and Os, for example, the M-H frequency increases by about 100 cm^{-1} from Fe to Ru, and from Ru to Os, corresponding to the increasing stability of the M-H bond down the Group. Similar examples occur in all the Groups, with the exception of the carbonyl hydrides where the heavy metal compound is usually too unstable for its spectrum to be recorded.

Other effects on the M-H stretching frequency are less clear-cut. For example, in the extensive series of *trans*-$PtHX(PR_3)_2$ compounds, the Table shows the frequency drops with the increasing *trans* effect of the substituent, in the order $NO_3 > Cl > Br > I > CN$, as expected. The discovery that both isomeric forms of NCO and NCS co-exist, and that the NO_2 species is nitrito, not nitro, helps to improve this correlation with the *trans* effect. The very low frequency in the dihydride could be ascribed to its high *trans* effect. In the platinum complexes, where the stretching frequency changes with the *trans* effect of the ligand opposite to the hydrogen, there is also a general correlation to be found in the nmr spectrum. Here, the proton shift decreases, approximately in the order that the *trans* effect of the second ligand increases [18]. However, in the octahedral complexes of iron, ruthenium, and osmium, the frequency of the M-H stretch *increases* from Cl to I, that is, it changes in the opposite sense from that observed in the square planar platinum complexes. However, some part of the pattern remains, in that the frequency is greater for the halides than for SCN, CN, and H in the *trans* position. The change in the halide complexes in this case can, of course, be ascribed to the simple change in inductive effect from chlorine to iodine, but then the reason for this becoming the dominant effect would be needed.

The M-H frequency also shows shifts with the solvent used to dissolve the species, and on going from solid to solution. One study of this effect has appeared [24], in which it was found that frequencies were highest in polar solvents, with a maximum difference in frequency found between hexane (low) and chloroform (high). The hydrogens *trans* to chlorine were most affected, so that in the isomer of $IrH_2Cl(PR_3)_3$, where one H is *trans* to the Cl and the other is *trans* to a phosphine, the solvent shift on going from hexane to chloroform was 34 cm^{-1} for the H *trans* to Cl, and zero for the H *trans* to phosphine. Although only a limited number of examples were studied, it seems that H *trans* to a phosphine or arsine is solvent insensitive, H *trans* to Cl is most solvent sensitive, while H *trans* to I shows about ¾ of the chlorine solvent shift. Although no general correlation has been found between the proton resonance shift and the infra-red frequency, it was found that the solvent shift from polar to non-polar solvent did correlate with the nmr shift. Further work on this subject, with some of the other fairly extensive sets of related complexes now available, would be of great interest.

Marked shifts also occur when changes are made in the substituents on the phosphine ligands, and these are surprisingly large. Thus, in the ruthenium compounds, *trans*-$RuHCl(diphos)_2$, the frequencies of the M-H stretch vary from 1889 cm^{-1} for diphos = $C_2H_4(PMe_2)_2$ to 1978 cm^{-1} for diphos = o-$C_6H_4(PEt_2)_2$, and even the replacement of the methyls by ethyl groups in the ethylenediphosphine causes a shift of 50 cm^{-1}. These shifts probably reflect steric and electronic effects in the P-M bond which alters the extend of π-bonding, and hence affects the strength of the remaining bonds to the metal.

Electronic Spectra and the Place of Hydride in the Spectrochemical Series. Two separate and conflicting determinations of the position of hydrogen in the spectrochemical series have been made. In the earlier, [98], the spectrum of $RuHCl\{C_2H_4(PMe_2)_2\}_2$ was examined and compared with the dihalides, and with the spectra of complexes with organic groups in the place of the hydrogen. In the dihalides, a distinct band is seen which can be ascribed to the $^1A_{2g}, ^1E_g \leftarrow {}^1A_{1g}$ transition. In the hydride-chloride, and in the organic derivatives, this band is shifted under the strong charge-transfer bands by more than 4,100 cm^{-1} for the methyl compound (where a shoulder remains) and by at least 2,900 cm^{-1} (lower limit) in the hydride where no sign of the band is seen. Gaussian analysis of the curves allowed the exact location of the methyl absorption, and the approximate location of the hydride band. These are compared with an estimated position of the band in the cyanide complex, derived from that in the dicyanide and dichloride complexes.

Band position (cm^{-1})	24,300,	28,700 ,	> 27,500 ,	29,500
X, in Ru(Cl)X(diphos)$_2$, =	Cl	CH_3 (by gaussian analysis)	H (lower limit)	CN (estimated from $Ru(CN)_2(diphos)_2$)
		(phenyl and tolyl similar)		

This result would put hydride, and organic groups σ-bonded to the metal, among the high field ligands in the spectrochemical series, just below cyanide.

This result is in accord with the high *trans* effect of hydride [99] which has to be ascribed to a large electrostatic interaction, which, in turn, would imply a high ligand field for hydride. It is also supported by the high energy of the bonding → anti-bonding transition observed in the electronic spectrum of the ReH_9^{2-} ion, where no interference is found. However, this comparison depends on finding similar compounds with other ligands, in order to be put on a certain footing, and the argument from the *trans* effect is an indirect one.

These objections are pertinent, as a recent study of the electronic spectra of the rhodium amine hydrides and related compounds would indicate a much lower position for hydrogen in the spectrochemical series [85]. This study is important, as it applies to a series of compounds in which there are no π-bonding ligands and therefore no interference from the much more intense charge transfer bands. Typical of the results, for a similar transition as that in the ruthenium species with a d^6 ground state, are the following values for the complexes

trans-$Rh(en)_2X_2^+$, X =	I	Br	Cl	N_3	H	NO_2
band position (cm^{-1})	21,650	23,530	24,630	26,670	29,410	33,330

Results for $Rh(en)_2XCl^+$ were similar, with H lying above water, below ammonia, and approximately equal to isothiocyanate. Other complexes, including the pentammines, gave similar results, so that the position of hydrogen is

$$I^- < Br^- < Cl^- < OH^- < H_2O < H^- \approx NCS < NH_3 < NO_2^-.$$

These results are paradoxical in that the rhodium ones, which are directly determined and thus more reliable than those found for the ruthenium complexes, fit less well with the *trans* effect and other properties of hydrogen in the hydrides. It is unfortunate that the only ligands common to the two experiments are the halides, which all lie below H on both scales, and hydride which is in dispute. As the results with the rhodium complexes do not involve any interference from allowed transitions, and therefore are direct measurements not relying on curve analysis, they must be preferred to the results of the ruthenium experiment. It is to be hoped that further work will speedily follow to clarify the position. The main objection that might be raised against the rhodium work lies in the instability of the hydride complexes but the work seems satisfactory in this respect.

The position is not improved by the fact that Buckingham's treatment of the proton shift in the nmr spectrum uses a high ligand field value for hydrogen, [85], and that he quotes a private communication from Pratt that the ligand field strength, in $Co(CN)_5H^{3-}$, of the hydride ion is greater than that of the cyanide! The whole gamut of results raises the question whether the position of hydrogen in the spectrochemical series is indeed a fixed one? Chatt [33] suggests that in the $PtHX(PR_3)_2$ complexes, not only the hydrogen is strongly bonded to the metal, but the phosphines also seem to become more tightly held on hydrogen substitution. A general sensitivity of the bond to hydrogen in the environment, as shown in the differences in stretching frequency and bond length, might well alter the hydrogen ligand field depending on the presence of overall π-bonding, or other factors leading to strong bonding.

The Stabilization of Hydride Complexes. The simple theory proposed in Section 5, to account for the existence of ReH_9^{2-}, can be extended to give a general qualitative explanation for the observed hydride types, and for most of the stabilities. Returning to Figure 3, in an octahedral complex there are electrons present in the non-bonding t_{2g} levels (in all d^n configurations), and none in the anti-bonding levels up to the d^6 configuration – as long as the strong field case holds. Thus, for configurations up to d^6, octahedral – or complexes which can be approximated to octahedral – complexes will be the more stable as the ΔE gap increases, that is, as the t_{2g} level is lowered or the antibonding levels are raised. Both these effects are achieved if π-bonding ligands are present, as these interact with the t_{2g} levels in forming the π bonds (lowering them), and also strengthen the overall bonding (note that the antibonding π orbitals are too high in energy to enter the picture). Although the symmetry labels change, this argument essentially applies to all six-co-ordinate species: in unsymmetrical complexes such as MHLL′L″L‴L⁗L⁗′, the various degenerate levels split, but remain in approximately the same average positions. An exactly similar argument applies to square planar complexes of d^7 or d^8 configurations, where ΔE between the highest non-bonding level and the anti-bonding levels is very nearly the same as the corresponding value for the octahedral field. Thus, six-coordinated hydride complexes up to d^6, and square-planar d^8 hydride complexes, should be more stable than d^9, or d^7 and d^8 octahedral complexes: no examples of any of the latter are known. Further, the stability of the allowed configurations is increased with the size of the ligand field, so that complexes of metals in the III or IV oxidation states, and complexes of elements of the second and third transition series, should be the more stable: the Table illustrates this. Finally, the presence of π-bonding ligands such as phosphines, carbonyl, cyanide, or unsaturated organic systems should stabilize the hydride complexes: the Tables show only the rhodium amines as forming hydride complexes with no π-bonding ligand present, and these are relatively unstable. Further, no hydride complexes of tetrahedral configurations are expected, as these have a much smaller ΔE value than octahedral or square-planar species.

On the basis of this discussion, the instability of carbonyl complexes would result from the low oxidation states of the metals, while the stability order of the other complex hydrides follows roughly the order of ligand field strengths of the remaining ligands. The discussion can clearly be applied to cases of other than four or six-coordination. This discussion follows that of Chatt [33], and is only a simple qualitative theory. It does seem to rationalize many of the observed stability patterns.

Concluding Remarks. The distribution of hydride complexes of the transition elements is located towards the centre and right of the transition block, filling the 'hydride gap' left between the binary hydrides of the metallic and electron-deficient types. It is noteworthy that the elements which most readily react with hydrogen to form binary hydrides, the titanium Group, the vanadium Group, and palladium, form no, or only a few hydride complexes. The vanadium carbonyl hydrides parallel the instability of vanadium carbonyl. The only stable hydride of the vanadium Group is $(C_5H_5)_2TaH_3$ – though no doubt other examples will be reported, and the corresponding niobium compounds as well. At the right-hand end of the transition series, platinum forms a variety of hydrides but the palladium analogues are very unstable and the nickel ones non-existent. This parallels exactly the behaviour of the corresponding organic compounds of the type $MRX(PR_3)_2$, where a variety of platinum compounds, both *cis* and *trans*, exists while only a few *trans* palladium compounds are known, and the nickel analogues exist only under special conditions. The few known nickel hydrides are carbonyl compounds of low stability. Of course, palladium and platinum form no carbonyls.

The behaviour of hydrogen in the hydride complexes reflects a change from acidic hydrogen in the carbonyl hydrides to basic, hydridic, hydrogen in the other compounds. The latter are much more stable. This range in properties throws little light on the nature of the hydrogen in the metallic hydrides, except to warn that a range of behaviour is possible and that it may not be appropriate to try and find a single theory to cover all the compounds.

The nuclear magnetic resonance and infra-red spectra of the transition metal hydride complexes are now reasonably well understood, and more experiments are to be expected to clarify and extend the observations and predictions already made. The recent work on the electronic spectrum indicates that hydrogen falls about the middle of the spectrochemical series. Further studies are needed to verify this, in view of the earlier finding that hydrogen had a high ligand field strength.

Table 5.1. *Hydride Complexes of the Transition Metals*

Compound	General Properties	M-H proton Resonance in τ (ppm)	M-H stretch (cm^{-1})	References
VANADIUM GROUP				
$VH(CO)_6$	H as acidic as in $CoH(CO)_4$			[73]
$VH(CO)_5(PPh_3)$				[73]
$TaH_3(C_5H_5)_2$	white	11·63 (A) 13·02 (B_2)	1735	[40, 41, 42]
CHROMIUM GROUP				
$CrH_2(CO)_5$	white, volatile, unstable			[81]
$CrH(CO)_5^-$	yellow, red salts with large cations			[81, 84]
$CrH(CO)_3(C_5H_5)$	yellow, mpt. 57°C	15·95		[70, 71]
$CrH(CO)_3(C_6H_6)^+$	yellow soln. in BF_3/CF_3COOH	13·55		[61]
(similar solutions with other aromatic groups: τ values up to 14·27 ppm, all solns. yellow [61])				
$Cr_2H(CO)_{10}^-$	red			[84]
$Cr_2H(CO)_6(OR)_3^{2-}$(R=H.Me)	red-orange			[82]
$MoH_2(C_5H_5)_2$	yellow	18·76	1847	[42, 40]
$MoH_3(C_5H_5)_2^+$	in CF_3COOH solution	16·08	1915	[42]
$MoH(CO)_3(C_5H_5)$	yellow, mpt. 54, decomp. 110°C	15·52	1790	[44]
$Mo_2H(CO)_4(C_5H_5)_2(PMe_2)$	orange; bridging PMe_2 group: unique H associated with both Mo atoms.	21·73		[69]
$Mo_2H(CO)_6(C_5H_5)_2^+$	red-brown soln. in H_2SO_4; H associated with both Mo atoms	30·99		[61]
$Mo_2H(CO)_{10}^-$				[84]
$Mo_2H(CO)_6(OH)_3^{2-}$				[82]
$WH_2(C_5H_5)_2$	yellow, mpt. 193°C	22·4	1918	[42, 60]
$WH_3(C_5H_5)_2^+$	in acid solution	16·08 (A) 16·44 (B_2)	1943	[41, 42]
$WH_2(C_5H_4Li)_2$	golden			[39]

$WH_2(C_5H_4D)_2$		22·4		[39]
$WH(CO)_3(C_5H_5)$	yellow, mpt. 69, decomp. below 180°C	17·3	1845	[44, 70]
$WH_2(C_5H_5)_2.BF_3$			1917, 1922	[60]
$WH_2(C_5H_5)(CO)_3^+$	in BF_3/CF_3COOH	11·93		[61]
$W_2H(C_5H_5)_2(CO)_6^+$	red-brown; in H_2SO_4 and as PF_6^- salt: H associated with both metal atoms	34·77		[61]
$WMoH(C_5H_5)_2(CO)_6$	as above	32·88		[61]
$W_2H(CO)_6(OH)_3^{2-}$	yellow			[62]
$W_3H(CO)_9(OH)(OMe)(MeOH)^{3-}$	orange-yellow			[62]
$W_3H_4(CO)_9(OH)_2(H_2O)$	yellow: bridging OH groups			[63]
(also $W_3H_4(CO)_9(OH)(OMe)(MeOH)$	with bridging OH and OMe groups; a variety of similar polynuclear carbonyl hydrides is reported [63])			
$\{WH(C_6H_5Li)_2\}_n$ ($n \geqslant 2$)	black: stable to 150°C			[64]
MANGANESE AND RHENIUM (Technetium compounds similar to Rhenium ones as far as is known)				
$MnH(CO)_5$	colourless, mpt. −24·6°C	17·50	1783	[23, 74]
$MnH(CO)_4(PPh_3)$	pale yellow, mpt. 137°C		1790?	[75]
$MnH(NO)_2(PPh_3)_2$	yellow, mpt. 153°C			[80]
$MnH(CO)_4(PEt_3)$	brown?, distills 65°C *in vacuo*			[75]
$MnH(CO)_4\{P(C_6H_{11})_3\}$	colourless, mpt. 155°C			[75]
$MnH(CO)_4\{P(OPh)_3\}$	orange, decomp, 135°C			[75]
$Mn_2H(CO)_8(PPh_2)$	yellow, mpt. 154°C: bridging PPh_2 group; H associated with both Mn atoms	26·8		[79]
$Mn_2H_2(CO)_9$	red, subl. 70°C			[78]
$Mn_2H(CO)_{10}^+$?	in acid solvent? No nmr signal (solubility low) but there is a change in electronic spectrum indicating hydride formation [61]			
$MnFeH(CO)_7(C_5H_5)^+$	see list of Fe compounds			
$ReH(CO)_5$	white, mpt. 100°C	15·66	1832	[44]
$ReH(C_5H_5)_2$	yellow, mpt. 161, decomp. > 250°C	23·53	2037, 2000	[39, 41, 43]
$ReH_2(C_5H_5)_2^+$	white	23·6	2330–2070?	[41, 43]
$ReH(C_5H_4Li)_2$	white			[39]
$ReH(C_5H_4HgCl)$	yellow, also $ReH_2(C_5H_4HgCl)_2^+$	(C_5H_4 resonance split by Re-H)		[39]

Table 5.1—*continued*

Compound	General Properties	M-H proton Resonance in τ (ppm)	M-H stretch (cm^{-1})	References
$ReH(C_5H_4D)_2$	yellow	23·3		[39]
$ReH_3(PPh_3)_3$	red, mpt. 155°C		2000	[58]
$ReH_3(PPh_3)_4$	yellow, mpt. 147°C		2050	[58]
$Re_2H(CO)_8O_2^+$?				[59]
$Re_3H_3(CO)_{12}$	white	not detected	(M-H bend at 625?)	[57]
K_2ReH_9		19·1	1931, 1846, 1814	(sect. 5.1)
IRON GROUP				
$FeH_2(CO)_4$	yellow, mpt. −70°C	21·1		[21, 67, 68, 71]
$FeH(CO)_2(C_5H_5)$	pale yellow, mpt. −10°C	21·91	1835	[44]
$FeH(C_5H_5)_2^+$	in various acidic solvents	11·9 – 12·1		[66]
$FeH(CO)_5^+$	in H_2SO_4, green, weak base	18·14		[61]
$FeH(CO)_4(PPh_3)^+$	in H_2SO_4, yellow, strong base	17·75		[61]
$FeH(CO)_3(PPh_3)_2^+$	in H_2SO_4, yellow, strong base	17·78		[61]
(Also the two $AsPh_3$ compounds corresponding to the two PPh_3 compounds above; here τ = 18·11. The $SbPh_3$ analogue produces a transient yellow colour in strong acid but rapidly decomposes [61])				
tr-FeH_2(diphos I)$_2$	unstable		1817?	[35]
tr-FeH_2(diphos III)$_2$	orange, decomp. 248°C	23·1	1726 (bend 716)	[36]
tr-FeHCl(diphos I)$_2$	red, decomp. 155°C	44·3	1849	[35]
tr-FeHCl(diphos II)$_2$	red, decomp. 180°C		1810	[35]
tr-FeHCl(diphos III)$_2$	red	40·5		[37]
tr-FeHCl(diphos IV)$_2$	red, decomp, 230°C	41·2	1870	[35]
tr-FeHI(diphos I)$_2$	red-brown, decomp. 173°C	39·1	1872	[35]
$Fe_2H(PMe_2)(C_5H_5)_2(CO)_2$	dark brown, decomp. 137°C: PMe_2 group bridging; H associated with both metal atoms – bridging?	28·73		[35]

$Fe_2H(PPh_2)(C_5H_5)_2(CO)_2$	dark brown, mpt. 153°C: PPh_2 group bridging; H associated with both Fe atoms – bridging?.	28·67	1932?	[65]
$Fe_2H(CO)_4(C_5H_5)_2^+$	red, in H_2SO_4 and as PF_6^- salt: H associated with both Fe atoms – but not bridging?.	36·30	1767	[61]
$FeMnH(CO)_7(C_5H_5)^+$	cherry-red, in H_2SO_4 and as PF_6^- salt: H associated with Fe but not with Mn atom	38·1	1760	[61]
$Fe_2H_2(CO)_8$	red-brown			[72]
$Fe_3H_2(CO)_{11}$	cherry-red	24·9		[8, 72]
$Fe_3H(CO)_{11}^-$		24·9		[8, 72]
$Fe_4H(CO)_{13}$	red			[72]
tr-RuHCl(diphos I)$_2$	white, mpt. 174°C	32·3	1938	[34]
tr-RuHBr(diphos I)$_2$	yellow, decomp. 188°C	31·5	1945	[34]
tr-RuHI(diphos I)$_2$	yellow, decomp. 212–224°C	29·8	1948	[34]
tr-RuH(SCN)(diphos I)$_2$	white, decomp. 245°C		1919	[34]
tr-RuH(CN)(diphos I)$_2$	white (impure)		1803	[34]
tr-RuH$_2$(diphos I)$_2$	white, mpt. 147–53°C		1615	[34]

The corresponding compounds containing (diphos II)$_2$ show the same colours and trends in parameters. The melting points average 50°C higher, and the M-H stretching frequencies are almost uniformly 50 cm^{-1} lower in frequency [34]. The dihydride with diphos II was not made.

tr-RuH(NO$_2$)(diphos II)$_2$	yellow, decomp. 240°C		1858	[34]
tr-RuHCl(diphos III)$_2$	yellow, decomp. 250°C		1978	[34]
tr-RuHI(diphos III)$_2$	brown, decomp. 278°C		1976	[34]
tr-RuH$_2$(diphos III)$_2$	yellow, decomp. 276°C		1617	[34]
tr-RuHCl(diphos IV)$_2$	yellow, crystallizes with $\frac{1}{2}$ mole benzene, decomp. 283°C		1978	[34]
tr-RuHCl(diars)$_2$	white, decomp. 190°C		1804	[34]
cis-RuH(CH_3)(diphos I)$_2$	mpt. 247°C, white	18·9 (double quartet)	1884	[37]
tr-RuH(CH_3)(diphos I)$_2$	mpt. 290°C, white	18·4 (double quartet)	1868	[37]
cis-RuH(C_5H_5)(diphos I)$_2$	white, mpt. 289°C		1873	[37]
cis-RuH(C_3H_7)(diphos I)$_2$	white, mpt. 278°C		1867	[37]
cis-RuH(C_6H_5)(diphos I)$_2$	white, mpt. 136°C		1806	[38]

Table 5.1—*continued*

Compound	General Properties	M-H proton Resonance in τ (ppm)	M-H stretch (cm^{-1})	References
tr-$RuH(C_6H_5)$(diphos I)$_2$	white, mpt. 159°C: the *p*-tolyl derivative is very similar	23·3 (quintet)	1757	[37]
cis-RuH_2(diphos I)$_2$	white, mpt. 82°C	18·6	1806	[38]
cis-$RuH(2\text{-}C_{10}H_7)$(diphos I)$_2$	white, mpt. 182°C	17·6, 19·8	1802	[38]
cis-$RuH(C_{14}H_9)$(diphos I)$_2$	(i) $C_{14}H_9$ = *anthryl*, orange, mpt. 185°C		1802	[38]
	(ii) $C_{14}H_9$ = *phenanthryl*, white, decomp. 202°C		1796	[38]
$RuH(CO)_5(C_5H_5)$	colourless liquid	20·92	1853	[44]
$RuHCl(CO)(PPh_3)_3$			2020	[49]
$RuHCl(CO)(PEt_2Ph)_3$	white, mpt. 99°C	17·1	1880	[45]
$RuHBr(CO)(PEt_2Ph)_3$	white, mpt. 110°C	17·7		[45]
$RuHI(CO)(PEt_2Ph)_3$	white, decomp. 141°C			[45]
tr-OsHCl(diphos I)$_2$	white, mpt. 171, decomp. 315°C	36·5	2039	[34]
tr-OsHI(diphos I)$_2$	yellow, mpt. 224°C	31·3	2051	[34]
tr-OsH(SCN)(diphos I)$_2$	white, decomp. 200°C		2009	[34]
tr-OsH_2(diphos I)$_2$	white, mpt. 150, decomp. 295°C		1721	[34]
tr-OsHCl(diphos II)$_2$	white, decomp. 190°C		2014	[34]
tr-OsHCl(diphos V)$_2$	yellow, decomp. 314°C; cryst. with 1 C_6H_6 molecule		2046	[34]
tr-OsHCl(diphos VI)$_2$	yellow, decomp. 295°C; cryst. with 1 C_6H_6 molecule		2045	[34]
tr-OsH_2(diphos III)$_2$	lemon-yellow, mpt. 293°C		1720	[34]
$OsH(CH_3)$(diphos V)$_2$	pale yellow, mpt. 145°C; cryst. with 1 C_6H_6 molecule		1948	[37]
$OsH(C_2H_5)$(diphos V)$_2$	pale yellow, mpt. 311°C; cryst. with $\frac{1}{2}$ C_6H_6 molecule		1941	[37]
$OsHCl(CO)(PPh_3)_3$	white, mpt. 177, decomp. 277°C		2097 (bend 730–870)	[10]
$OsHBr(CO)(PPh_3)_3$	white, mpt. 172, decomp. 276°C		2100 (bend 730–780)	[10]

$OsHCl(CO)(AsPh_3)_3$	white, mpt. 200, decomp. 247°C		2085 (bend 730–870)	[10]
$OsHBr(CO)(AsPh_3)_3$	tan, mpt. 195, decomp. 243°C		2087 (bend 730–870)	[10]
Cobalt Group				
$CoH(CO)_4$	yellow, mpt. −26°C	20·7	1934 (bend 703)	[51]
$CoH(PF_3)_4$	pale green, mpt. −51, bpt. 80°C	22·5		[50]
$CoH(PPh_3)_4$	very unstable		1739	[52]
$CoH(CO)_3(PPh_3)$	yellow, decomp. 20°C			[53]
$CoH(CO)_3\{P(OPh)_3\}$	yellow, decomp. 0°C			[53]
$CoH(\text{diphos V})_2$	red, mpt. 265, decomp. 280°C		1884	[48, 52]
$CoH_2(\text{diphos V})_2^+$	in *cis* configuration		1985, 1940	[48]
$CoH(CN)_5^{3-}$	yellow solution	22·6		[28, 56]
vitamin B_{12s}	'hydrido-cobalamin'. This is thought to contain a Co-H bond [54] but other workers reject this formulation [55].			
$RhH(CO)_4$	pale yellow, mpt. −10, decomp. 20°C			[26]
$RhH(CO)(PPh_3)_3$	yellow	19·9	2004 (bend 784)	[19, 20]
$RhH(\text{diphos V})_2$	orange, decomp. 280°C		1902 (bend 625)	[48]
$\{RhH(Cl)(\text{diphos V}_2)\}Cl$	above compound $+2HCl-H_2$			[48]
$RhH(Cl)_2(AsMePh_2)_3$	yellow, mpt. 172°C		2077	[32, 29]
$RhH(Br)_2(AsMePh_2)_3$	yellow-orange, mpt. 175°C		2073	[32]
$RhH(I)_2(AsMePh_2)_3$	orange-brown, mpt. 164°C		2058	[32]
$RhH(CN)_5^{3-}$	in solution	20·8		[28]
$RhH(NH_3)_5^+$	brown, decomp. 0°C		2079	[25]
$RhHCl(DMG)^+$	brown solution, decomp. 0°C	26·4		[25]
cis-$RhH_2(en)_2^+$	brown, decomp. 0°C. (Later [85] this was regarded as the *trans* isomer)	31 (doublet)	2100	[25]
cis-$RhHCl(trien)^+$	brown	28·5 (doublet)	2081	[25, 85]

Table 5.1—*continued*

Compound	General Properties	M-H proton Resonance in τ (ppm)	M-H stretch cm^{-1})	References
tr-$RhHCl(C_5H_5N)_4^+$	brown soln., decomp. 0°C	28·6		[25, 85]
tr-$RhHCl(en)_2^+$	Also possible *cis* isomer, as intermediates in preparation of the dihydride			[25]
tr-$RhH_2(en)_2^+$	in solution and as BPh_4^- salt	31·6		[95]
tr-$RhHCl(en)_2^+$	in solution and as BPh_4^-		2100	[85]
tr-$RhHBr(en)_2^+$	in solution and as BPh_4^-		2120	[85]
tr-$RhHI(en)_2^+$	in solution and as BPh_4^- salt	30·2	2140	[85]
tr-$RhHCl(NH_3)_4^+$	in dilute, ice-cold solution; shown by electronic spectrum only			[85]
tr-$RhHBr(C_5H_5N)_4^+$	in solution and as salt	28·5	1976	[85]
cis-$RhHCl(en)_2^+$	in solution and as BPh_4^- salt		2105	[85]
cis-$RhH_2(en)_2^+$	in solution and as BPh_4^- salt. Note the relatively high value of the stretching frequency compared with other dihydrides. See '*cis*' compound above, of same formula [25]	32·0	1969	[85]
cis-$RhH_2(trien)^+$	in solution and as BPh_4^- salt	32·5	1969	[25, 85]
$IrH(CO)_4$				[27]
$IrH_3(PPh_3)_3$	white, mpt. 227°C: isomer mixture??		2100, 1745	[30]
$IrH_3(PPh_3)_3$(*trans* H_2)	white, mpt. 173°C		2130, 1750	[100]
$IrH_3(PPh_3)_3$(*cis* H_3)	mpt. 152°C		2075	[100]
$IrH(CN)_5^{3-}$		29·4		[8]
$IrH(Cl)_2(PPh_3)_3$ (three possible positional isomers)	(i) *yellow*, mpt. 256°C		2197 (bend, 860, 804)	[11]
	(ii) *white* (*I*), different X-ray powder pattern from yellow form		2049 (bend 835, 820)	[11]
	(iii) *white* (*II*), mpt. 261°C. Results from HCl + $IrH_2Cl(PPh_3)_3$		2243 (bend 806)	[11]
$IrH(Cl)_2(AsPh_3)_3$	yellow, mpt. 240°C		2170	[11]

$IrH(Cl)_2(SbPh_3)_3$	yellow, mpt. 201		2100	[11]
$IrH(Br)_2(PPh_3)_3$				[100]
$IrH(Cl)_2(PEt_3)_3$	(i) yellow, *trans*-Cl_2, mpt. 81°C	23·1	2114	[24, 33]
	(ii) white, *cis*-Cl_2, mpt. 99°C	32·2	2213	[24, 33]
$IrH(Br)_2(AsMePh_2)_3$	yellow, mpt. 248°C		2094 (bend 789)	[32]
$IrH_2Cl(PPh_3)_3$	(i) *white I*, mpt. 250°C		2215, 2110	[11]
	(ii) *white II*, mpt. 218°C		2210, 2130	[30]
$IrH_2Br(PPh_3)_3$	white, mpt. 242°C		2240, 2090	[11]
$IrH(CO)(PPh_3)_3$	yellow: genuinely five-coordinate and isomorphous with Rh analogue (qv) whose structure is known	21·2 (quartet)	2068 (bend 822)	[19]
$IrH_2Cl(CO)(PPh_3)_2$		2190, 2100		[9]
$IrH_2Br(CO)(PPh_3)_2$				[47]
$IrHCl_2(CO)(PPh_3)_2$	also the $PEtPPh_2$ analogue [24]: this reference discusses solvent effects on M-H stretching		2245	[9]
$IrH_2Cl_2(CO)(PPh_3)_3^+$	as chloride			[47]
$IrHCl_2(CO)(PPhEt_2)_2$	(i) yellow, *trans*-Cl_2, *trans*-H, CO mpt. 110°C	19·0 (triplet)	2101, 2008	[31]
	(ii) white, *trans-H*,Cl, *trans*-Cl, CO mpt. 123–26°C	26·05 (triplet)	2237, 2032	[31]
$IrHBr_2(CO)(PPhEt_2)_3$	white, mpt. 140°C		2232, 2035	[31]
$Ir_2H_2Cl_4(CO)_2(PEt_3)_2$	bridging Cl with H *trans* to them; mpt. 170°C		2242, 2058	[31]
$Ir_2H_2Cl_4(C_8H_{12})_2$	cream, decomp. 200°C		2261	[46]
NICKEL GROUP				
$NiH_4(CO)_3$; $Ni_2H_2(CO)_6.4NH_3$; $Ni_2H(CO)_9^-$; $Ni_2H_2(CO)_6$; $Ni_4H_2(CO)_9$; $Ni_4H(CO)_9^-$:	all these compounds are reported as resulting from the acidification of nickel carbonyl salts, formed from nickel carbonyl by the action of alkali metals, usually in liquid ammonia. Most of the compounds are red, and all are of low stability [83]			
$NiHCl(PPr_3)_2$	very unstable, not isolated			[76]
$PdHCl(PPh_3)_2$	very unstable		2035?	[77]

Table 5.1—*continued*

Compound	General Properties		M-H proton Resonance in τ (ppm)	M-H stretch (cm^{-1})	References
tr-$PtHX(MEt_3)_2$	similar complexes of other phosphines, e.g. PMe_3, are also formed				[17, 18]
M = P, X =	*mpt.* (°C)	τ *Pt-H (ppm)*	*Pt-H coupling (c/s)*	*Pt-H stretch* (cm^{-1})	
NO_3	47	33·6	1322	2242	
ONO (nitrito)	95	29·4	1003	2150	
NCO } coexist	65	27·7	1080	2234	
OCN } coexist		27·0			
NCS } coexist	61	27·6	1086	2195	
SCN } coexist		22·95			
Cl	82	26·6	1275	2182	
Br	94	25·6	1346	2178	
I	73	22·7	1369	2112	
CN	106	17·6	778	2072	
M = As, X = NCS } coexist	56	29·9	1046	2108	
SCN } coexist		24·8			
Cl	91	29·3	1117	2174	
Br	107	27·8	1185	2167	
I	109	24·6	1220	2108	
$PtH_2(PPh_3)_2$	white, mpt. 175°C			1670 (bend 815)	[13, 15]
$PtH(GePh_3)(PEt_3)_2$	decomp. 150°C: prepared by action of molecular hydrogen on $Pt(GePh_3)_2(PPh_3)_2$ at 25°C, atmospheric pressure, and no catalyst			2051	[16]

Note In Table 5.1, *tr* = *trans*, diphos I = $C_2H_4(PEt_2)_2$, diphos II = $C_2H_4(PMe_2)_2$, diphos III = *o*-$C_6H_4(PEt_2)_2$, diphos IV = *o*-$C_6H_4(PPh_2)_2$, diphos V = $C_2H_4(PPh_2)_2$, diphos VI = $CH_2(PPh_2)_2$, diars = *o*-$C_6H_4(AsMe_2)_2$, en = ethylenediamine, trien = triethylenetetramine, DMG = dimethylglyoxime.

REFERENCES

[1] K. KNOX and A. P. GINSBERG, *Inorg. Chem.*, 1964, **3**, 555; compare idem, *ibid*, 1962, **1**, 945: A. P. GINSBERG, J. M. MILLFR, and E. KOUBEK, *J. Amer. Chem. Soc.*, 1961, **83**, 4909: J. G. FLOSS and A. V. GROSSE, *J. Inorg. Nucl. Chem.*, 1960, **16**, 36.

[2] S. C. ABRAHAMS, A. P. GINSBERG, and K. KNOX, *Inorg. Chem.*, 1964, **3**, 558.

[3] A. P. GINSBERG, *Inorg. Chem.*, 1964, **3**, 567.

[4] (*a*) G. E. F. LUNDELL, and H. B. KNOWLES, *J. Res. Nat. Bur. Stand.*, 1937, **18**, 629: (*b*) A. P. GINSBERG and E. KOUBEK, *Zeit. anorg. Chem.*, 1962, **315**, 278.

[5] J. BRAVO, E. GRISWOLD, and J. KLEINBERG, *J. Phys. Chem.*, 1954, **58**, 18.

[6] J. D. FARR, *J. Inorg. Nucl. Chem.*, 1960, **14**, 202.

[7] C. C. OTTINGER, I. E. MCFALL, and C. W. KEENAN, *Inorg. Chem.*, 1964, **3**, 1321.

[8] M. L. H. GREEN, *Angew. Chem.*, 1960, **72**, 719.

[9] L. VASKA and J. W. DILUZIO, *J. Amer. Chem. Soc.*, 1962, **84**, 679.

[10] L. VASKA, *J. Amer. Chem. Soc.*, 1964, **86**, 1943.

[11] L. VASKA, *J. Amer. Chem. Soc.*, 1961, **83**, 756: with J. W. DILUZIO, *ibid*, 1962, **84**, 4989.

[12] J. CHATT, B. L. SHAW, and A. E. FIELD, *J. Chem. Soc.*, 1964, 3466.

[13] L. MALATESTA and R. UGO, *J. Chem. Soc.*, 1963, 2080.

[14] G. W. WATT, E. M. POTRAFKE, and D. S. KLETT, *Inorg. Chem.*, 1963, **2**, 868.

[15] J. A. CHAPOORIAN, J. LEWIS and R. S. NYHOLM, *Nature*, 1961, **190**, 529: J. CHATT and G. A. ROWE, *ibid*, 1961, **191**, 1191.

[16] R. J. CROSS and F. GLOCKLING, *Proc., Chem. Soc.*, 1964, 143.

[17] J. CHATT and B. L. SHAW, *J. Chem. Soc.*, 1962, 5075.

[18] J. POWELL and B. L. SHAW, *J. Chem. Soc.*, 1965, 3879.

[19] S. S. BATH and L. VASKA, *J. Amer. Chem. Soc.*, 1963, **85**, 3500.

[20] S. J. LAPLACA and J. A. IBERS, *Acta Cryst.*, 1965, **18**, 511.

[21] E. O. BISHOP, J. L. DOWN, P. R. EMTAGE, R. E. RICHARDS and G. WILKINSON, *J. Chem. Soc.*, 1959, 2484.

[22] F. A. COTTON, *J. Amer. Chem. Soc.*, 1958, **80**, 4425.

[23] F. A. COTTON, J. L. DOWN, and G. WILKINSON, *J. Chem. Soc.*, 1959, 833.

[24] D. M. ADAMS, *Proc. Chem. Soc.*, 1961, 2605.

[25] R. D. GILLARD and G. WILKINSON, *J. Chem. Soc.*, 1963, 3594.

[26] W. HIEBER and H. LAGALLY, *Zeit. anorg. Chem.*, 1943, **251**, 96.

[27] idem, *ibid*, 1940, **245**, 321.

[28] W. P. GRIFFITHS and G. WILKINSON, *J. Chem. Soc.*, 1959, 2757.

[29] R. S. NYHOLM and K. VRIEZE, *Proc. Chem. Soc.*, 1963, 138.

[30] R. G. HAYTER, *J. Amer. Chem. Soc.*, 1961, **83**, 1259.

[31] J. CHATT, N. P. JOHNSON, and B. L. SHAW, *J. Chem. Soc.*, 1964, 1625.

[32] J. LEWIS, R. S. NYHOLM, and G. K. N. REDDY, *Chem. and Ind.*, 1960, 1386.

[33] J. CHATT, *Proc. Chem. Soc.*, 1962, 318.

[34] J. CHATT and R. G. HAYTER, *J. Chem. Soc.*, 1961, 2605.

[35] idem, *ibid*, 1961, 5507.

[36] J. CHATT, F. A. HART, and D. T. ROSEVEAR, *J. Chem. Soc.*, 1961, 5504.

[37] J. CHATT and R. G. HAYTER, *J. Chem. Soc.*, 1963, 6017.

[38] J. CHATT and J. M. DAVIDSON, *J. Chem. Soc.*, 1965, 843.

[39] R. L. COOPER, M. L. H. GREEN, and J. T. MOELWYN-HUGHES, *J. Organomet. Chem.*, 1965, **3**, 261.

[40] M. GERLOCH, and R. MASON, *J. Chem. Soc.*, 1965, 296.

[41] C. J. BALHAUSEN and J. P. DAHL, *Acta Chem. Scand.*, 1961, **15**, 296.

[42] M. L. H. GREEN, J. A. MCCLEVERTY, L. PRATT, and G. WILKINSON, *J. Chem. Soc.*, 1961, 4854.

[43] M. L. H. GREEN, L. PRATT, and G. WILKINSON, *J. Chem. Soc.*, 1958, 3916.
[44] A. DAVIDSON, J. A. MCCLEVERTY, and G. WILKINSON, *J. Chem. Soc.*, 1963, 1133.
[45] J. CHATT, B. L. SHAW, and A. E. FIELD, *J. Chem. Soc.*, 1964, 3466.
[46] S. D. ROBINSON and B. L. SHAW, *Tetrahedron Letters*, 1964, 1301.
[47] L. VASKA, 1963, quoted in [48].
[48] A. SACCO and R. UGO, *J. Chem. Soc.*, 1964, 3276.
[49] L. VASKA and J. W. DILUZIO, *J. Amer. Chem. Soc.*, 1961, **83**, 1262.
[50] T. KRUCK, W. LANG, and A. ENGELMANN, *Angew. Chem. Int.*, 1965, **4**, 148.
[51] W. F. EDGELL and R. SUMMITT, *J. Amer. Chem. Soc.*, 1961, **83**, 1772.
[52] F. ZINGALES, F. CANZIANI, and A. CHIESA, *Inorg. Chem.*, 1963, **2**, 1303.
[53] W. HIEBER and E. LINDER, *Zeit. Naturf.*, 1961, **16b**, 137; *Chem. Berichte*, 1961, **94**, 1417.
[54] See A. W. JOHNSON and co-workers, *J. Chem. Soc.*, 1963, 4416; *Pure and Applied Chem.*, 1963, **7**, 539; *Nature*, 1962, **194**, 1175.
[55] J. W. COLLAT and J. C. ABBOTT, *J. Amer. Chem. Soc.*, 1964, **86**, 2308.
[56] N. N. KING and M. E. WINFIELD, *J. Amer. Chem. Soc.*, 1961, **83**, 3366.
[57] D. K. HUGGINS, W. FELLMANN, J. M. SMITH, and H. D. KAESZ, *J. Amer. Chem. Soc.*, 1964, **86**, 4821.
[58] L. MALATESTA, M. FRENI, and V. VALENTI, *Angew. Chem.*, 1961, **73**, 273; *Gazzetta*, 1961, **91**, 1357.
[59] W. HIEBER and L. SCHUSTER, *Zeit. anorg. Chem.*, 1956, **285**, 205.
[60] D. F. SHRIVER, *J. Amer. Chem. Soc.*, 1963, **85**, 3509.
[61] A. DAVISON, W. MCFARLANE, L. PRATT, and G. WILKINSON, *J. Chem. Soc.*, 1962, 3653.
[62] W. HIEBER, K. ENGLERT, and K. RIEGER, *Zeit. anorg. Chem.*, 1959, **300**, 304.
[63] W. HIEBER and K. ENGLERT, *Zeit. anorg. Chem.*, 1959, **300**, 311.
[64] B. SARRY, M. DETTKE, and H. GROSSMANN, *Zeit. anorg. Chem.*, 1964, **329**, 218.
[65] R. G. HAYTER, *J. Amer. Chem. Soc.*, 1963, **85**, 3120.
[66] T. J. CURPHY, J. O. SANTER, M. ROSENBLUM, and J. H. RICHARDS, *J. Amer. Chem. Soc.*, 1960, **82**, 5249.
[67] W. HIEBER and F. LEUTERT, *Zeit. anorg. Chem.*, 1932, **204**, 145; W. HIEBER and J. VELTER, *ibid*, 1933, **212**, 145.
[68] W. HIEBER and H. FRANKEL, *Chem. Berichte*, 1953, **86**, 710.
[69] R. G. HAYTER, *Inorg. Chem.*, 1963, **2**, 1031.
[70] E. O. FISCHER, *Inorganic Syntheses*, (edited J. Kleinberg). McGraw-Hill, 1963, **7**, 136.
[71] T. S. PIPER and G. WILKINSON, *J. Inorg. Nucl. Chem.*, 1956, **3**, 116.
[72] W. HIEBER and G. BRENDELL, *Zeit. anorg. Chem.*, 1957, **289**, 324; W. HIEBER and R. WERNER, *Chem. Berichte*, 1957, **90**, 286; W. HIEBER and N. KAHLEN, *ibid*, 1958, **91**, 2223.
[73] W. HIEBER, E. WINTER, and E. SCHUBERT, *Chem. Berichte*, 1962, **95**, 3070.
[74] W. HIEBER and G. WAGNER, *Zeit. Naturf.*, 1958, **13b**, 339.
[75] W. HIEBER, G. FAULHABER and F. THEUBERT, *Zeit. anorg. Chem.*, 1962, **314**, 125.
[76] M. L. H. GREEN, C. M. STREET, and G. WILKINSON, *Zeit. Naturf.*, 1959, **14b**, 738.
[77] J. CHATT, L. A. DUNCANSON, and B. L. SHAW, *Chem. and Ind.*, 1958, 859.
[78] W. HIEBER, W. BECK, and G. ZEITLER, *Angew. Chem.*, 1961, **73**, 364.
[79] M. L. H. GREEN and J. T. MOELWYN-HUGHES, *Zeit. Naturf.*, 1962, **17b**, 783: R. G. HAYTER, *ibid*, 1963, **18b**, 581; see also [65].
[80] W. HIEBER and H. TENGLER, *Zeit. anorg. Chem.*, 1962, **318**, 136.
[81] M. G. RHOMBERG and B. B. OWEN, *J. Amer. Chem. Soc.*, 1951, **72**, 5901.
[82] W. HIEBER and K. RIEGER, *Zeit. anorg. Chem.*, 1959, **300**, 288.
[83] H. BEHRENS and H. ZIZLSBERGER, *J. Prakt. Chem.*, 1961, **14**, 249: idem with R. RAUCH, *Chem. Berichte*, 1961, **94**, 1497: H. BEHRENS and F. LOHOFER, *ibid*, 1961, **94**, 1391.

[84] H. BEHRENS and R. WEBER, *Zeit. anorg. Chem.*, 1957, **291**, 122; H. BEHRENS and W. KLEK, *ibid*, 1957, **292**, 151; H. BEHRENS and W. HAAG, *Chem. Berichte*, 1961, **94**, 312.

[85] J. A. OSBORN, R. D. GILLARD, and G. WILKINSON, *J. Chem. Soc.*, 1964, 3168.

[86] A. D. BUCKINGHAM and P. J. STEPHENS, *J. Chem. Soc.*, 1964, 2747; 4583.

[87] L. L. LOHR, Jr. and W. N. LIPSCOMB, *Inorg. Chem.*, 1964, **3**, 22; R. M. STEVENS, C. W. KERN, and W. N. LIPSCOMB, *J. Chem. Phys.*, 1962, **37**, 279, 260.

[88] J. B. WILFORD and F. G. A. STONE, *Inorg. Chem.*, 1965, **4**, 93.

[89] J. KWIATEK and J. K. SEYLER, *J. Organomet. Chem.*, 1965, **3**, 421.

[90] (*a*) J. B. WILFORD, P. M. TREICHEL, and F. G. A. STONE, *J. Organomet. Chem.*, 1964, **2**, 119: (*b*) R. MASON and D. R. RUSSELL, *Chem. Comm.*, 1965, 182.

[91] R. B. KING and F. G. A. STONE, *Inorganic Syntheses*, edited by J. Kleinberg, McGraw-Hill, 1963, **7**, 196.

[92] P. M. TREICHEL, J. H. MORRIS, and F. G. A. STONE, *J. Chem. Soc.*, 1963, 720.

[93] E. R. ANDREW and R. G. EADES, *Discussions Faraday Soc.*, 1962, **32**, 38.

[94] S. J. LAPLACA, W. C. HAMILTON, and J. A. IBERS, *Inorg. Chem.*, 1964, **3**, 1491.

[95] P. G. OWSTON, J. M. PARTRIDGE, and J. M. ROWE, *Acta Cryst.*, 1960, **13**, 246.

[96] P. L. ORIOLI and L. VASKA, *Proc. Chem. Soc.*, 1962, 333.

[97] R. J. DOEDENS and L. F. DAHL, *J. Amer. Chem. Soc.*, 1965, **87**, 2576.

[98] J. CHATT and R. G. HAYTER, *J. Chem. Soc.*, 1961, 772.

[99] F. BASOLO J. CHATT, H. B. GRAY, R. G. PEARSON, and B. L. SHAW, *J. Chem. Soc.*, 1961, 2207.

[100] L. MALATESTA, M. ANGOLETTA, A. ARANEO and F. CANZIANI, *Angew. Chem.*, 1961, **73**, 273: A. ARANEO and S. MARTINENGO, *Gazzetta*, 1965, **95**, 61.

[101] R. EISENBERG and J. A. IBERS, *Inorg. Chem.*, 1965, **4**, 773.

CHAPTER 6

The Tetrahydroborates, Tetrahydroaluminates, and Related Species

6.1 Introduction

Compounds containing the BH_4 or AlH_4 groups are formed by most metals and are discussed briefly in this chapter, along with other boron hydride ions and related species [79]. These compounds are of wide importance in synthetic chemistry, and also parallel in their properties the corresponding hydrides of the metals. They thus give some guidance to the properties of the hydrides, especially to the less stable compounds.

The compound $NaBH_4$ is systematically named *sodium tetrahydroborate*, but the name *sodium* borohydride is well-established by common usage. Similarly *lithium tetrahydroaluminate* is less-commonly used than *lithium aluminium hydride*. In the following sections, the systematic name and the common one is used interchangeably.

It is not intended to discuss here the applications of these hydrides in syntheses, although a number of uses have been indicated in the previous chapters. Gaylord's book [1], gives a full account. The aim of this chapter is to review the more recent preparations of complex hydrides, and to highlight recent developments. Wiberg [3], and Schlesinger [2], review earlier work, and accounts are to be found in the boron hydride reviews [4, 5, 6, 7]. An interesting personal account of early developments is given by Brown in his lecture to the 1959 Munich Conference [8].

Compounds containing the BH_4 and AlH_4 groups range in properties from ionic species like $NaBH_4$ to volatile covalent molecules like $Be(BH_4)_2$. The formation of the MH_4^- ions may be regarded, in a formal sense at least, as a Lewis acid-base reaction in which the MH_3 group accepts the electron pair from the hydride ion,

$$H^- + MH_3 = MH_4^- \ (M = B, Al, Ga).$$

Thus, the ions are produced by the action of excess hydride ion on a trihalide, or by direct reaction with the hydride,

$$4\,LiH + AlCl_3 = LiAlH_4 + 3\,LiCl \text{ (similarly for boron, where } BF_3.OEt_2 \text{ is a useful reactant)}$$

$$2\,LiH + B_2H_6 = 2\,LiBH_4.$$

Furthermore, the stabilities and properties follow the relative acceptor strengths which are in the order B > Al > Ga. This applies to the thermal stability – where the $MGaH_4$ compounds decompose around room temperature – and to the reactivity with H^+, which combines with the H^- to give hydrogen (again in a purely formal representation). Thus, sodium borohydride is stable in slightly alkaline solution and is decomposed only in acid, but the corresponding aluminium and gallium compounds are rapidly hydrolysed by water, $NaGaH_4$ explosively.

The general stabilities depend on the degree of ionic character in the compound. The alkali and alkaline earth compounds, which are essentially ionic, are relatively stable, while the volatile, covalent compounds like beryllium or aluminium borohydrides explode in air and are as reactive as the boron hydrides. Activities can be greatly changed by partial substitution, and reagents like $NaHB(OR)_3$ [35] or $LiHAl(OBu^t)_3$ have modified properties which are valuable in syntheses, either giving better yields, as in the reduction of $GeCl_4$ by $LiAlH(OR)_3$, or in providing a more selective reagent.

While the ionic borohydrides are prepared by the action of an ionic hydride on a trihalide, the more covalent species are best made from an ionic borohydride,

$$AlCl_3 + LiBH_4 \rightarrow Al(BH_4)_3 \text{ [9].}$$

The reaction of B_2H_6 with the metal halide or alkoxide is also used. The preparation of the aluminohydrides and gallohydrides is similar, but the range of metals which form these complex hydrides is much narrower so that only gallohydrides of the alkali metals have been reported.

An important extension of the synthetic methods is the development of the direct synthesis of the complex hydride from the elements. In the preparation of $LiAlH_4$ from aluminium trichloride, three-quarters of the lithium used as LiH ends up as LiCl and is lost. As lithium is by far the most expensive element involved in the preparation, this is a serious disadvantage and accounts for the high price of $LiAlH_4$. A number of workers including Clasen [10] and Russian workers [34] have studied the preparation of $MAlH_4$ from the elements, and the recent account by Ashby [11] gives full details. Further, the reaction goes equally well with sodium in the place of lithium (in contrast to the synthesis from the hydride where NaH is a much poorer reagent than LiH as it is insoluble in the ether used as solvent), and this reduces the cost even further since sodium and lithium aluminium hydrides are essentially equivalent reducing agents. The reaction used in the preparation is

$$M + Al + 2H_2 \xrightarrow[\text{1000–5000 psi, 120–150°C}]{\text{ether solvent}} MAlH_4 \text{ 90–99\% yield.}$$

The ether may be tetrahydrofuran or monoglyme and the time required depends on the temperature and pressure used. However, it is dangerous to exceed 160–170°C as the cleavage of ethers by alkali metals becomes explosively rapid in the range 180–200°C. Typical conditions, using sodium and tetrahydrofuran, are to heat for six hours at 150°C and 2000 psi pressure giving

95% yield, or three hours at 140°C and 5000 psi giving 99% yield. Commercial aluminium gives only a slow reaction but the aluminium may be activated, either by treatment with triethylaluminium or by recycling from a preparation run, to give reaction under the conditions above. For lithium and sodium, tetrahydrofuran and diglyme are suitable solvents, potassium is best used in diglyme with a relatively low temperature of reaction, while cesium cleaves any ether too rapidly to be used. However, cesium, or any of the other alkali metals, can be used with a non-solvating medium such as toluene or hexane, provided triethylaluminium is added. It is presumed that this acts *via* the formation of intermediates like $MAlH_2Et_2$ which are soluble in the hydrocarbon thus allowing a clean metal surface to be maintained. Even mineral oil can be used as solvent in the alkylaluminium catalysed reaction and allows a 50% yield. This synthesis thus allows the ready and inexpensive preparation of the tetrahydroaluminates and it is to be expected that their wider use in large-scale syntheses, especially of fine chemicals, will follow.

The direct synthesis may be extended to a wider variety of hydride syntheses, as was indicated in Chapter 4, by heating an appropriate element, halide, or oxide, with an active metal and hydrogen under pressure, when the element-hydride is formed, presumably *via* the active metal hydride. Other extensions are also possible. Thus Clasen [10] and Ashby [11] report the reaction, under similar conditions,

$$Na + Al + 2H_2 + n(RCH{=}CH_2) = NaAl(CH_2CH_2R)_nH_{(4-n)}.$$

Apart from the simple compounds containing the MH_4 group, a variety of more complex hydride anions exist, mainly of boron. While these are outside the scope of this account, one or two of their properties may be mentioned briefly. First, the boron hydride ions are not necessarily derivatives of the parent hydrides. Thus, the anions $B_3H_8^-$ and $B_{12}H_{12}^{2-}$ exist with no corresponding hydrides, and also the ions like $B_{10}H_{12}^{2-}$ which do have the same number of boron atoms as a hydride, do not always have the same structure. Like the parent hydrides, most of the boron hydride ions have boron atom skeletons which are icosahedral fragments, and the $B_{12}H_{12}^{2-}$ ion has, in fact, a regular icosahedron of boron atoms, each with one terminal hydrogen bonded to it. Another highly symmetrical anion is $B_6H_6^{2-}$ [12] in which the six borons form a regular octahedron, each with a single terminal hydrogen bonded to it.

Although a number of special preparations are available, these hydride anions can all be derived from the same type of general reaction. Thus the reaction between diborane and $NaBH_4$ will yield $B_3H_8^-$, $B_6H_6^-$, $B_{10}H_{10}^{2-}$, $B_{11}H_{14}^-$, or $B_{12}H_{12}^{2-}$ depending on the conditions used. Ions of complexity as great as that of the hydrides are known, such as $B_{20}H_{19}^{3-}$ [13]. Furthermore, anions of the carboranes and other related species also exist. One very interesting example of the latter species is the anion $B_9C_2H_{11}^{2-}$. In structure, this may be derived from the regular dodecahedron of the $B_{12}H_{12}^{2-}$ ion by removing one apical B atom, with its hydrogen, leaving a five-membered ring as the exposed face, this ring containing three boron atoms and the two carbons. Now, this face has five equivalent atomic orbitals directed towards the empty apex – just as cyclopentadienyl anion has – and these may be used to form three bonding molecular orbitals containing six electrons, just as the cyclopentadienyl ring does in ferrocene and related compounds. It is reported [14] that anhydrous ferrous chloride reacts with the carborane anion to give $Fe(C_2B_9H_{11})_2^{2-}$ which is diamagnetic and may well be analogous to ferrocene. Oxidation gives the red, paramagnetic ion $Fe(B_9C_2H_{11})_2^-$, analogous to the ferricinium ion. Furthermore, stable anions $(B_9C_2H_{11})M(CO)_3^-$ (M = Mn or Re) are formed analogous to the cyclopentadienyl carbonyls. These are only preliminary reports of possible structures, but if these are proven a most exciting new class of compounds becomes possible, and this work of Hawthorne and his colleagues opens up a new field on the boundary between the boron hydrides and the metallocenes.

The boron hydride anions fit in with the boron hydrides in general behaviour, and they are amenable to the same type of theoretical and topological discussion as are the hydrides [4]. Indeed, the hydrides and hydride ions of boron form one continuous field which is not to be divided up merely because some of the species carry a charge.

6.2 Structures and Physical Properties

Some recently determined heats of formation and estimated free energies of formation of the alkali borohydrides and aluminohydrides are listed here [15].

Compound	$-\Delta H_f^\circ$ at 25°C (kcal/mole)	$-\Delta G_f^\circ$ at 25°C (kcal/mole)	Heat of decompn. to $MH + M + 3/2H_2$
$LiBH_4$	46·37	30·75	24·7
$NaBH_4$	45·63	30·19	32·1
KBH_4	54·70; 55·5 [26]	38·70	
$RbBH_4$	56·6 [26]; 59 [40]		
$CsBH_4$	63 [40]		
$LiAlH_4$	28·5; 25·74 [16]; 24·67 [17]	12·9	6·8
$NaAlH_4$	27·0	11·6	13·5
$KAlH_4$	39·8	23·8	26·0
$CsAlH_4$	39·4	23·5	27·5

It can be seen that the borohydrides are markedly more stable than the aluminohydrides, as expected from the greater acceptor strength of the BH_3 group. The close similarity of $LiAlH_4$ and $NaAlH_4$ is also marked, and corresponds to the close similarity in their chemical behaviour. The greater stability of the potassium and cesium compounds is probably largely a lattice energy effect. The heat capacity and thermodynamic properties of potassium borohydride up to 700°K have been reported [18]. An early determination of the heat of formation of liquid $Al(BH_4)_3$ gave a value of $-72{\cdot}1 \pm 4$ kcal/mole at 289°K [39]. The thermal decomposition of $LiAlH_4$ has been studied

[76], and its reaction with hydrides to give compounds like $LiAl(PH_2)_4$ [77]. The stability of borohydrides has been treated theoretically [78].

In the alkali borohydrides, the BH_4^- ion is tetrahedral and only two frequencies are observed in the infra-red. These are the triply degenerate stretching and bending modes, ν_3 and ν_4 respectively. All four modes are allowed in the Raman spectrum. Observed values are

	ν_1(R)	ν_2(R)	ν_3(IR,R)	ν_4(IR,R)
		(all values in wave numbers)		
$LiBH_4$	2265	1202	2320	1094 (1082)
$NaBH_4$	2264	1210	2280	1120 (1080)
KBH_4	2269	1214	2280	1117 (1084)
$TlBH_4$			2180	1050

(Values are taken from references [20], [61], [62] and cover a variety of experimental conditions. Values are averaged except for ν_4 where the unbracketed figures are for KBr discs and the bracketed ones for solutions in liquid ammonia.)

The frequencies found are almost independent of the cation, but depend on the experimental conditions and change with the dispersion medium [62]. The infra-red modes are commonly split, and the degree of splitting depends on the medium and the cation. The thallium values are consistently lower than the alkali metal compounds, suggesting that weak bridging may be occurring.

The spectrum of the AlH_4^- ion is similar; a solution of $LiAlH_4$ in ether showing rather broad bands at 1790 (R), 1741 (IR,R), 799(R), and 767 (IR,R) cm^{-1} [63]. The broadening may reflect weak coordination by the solvent or an interaction with the lithium. In Me_4NAlH_4, the stretching mode occurs as a broad band at 1660 cm^{-1} with a shoulder at 1690 cm^{-1}: $(Oct)_3PrNAlH_4$ has a sharp band at 1660 cm^{-1} (all these in the infra-red spectrum [48].

The alkali borohydrides have cubic structures except for $LiBH_4$ [74], with a transition to a tetragonal form at low temperatures. Properties of the solids are tabulated below.

	Lattice Parameters (Å) [64]	Lattice Energy (kcal/mole) [40]	Order-Disorder Transition Temperature [65] (°K)
$LiBH_4$	$a = 6{\cdot}82$, $b = 4{\cdot}44$, $c = 7{\cdot}72$ (orthorhombic)	186	
$NaBH_4$	$a = 6{\cdot}164$ (below -80°C, tetragonal) (with $a = 4{\cdot}354$, $c = 5{\cdot}907$)	168	
KBH_4	$a = 6{\cdot}727$	159	76
$RbBH_4$	$a = 7{\cdot}029$	155	44
$CsBH_4$	$a = 7{\cdot}419$	150	27
$TlBH_4$	$a = 6{\cdot}88$ [20]		

A further study of $NaBH_4$ and KBH_4 at room temperature and at 90°K gave values agreeing with the above, and found that KBH_4 was still cubic at 90°K with $a = 6{\cdot}636$ Å [66].

Of the volatile borohydrides, most information available concerns the beryllium and aluminium compounds. In both cases the infra-red spectrum [72] indicates the presence of bridges so that aluminium is surrounded by six hydrogens, bridging to the three borons in $Al(BH_4)_3$ and beryllium has four hydrogens bridging to the two borons in $Be(BH_4)_2$. The electron diffraction results may be interpreted in accordance with such structures if the bridges are unsymmetrical with the hydrogens nearer the boron in each case. The structural parameters are shown herewith [67].

	$Be(BH_4)_2$	$Al(BH_4)_3$	
Terminal B-H distance (Å)	1·22	1·21	(cf. 1·25 in BH_4^- [66])
Bridge B-H distance (Å)	1·28	1·28	(cf. 1·33 in diborane)
Bridge metal-H distance (Å)	1·63	2·1	
Angle of bridge bonds at B	130°	120°	

These compounds were the first borohydrides to be prepared, and though relatively unstable, they still find some uses in the preparation of borohydrides of relatively inert elements as Table 6.1 shows. The simplest preparation is by the action of an alkali borohydride on the halide [9] and the intermediate formation of halide-borohydrides has been demonstrated [68]. Reducing power increases in the order, alkali borohydrides < alkaline earth borohydrides < aluminium borohydride, and handling problems increase in the same order.

Aluminium borohydride has been shown to act as an acceptor and the presence of both 1:1 and 1:2 adducts with alkyl amines, phosphines, arsines, ethers, and sulphides has been demonstrated [36, 69, 70]. It is also possible to make hydride-borohydrides of aluminium in presence of amines [70] – for example, $HAl(BH_4)_2.NMe_3$. It is interesting that, while oxygen is a stronger donor to aluminium borohydride than is sulphur, nitrogen and phosphorus are approximately equally effective, indeed for the 2:1 adducts $(Me_3M')_2.Al(BH_4)_3$ ($M' = N, P$) the phosphine compound is more stable than the amine [36]. In these compounds, it has been shown that the donor atom is attached to the aluminium and it is thought that the bridge bonding may alter – to involve only one aluminium orbital, for example – to avoid seven-coordinate aluminium in $D.Al(BH_4)_3$ species. However, the infra-red spectra show bridging hydrogen is still present, and the structures of these species is still unsolved. When aluminium borohydride is treated with ammonia at −78°, the hexammine is formed which gives $Al(BH_4)_3.\ 5{\cdot}5\ NH_3$ at room temperature [28]. This species has very broad bands in the infra-red and nothing is known of its structure. It is much less reactive than the uncoordinated borohydride. The exchange reactions of $Al(BH_4)_3$ with D_2 and $B_2^{10}D_6$ are also reported [28].

Rather less is known of beryllium borohydride. The crystal structure has been examined and the space group determined [71]. The unit cell is tetragonal with $a = 13{\cdot}59$ Å and $c = 9{\cdot}92$ Å, and it contains sixteen molecular units. As these are in general positions, no deductions about the molecular shape could be drawn. The infra-red spectrum has been examined by Price [72], whose pioneering work led to the correct structure for $Al(BH_4)_3$, in place of an earlier electron diffraction study which gave metal-boron bonds. Beryllium borohydride reacts with ethers and amines to give compounds of the type $BeD_4(BH_4)_2$ (D = THF, $BuNH_2$ etc), but reaction with phosphines does give products analogous to the aluminium borohydride adducts [75]. The 1:1 adducts, $Ph_3P.Be(BH_4)_2$ and the corresponding trimethylphosphine compound, are reported. As the boron-11 magnetic resonance spectrum shows a quintuplet, like that of $Al(BH_4)_3$ [73], it is thought that the phosphine is coordinated to the beryllium.

Tables 6.1 and 6.2 list the tetrahydroborates and tetrahydroaluminates known for elements other than the alkali metals and the beryllium and aluminium borohydrides which are discussed separately. It will be seen that the tetrahydroaluminates are of more limited occurrence and are generally less stable than the boron compounds. Furthermore, many of the compounds are reported only in preliminary communications and must be treated with some reserve. Thus, it will be interesting if tin does form $Sn(AlH_4)_4$ while SnIV is reduced to give $Sn(BH_4)_2$ only, but the aluminium compound report is, as yet unconfirmed. The stabilities of the Main Group compounds, and those of the copper and zinc Group elements, parallel the stabilities of the hydrides of these elements, with the complex hydrides being somewhat more stable on average.

The transition elements, apart from the titanium Group borohydrides, form only unstable or transient simple borohydrides or aluminohydrides, but some of the complex compounds are much more stable. Among the interesting cases is $Cr(NH_3)_6(BH_4)_3$, formed in liquid ammonia, which is stable to 60°C. It forms an aqueous solution which decomposes only slowly. A growing class of compounds is the set of borohydrides of transition elements with π bonding ligands such as cyclopentadienyl or triphenylphosphine. Although only a handful of examples are known at present, it seems likely that a wider range of such compounds will be stable. The bonding in these species is of interest, and the infra-red spectra indicate bridge formation, as in

$(Ph_3P)_2Cu(-H-)_2BH_2$ or $[(C_5H_5)_2Zr(-H-)_2BH_2]_2$ [52]

For example, the copper compound [51] has absorptions at 2385 and 2353 cm^{-1}, (terminal BH stretch), 2001 and 1959 cm^{-1} (bridge CuH_2B) and

Table 6.1. *Some Tetrahydroborates*

The alkali metal, aluminium, and beryllium compounds are discussed in the text and are excluded here.

Compound	Preparation	Decompn. Temp. (°C)	Other Properties	References
$Mg(BH_4)_2$	B_2H_6 + MgH_2 at 80°C in glycol ether, or + $MgEt_2$ at room temp. with $AlEt_3$	280		[24, 40, 41, 42]
$Ca(BH_4)$	B_2H_6 + $Ca\{B(OMe)_4\}_2$/THF (or CaH_2 or $Ca(OMe)_2$)	320	preparative uses [44]	[44]
Sr and $Ba(BH_4)_2$	as Ca cpd.	above 350		[42, 44]
NH_4BH_4	NH_4F + $NaBH_4$/liq. NH_3	−20	Decompn. to $(BNH_6)_x$	[30]
$TlBH_4$	$TlNO_3$ + KBH_4/aq. alkali		insoluble in H_2O, white, slow decompn. in water	[20]
$Sn(BH_4)_2$	$Sn(OMe)_2$ or $Sn(OMe)_4$ + B_2H_6 at −78°C/Et_2O	> −65	yellow: 0·198 mg/ml soly. in Et_2O at −78°C	[29]
$Me_2Sn(BH_4)_2$	$SnMe_4$ + $Al(BH_4)_3$	unstable intermediate		[31]
Me_3PbBH_4	$PbMe_4$ + $Al(BH_4)_3$	unstable intermediate (cf. Me_3PbH in Chapter 4)		[31]
$CuBH_4$	$CuCl_2$ + $LiBH_4$/Et_2O (−45°C)	−12	pyridine gives a complex	[50, 55]
$(Ph_3P)_2CuBH_4$	$CuSO_4$/Ph_3P/EtOH + $NaBH_4$	177 (mpt)	IR spectrum suggests $Cu(H_2)BH_2$ bridged structure	[51]
$AgBH_4$	not found [20]: prepd. −80°C	−30		[56]
$Zn(BH_4)_2$	chloride + $LiBH_4$	120	$Li\{ZnCl(BH_4)_2\}$ isolated	[57, 58]
$Cd(BH_4)_2$	as zinc cpd	80	$Li\{CdCl(BH_4)_2\}$ also isolated	[57]
'Onium' Base Borohydrides (of Ph_4P^+. Ph_3S^+. Ph_2I^+) also occur				[19]
Scandium, yttrium, lanthanum and lanthanide borohydrides				
$M(BH_4)_3$ (M = Y, Sm, Eu, Gd, Tb, Dy, Ho, Er, Tm, Yb, Lu)	$M(OMe)_3$ + B_2H_6/THF			[27]
$SmCl(BH_4)_2$	$SmCl_3$ + $LiBH_4$/THF	stable to 80	yellow: also Dy, Y, Gd, Tb, Er, Tm but not La	[21, 25]

Table 6.1—*continued*

Compound	Preparation	Decompn. Temp. (°C)	Other Properties	References
$M(BH_4)(OMe)_2$ and $MB(H,OMe)_n$ (M = Sm, Gd, Dy, Y, Ho, Yb, Er)				[32]
Other Compounds				
$Th(BH_4)_4$	$ThF_4 + Al(BH_4)_3$	204 (at mpt)	white, salt-like, involatile isomorphous with $U(BH_4)_4$	[47, 45]
$U(BH_4)_4$	$UF_4 + Al(BH_4)_3$	stable up to 70	green, volatile ($\log p_{mm} = -4{,}265/T + 13{\cdot}354$)	[37]
$U(BH_4)_3(BH_3Me)$	$U(BH_4)_4 + BMe_3$/70°C		most volatile U^{IV} cpd	[38]
$U(BH_4)_3$	$U(BH_4)_4$ at 100°C	150	reddish brown, pyrophoric	[37]
$Ti(BH_4)_3$	$TiCl_4 + LiBH_4$	25 (slowly)	green: $Al(BH_4)_3$ reduction is complex and blue $TiCl(BH_4)_2$ is one product $(C_5H_5)_2TiBH_4$ is also found: thought to contain Ti-H and coordinated BH_3 [53]	[47]
$Zr(BH_4)_4$	$NaZrF_5 + Al(BH_4)_3$		white, mpt 28·7, v. press. = 15 mm at 25°C: $\log p = -2039/T + 8{\cdot}032$	[47]
$Hf(BH_4)_4$	as Zr compound		white, mpt 29·0, v. press. = 14·9 mm at 25°C: $\log p = -2097/T + 8{\cdot}247$	[47]
$(C_5H_5)_2Zr(BH_4)_2$ (and $(C_5H_5)_2Zr(BH_4)Cl$ as intermediate)			yellow, mpt 155°C, stable to air formulated with bridge bonding	[52]
$(C_5H_5)_2Nb(BH_4)Cl$ is also known				[54]
Mn, Fe, or $Co(BH_4)_2$ are reported as unstable species				[22]
$Cr(NH_3)_6(BH_4)_3{\cdot}\frac{1}{2}NH_3$	The fluoride + $NaBH_4$ in liq. NH_3 at −45°C	>60	yellow, gives relatively stable yellow soln. in water	[30]
$Co(NH_3)_6(BH_4)_3.NH_3$	As Cr compound	25	yellow, (transient yellow solution)	[30]
$Fe(BH_4)_2$	$FeCl_3 + LiBH_4/Et_2O$	−10	white, involatile, Et_2O-insoluble	[46]

1153 cm^{-1} (BH_2 deformation). The titanium compound, $(C_5H_5)_2TiBH_4$ [53], has a similar spectrum with an additional band at 1942 cm^{-1}. This was interpreted as showing a Ti-H bond and coordinated BH_3, but is also in the right region for a bridging mode. The spectra of the copper, titanium, and zirconium compounds are similar to that of aluminium borohydride.

The formation of titanium borohydride involves reduction to the III state, but zirconium and hafnium form tetravalent borohydrides, as do thorium and uranium. These compounds are of reasonable stability and the zirconium, hafnium and uranium compounds are volatile. Indeed, $U(BH_4)_4$ was probably considered as an alternative to UF_6 for the separation of uranium isotopes by diffusion. This volatility implies that these compounds, like $Al(BH_4)_3$, have bridge bonding, as in the boron hydrides. By contrast, thorium forms a white, involatile compound, $Th(BH_4)_4$, which is more salt-like. It is said to be isomorphous with $U(BH_4)_4$, although neither of these structures has been published in the open literature. Heating $U(BH_4)_4$ to 100°C causes the loss of one borohydride group and the formation of what is probably $U(BH_4)_3$.

The borohydride of thallium is a compound of the I state and appears to resemble the alkali borohydrides and be ionic. Like thallous chloride, it is insoluble in water. Its existence lends support to the view that TlH might be capable of preparation.

Table 6.2 *Tetrahydroaluminates*

Compounds of all elements except the alkali metals.

	Preparation and properties	
$Be(AlH_4)_2$	$BeCl_2$ + $LiAlH_4/Et_2O$, 20°C: colourless, ether soluble	[2]
$Mg(AlH_4)_2$	Halide + $NaAlH_4$/ether or amine: decomp. 140°C *in vacuo*	[23] [60]
$Ca(AlH_4)_2$	As Mg compound: also CaH_2 + $AlCl_3$	[23, 33, 59]
$CuAlH_4$	$CuBr_4^{2-}$ + $LiAlH_4/Et_2O$: decomp. −70°C	[22]
$AgAlH_4$	$AgClO_4$ + $LiAlH_4/Et_2O$, −80°C: decomp. −50°C yellow	[2] [43]
(Note that a similar preparation of $AgGaH_4$, decomp. −75°C, is also claimed [2])		
$Sn(AlH_4)_4$	Similar preparation: decomp. −40°C	[2]
$Ce(AlH_4)_3$	Halide complex + $LiAlH_4/Et_2O$, −80°C: decomp. 25°C	[22]
$Ti(AlH_4)_4$	$TiCl_4$ + $LiAlH_4/Et_2O$: decomp. −85°C	[49]
$Mn(AlH_4)_2$	Halide complex + $LiAlH_4/Et_2O$: decomp. 25°C	[22]
$Fe(AlH_4)_2$?	$FeCl_3$ + $LiAlH_4$: very unstable and rapidly decomposes	[46]
$(R_4N)(AlH_4)$	R_4NX + $LiAlH_4/C_6H_6$, 25°C, 3 days: mpt. 61–3°C (decomp.) Where R_4N = (octyl)$_3$(propyl)N, X = Br For Me_4N, X = SPh^-, reaction in THF at 63°C, decomp. 175°C	[46]
$Ga(AlH_4)_3$	$GaCl_3$ + $LiAlH_4/Et_2O$, 0°C: decomp. + 35°C	[2] (a)
$In(AlH_4)_3$	$InCl_3$ + $LiAlH_4/Et_2O$, −70°C: decomp. −40°C	[2] (a)
$Tl(AlH_4)_3$	? possible intermediate, decomp. at −115°C, the temp. of the preparation	[2]

(a) These results should be treated with reserve in light of the findings on gallium hydride discussed in Chapter 4

REFERENCES

[1] N. G. GAYLORD, *Reductions with Complex Metal Hydrides*, Interscience, 1956.

[2] H. I. SCHLESINGER, H. C. BROWN, B. ABRAHAM, A. C. BOND, N. DAVIDSON, A. E. FINHOLT, J. R. GILBREATH, H. HOEKSTRA, L. HORVITZ, E. K. HYDE, J. J. KATZ, J. KNIGHT, R. A. LAD, D. L. MAYFIELD, L. RAPP, D. M. RITTER, A. M. SCHWARTZ, I. SHEFT, L. D. TUCK, and A. O. WALKER, *J. Amer. Chem. Soc.*, 1963, **75**, 186–222.

[3] E. WIBERG, *Angew. Chem.*, 1953, **65**, 16.

[4] W. N. LIPSCOMB, *Boron Hydrides*, W. A. Benjamin, 1963.

[5] G. W. CAMPBELL, *Progress in Boron Chemistry*, 1964, **1**, 167. Structures of the Boron Hydrides.

[6] T. ONAK, Carboranes. *Advances in Organometallic Chemistry*, 1965, **3**.

[7] W. N. LIPSCOMB, Recent Studies on the Boron Hydrides. *Advances in Inorganic Chemistry and Radiochemistry*, 1959, **1**, 118.

[8] H. C. BROWN, Reactions of Alkali Metal Hydrides and Borohydrides with Lewis Acids of Boron and Aluminium. *XVII Internat. Cong. Pure and Applied Chem.*, 1959, **1**, 167.

[9] H. I. SCHLESINGER, H. C. BROWN, and E. K. HYDE, *J. Amer. Chem. Soc.*, 1953, **75**, 209.

[10] H. CLASEN, *Angew. Chem.*, 1961, **73**, 322.

[11] E. C. ASHBY, G. J. BRENDAL, and H. E. REDMAN, *Inorg. Chem.*, 1963, **2**, 499; E. C. ASHBY, *Chem. and Ind.*, 1962, 208; French Pat. 1,235,680, May 1960.

[12] J. L. BOONE, *J. Amer. Chem. Soc.*, 1964, **86**, 5036.

[13] I. A. ELLIS, D. E. GAINES, and R. SCHAEFFER, *J. Amer. Chem Soc*, 1963, **85**, 3885: W. H. KNOTH, J. C. SAUER, D. C. ENGLAND, W. R. HERTLER, and E. L. MUETTERTIES, *J. Amer. Chem. Soc.*, 1964, **86**, 3973: N. N. GREENWOOD and J. H. MORRIS, *Proc. Chem. Soc.*, 1963, 338: M. F. HAWTHORNE, R. L. PILLING, P. F. STOKELY, and P. M. GARRETT, *J. Amer. Chem. Soc.*, 1963, **85**, 3704.

[14] M. F. HAWTHORNE, D. C. YOUNG, and P. A. WEGNER, *J. Amer. Chem. Soc.*, 1965, **87**, 1818; M. F. HAWTHORNE and T. D. ANDREWS, *ibid*, 2497.

[15] M. B. SMITH and G. E. BASS, *J. Chem. Eng. Data.*, 1963, **8**, 342.

[16] W. D. DAVIS, L. S. MASON, and G. STEGMAN, *J. Amer. Chem. Soc.*, 1949, **71**, 2775.

[17] L. G. FASOLINO, *J. Chem. Eng. Data*, 1964, **9**, 68.

[18] G. T. FURUKAWA, M. L. REILLY, and J. H. PICCIRELLI, *J. Res. Nat. Bur. Stand.*, 1964, **68A**, 651.

[19] H. G. HEAL, *J. Inorg. Nucl. Chem.*, 1961, **16**, 208.

[20] T. C. WADDINGTON, *J. Chem. Soc.*, 1958, 4783.

[21] A. BRUKL and K. ROSSMANITH, *Monatshefte*, 1959, **90**, 481.

[22] G. MONNIER, *Ann. chim.*, 1957, [13], **2**, 14: J. AUBRY and G. MONNIER. *Comptes rendus*, 1954, **238**, 2534.

[23] Brit. Pat., 905,985, 1962.

[24] H. D. BATHA, E. D. WHITNEY, T. L. HEYING, J. P. FAUST, and S. PAPETI, *J. Appl. Chem.*, 1962, **12**, 478: R. BAUER, *Zeit. Naturf.* 1962, **17b**, 277.

[25] K. ROSSMANITH and E. MUCKENHUBER, *Monatshefte*, 1961, **92**, 600; 768.

[26] L. V. COULTER, J. B. SINCLAIR, A. G. COLE, I. WARSHAWSKY, and M. WOLFE, U.S. Atomic Energy Comm., CCC–1024–TR–218 (1957).

[27] E. ZANGE, *Chem. Berichte*, 1960, **93**, 652.

[28] U.S. Dept. Comm. Office Tech. Service, 1961, AD 256,887, L. TAYLOR, 30; P. C. MAYBURY and J. C. LARRABEE, **2**, 17: *Inorg. Chem.*, 1963, **2**, 885.

[29] E. AMBERGER and M. R. KULA, *Chem. Berichte*, 1963, **96**, 2556; *Angew. Chem.*, 1963, **75**, 476.

[30] R. W. PARRY, D. R. SCHULTZ, and P. R. GIRADOT, *J. Amer. Chem. Soc.*, 1958, **80**, 1.

[31] A. K. HOLLIDAY and W. JEFFRY, *J. Inorg. Nucl. Chem.*, 1958, **6**, 134.
[32] K. ROSSMANITH and H. MACALKA, *Monatshefte*, 1963, **94**, 295.
[33] A. E. FINHOLT, G. D. BARBARAS, G. K. BARBARAS, G. URRY, T. WARTIK, and H. I. SCHLESINGER, *J. Inorg. Nucl. Chem.*, 1955, **1**, 317.
[34] L. I. ZAKHARKIN and V. V. GARRILENKO, *Dokl. Akad. Nauk. S.S.S.R.*, 1962, **145**, 793.
[35] H. C. BROWN, H. I. SCHLESINGER, I. SHEFT, and D. M. RITTER, *J. Amer. Chem. Soc.*, 1953, **75**, 192.
[36] P. H. BIRD and M. G. H. WALLBRIDGE, *Chem. Comm.*, 1965, 291.
[37] H. I. SCHLESINGER and H. C. BROWN, *J. Amer. Chem. Soc.*, 1953, **75**, 219.
[38] H. I. SCHLESINGER, H. C. BROWN, L. HORVITZ, L. D. TUCK, and A. O. WALKER, *J. Amer. Chem. Soc.*, 1953, **75**, 222.
[39] R. M. RULON and L. S. MASON, *J. Amer. Chem. Soc.*, 1951, **73**, 5491.
[40] A. P. ALTSHULLER, *J. Amer. Chem. Soc.*, 1955, **77**, 5455.
[41] R. BAUER, *Zeit. Naturf.*, 1962, **17b**, 277; 1961, **16b**, 557.
[42] E. WIBERG, H. NOTH, and R. HARTWIMMER, *Zeit. Naturf.*, 1955, **10b**, 292, 294–5.
[43] G. JANDER and K. KRAFFCZYK, *Zeit. anorg. Chem.*, 1956, **283**, 217.
[44] J. KOLLONITSCH, O. FUCHS, and U. GABOR, *Nature*, 1955, **175**, 346; 1955, **174**, 1081; 1954, **173**, 125.
[45] L. I. KATZIN, *Proc. Internat. Conf. Peaceful Uses Atomic Energy, Geneva*, 1955, **7**, 407.
[46] G. W. SCHAEFFER, J. S. ROSCOE, and A. C. STEWART, *J. Amer. Chem. Soc.*, 1956, **78**, 729.
[47] H. R. HOEKSTRA and J. J. KATZ, *J. Amer. Chem. Soc.*, 1949, **71**, 2488; and U.S. Pat. 2,575,760 (1961).
[48] R. EHRLICH, A. R. YOUNG, II, and D. D. PERRY, *Inorg. Chem.*, 1965, **4**, 758.
[49] E. WIBERG and R. U. LACAL, *Zeit. Naturf.*, 1951, **6b**, 392; *Rev. acad. cienc. exact., fis. quim. y nat. Zaragoza*, 1951, **6**, 15.
[50] T. J. KLINGEN, *Inorg. Chem.*, 1964, **3**, 1058.
[51] J. M. DAVIDSON, *Chem. and Ind.*, 1964, 2021.
[52] R. K. NANDA and M. G. H. WALLBRIDGE, *Inorg. Chem.*, 1964, **3**, 1798.
[53] R. NOTH and R. HARTWIMMER, *Chem. Berichte*, 1960, **93**, 2238.
[54] R. B. KING, *Zeit. Naturf.*, 1963, **18b**, 157.
[55] E. WIBERG and W. HENLE, *Zeit. Naturf.*, 1952, **7b**, 582.
[56] idem, *ibid*, 575.
[57] idem, *ibid*, 579, 582.
[58] G. D. BARBARAS, C. DILLARD, A. E. FINHOLT, T. WARTIK, K. E. WILZBACH, and H. I. SCHLESINGER, *J. Amer. Chem. Soc.*, 1951, **73**, 4585.
[59] W. SCHWAB and K. WINTERSBERGER, *Zeit. Naturf.*, 1953, **8b**, 690.
[60] E. WIBERG and R. BAUER, *ibid*, 1952, **7b**, 131.
[61] A. R. EMERY and R. C. TAYLOR, *J. Chem. Phys.*, 1958, **28**, 1029: R. C. TAYLOR, D. R. SCHULTZ and A. R. EMERY, *J. Amer. Chem. Soc.*, 1958, **80**, 27.
[62] C. J. H. SCHUTTE, *Spect. Acta.*, 1960, **16**, 1054: J. A. A. KETELAAR and C. J. H. SCHUTTE, *ibid*, 1961, **17**, 1240.
[63] E. R. LIPPINCOTE, *J. Chem. Phys.*, 1949, **17**, 1351.
[64] S. C. ABRAHAMS and J. KALNAJS, *J. Chem. Phys.*, 1954, **22**, 434.
[65] C. C. STEPHENSON, D. W. RICE, and W. H. STOCKMAYER, *J. Chem. Phys.*, 1955, **23**, 1960.
[66] P. T. FORD and H. M. POWELL, *Acta Cryst.*, 1954, **7**, 604.
[67] S. H. BAUER, *J. Amer. Chem. Soc.*, 1950, **72**, 622.
[68] W. M. OLSEN, and R. T. SANDERSON, *J. Inorg. Nucl. Chem.*, 1958, **7**, 228.
[69] J. K. RUFF, *Inorg. Chem.*, 1963, **2**, 515.
[70] P. H. BIRD and M. G. H. WALLBRIDGE, *J. Chem. Soc.*, 1965, 3923.
[71] A. STOSICK, *Acta Cryst.*, 1962, **5**, 151.
[72] W. C. PRICE, *J. Chem. Phys.*, 1949, **17**, 1044.

[73] R. A. OGG and J. D. RAY, *Discussions Faraday Soc.*, 1955, **19**, 239.
[74] P. M. HARRIS and E. P. MEIBOHM, *J. Amer. Chem. Soc.*, 1947, **69**, 1231.
[75] L. BANFORD and G. E. COATES, *J. Chem. Soc.*, 1964, 5591.
[76] J. BLOCK, and A. P. GRAY, *Inorg. Chem.*, 1965, **4**, 304.
[77] A. E. FINHOLT, C. HELLUNG, V. IMHOFF, L. NIELSON, and E. JACOBSON, *Inorg. Chem.*, 1963, **2**, 504.
[78] G. N. SCHRAUZER, *Naturwiss.*, 1955, **42**, 438.
[79] H. G. HEAL, *Royal Institute of Chemistry Lectures Monographs and Reports*, 1960, Number One.

Addendum

Attention is drawn to the following papers which have appeared up to December 1965.

Chapter Two

Pauling Crystal Radius of the Hydride Ion. D. F. C. Morris and G. L. Reed, *J. Inorg. Nucl. Chem.*, 1965, **27**, 1715.

Thermodynamics of the Reduction of Oxides by NaH in an Alkaline Melt. N. V. Bogoyavlenskaya, V. I. Cherenko, V. A. Babchenko, and E. I. Vydra, *Ukrain. Zhur. Khim.*, 1965, **31**, 790 (In Russian.)

Interatomic Forces and Crystal Energy of Alkali Hydrides. L. Dass and S. C. Saxena, *J. Chem. Phys.*, 1965, **43**, 1747.

Chapter Three

Lu-H System. (Resistivity studies.) J. N. Daou and J. Bonnet, *Comptes rendus*, 1965, **261**, 1657 (In French.)

Y-H System. (Thermodynamics). L. N. Yannopoulos, R. K. Edwards, and P. G. Wahlbeck, *J. Phys. Chem.*, 1965, **69**, 2510. YH_2 and YH_3 phases occur, similar to Gd and Yb hydride systems but with the defect dihydride phase occurring over a wider range of hydrogen content.

Nb-H System. (P.m.r. studies of H diffusion: structure of β-hydride.) B. Stalinski and O. J. Zogal, *Bull. Acad. polon. Sci.*, (*chim.*) 1965, **13**, 397.

Preparation and Properties of Chromium Hydride. A. A. Proskurnikov and E. I. Krylov, *Zhur. neorg. Khim.*, 1965, **10**, 1017 (Russian: approx. 551 in English translation.)

Pd-H electrode. R. V. Bucur, *J. Electroanalyt. Chem.*, 1965, **10**, 8 (In German)

Ni-H system. (Free energy and Entropy of formation.) B. Baranowski and K. Bochenska, *Z. phys. Chem.* (*Frankfurt*), 1965, **45**, 140.

Chapter Four

Na_2BeH_4 (compare also Chapter Six). N. A. Bell and G. E. Coates, *Chem. Comm.*, 1965, 582. Structure thought to contain polarised Na-H bridges, as in $NaHBe(C_2H_5)_2$.

$(GeH_3)_3P$ and GeH_3NCO (Compare references (231) and (152) – preliminary accounts of the structures of these species have now appeared). *Chem. Comm.*, 1965, 515 and 437 respectively.

Aluminium Hydride Reactions. A number of papers on Al-H compounds have appeared: S. Cesca, M. L. Santostasi, W. Marconi, and M. Greco, *Ann. Chim.* (*Italy*), 1965, **55**, 682; S. C., M. L. S., W. M., and N. Palladino, *ibid*, 704, (both in Italian with English summaries): A. R. Young Jr., and R. Ehrlich, *Inorg. Chem.*, 1965, **4**, 1358: W. Marconi, A. Mazzei, S. Cucinella, and M. Greco, *Ann. Chim.* (*Italy*), 1965, **55**, 897 (Italian with English summary.)

Comparative Stabilities of Gaseous AlH_3, GaH_3, and InH_3 (Mass spectrometer).

P. Breisacher and B. Siegel, *J. Amer. Chem. Soc.*, 1965, **87**, 4255. It was found that these transient species decreased in stability in the order $AlH_3 > GaH_3 > InH_3$: confirming the discussion in 4.5 on the improbability of the existence of stable solid indane or thallane species.

Hydroplumbation of Unsaturated Organic Compounds. W. P. Neumann and K. Kuhlein, *Angew. Chem.*, 1965, **7**, 808.

Chapter Five

$(Et_3P)_2PdH(Cl)$. E. H. Brooks and F. Glockling, *Chem. Comm.*, 1965, 510. First palladium hydride complex to be obtained pure: colourless, dec. 55°C, infra-red shows stretch at 2035 cm^{-1} and bending mode at 721 cm^{-1}.

$RhH(PF_3)_4$. T. Kruck, W. Lang, and N. Derner, *Zeit. Naturf.*, 1965, **20b**, 705.

$CoH(PF_3)_3CO$. T. Kruck and W. Lang, *Chem. Ber.*, 1965, **98**, 3060. mpt. – 67°C, $\tau = 21{\cdot}4$ ppm, strong monobasic acid.

$\{IrH(X)_2(C_8H_{12})\}_2$; $X = Cl, Br, I$. S. D. Robinson and B. L. Shaw, *J. Chem. Soc.*, 1965, 4997. *Ir-H* stretch at 2261, 2239, and 2188 cm^{-1} for X = Cl, Br, I, respectively.

Isotopic Exchange of trans- *$PtH(Cl)(PEt_3)_3$ with D_2O.* C. D. Falk and J. Halpern *J. Amer. Chem. Soc.*, 1965, **87**, 3523.

Probable Structure of $Fe_3(CO)_{12}$ from the Structure of $HFe_3(CO)_{11}^-$. L. F. Dahl and J. F. Blount, *Inorg. Chem.*, 1965, **4**, 1373.

Protonated Covalent Metal-Metal Bond in $HM_2(CO)_{10}^-$; $M = Cr, Mo, W$. U. Anders and W. A. G. Graham, *Chem. Comm.*, 1965, 499. Evidence that proton is associated with both metal atoms, as in $(C_5H_5)_2Mo_2H(Me_2P)(CO)_4$. Proton resonance spectrum gives metal-hydrogen signal at $\tau = 16{\cdot}7$, $22{\cdot}2$, and $22{\cdot}5$ for M = Cr, Mo, W. The tungsten compound shows a triplet, explained by coupling to two W atoms (W-183, spin $\frac{1}{2}$).

$HMn_3(CO)_{10}(BH_3)_2$. H. D. Kaesz, W. Fellman, G. R. Wilkes, and L. F. Dahl, *J. Amer. Chem. Soc.*, 1965, **87**, 2753. The X-ray structure shows the two BH_3 units bridge two Mn atoms and there is a Mn-H-Mn bridge. All carbonyls are terminal. This structure is like a mixed boron hydride-metal cluster and presents an important link between the boranes and metal-metal bonded species.

Chapter Six

Carborane Analogues of Cobalticinium Ion. M. F. Hawthorne and T. D. Andrews, *Chem. Comm.*, 1965, 433. $B_9C_2H_{11}^{2-}$ units replace C_5H_5, as for the iron and manganese compounds discussed in the text.

Structure of $C_5H_5FeB_9C_2H_{11}$. A. Zalkin, D. H. Templeton, and T. E. Hopkins, *J. Amer. Chem. Soc.* 1965, **87**, 3988. Confirms Hawthorne's prediction that this is a sandwich structure related to ferrocene.

Structure of $Al(BH_4)_3.NMe_3$. N. Bailey, P. H. Bird, and M. G. H. Wallbridge, *Chem. Comm.*, 1965, 443.

Table 1.4

The new boranes, *iso- B_9H_{15}*, (*J. Amer. Chem. Soc.*, 1965, **87**, 3522) and *B_8H_{18}* (*ibid*, 4072) should be added to Table 1.4.

Reviews

Two reviews of transition metal hydride complexes have appeared: A. P. Ginsberg, *Progr. Transition Metal Chem.*, 1965, **1**, 111. M. L. H. Green, *Advances in Inorganic Chemistry and Radiochemistry*, 1965, **7**, 115.

Index

acceptor properties of electron deficient hydrides 102
actinium hydride 64
actinide element hydrides 64–70
addition to double bonds,
  covalent hydrides 127–128
  hydride complexes 143
alkali hydrides 19–33, 181
aluminium hydride,
  $AlH_{1\cdot 02}$ 109
  AlH_3 and Al_2H_6 108, 182
  $(AlH_3)_x$, uncoordinated 109
  $(AlH_3)_x$ 108–112, 129–131, 181
  AlH_3 complexes with donor molecules 110–112
  AlH_4, compounds containing 168–177
  AlH_4Li, uses in hydride preparations 103–105, 141–142
  $Al_2H_5NMe_2$ structure 112
  $AlH_2B_{10}H_{12}^-$ 115
aluminium borohydride 101, 171, 173 182
aluminium-thorium hydrides 69
americium hydrides 64, 70
arsenic hydrides 6, 7, 125–127

barium hydride,
  BaH_2 20, 22–24, 29
  BaH_3Li 37
  $BaHX$ (X = Cl, Br, I) 34–35
beryllium hydride,
  BeH_2 101, 105–107
  BeH_4Na_2 107, 181
beryllium aluminium hydride 177
beryllium borohydride 101, 174
body-centred cubic lattice, configurational entropy 54–55
bond energies 129
bonding,
  electron-deficient 100–101
  transition metal hydrides 45–54, 92–93
boron hydrides, 5, 6, 8–10, 128, 182
  bonding, 100
borohydride ions 168–177
  BH_4Na in preparations of hydrides 103–105, 141–142
  $B_9C_2H_{11}^{2-}$ as cyclopentadienyl analogue 171, 182
  mixed decaborane-aluminium and -gallium ions 115

cadmium hydride 108
calcium hydride,
  CaH_2 20, 22–24, 27, 29, 31
  $CaHX$ (X = Cl, Br, I) 37
carboranes 8, 10, 171, 182
carbonyl hydrides 144, 145
  origin of CO and H in alcoholic preparation 142
catalyst, polymerisation 109, 110, 143, 181
cerium hydrides 56–59, 61
  cerium-other hydride systems 62
cesium hydride 18–22, 24, 28
cesium aluminohydride and borohydride 171, 172, 175, 177
chromium hydrides, binary 85, 181
  complexes 156, 182
cobalt, complex hydrides 161, 182
  cobalticinium ion, carborane analogue 182
configuration entropy 54–55, 77
copper hydride 41, 89–90
covalent hydrides 12, 90–105
crystal structures:
  actinide hydrides 64
  alkali hydrides 21, 29
  alkaline earth hydrides 23, 29
  aluminium hydride adducts 110–112
  $Al(BH_4)_3.NMe_3$ 182
  borohydrides 172
  chromium hydrides 85
  copper hydride 89–90
  europium dihydride 36–38
  ferrocene, carborane analogue 182
  $GaH_3.NMe_3$ 114
  halohydrides, MHX 34–35
  inverse perovskite phases, $LiMH_3$ 37
  lanthanide hydrides 56–59
  magnesium hydride 40
  $MnH(CO)_5$ 148
  $Mn_3H(CO)_{10}(BH_3)_2$ 182

crystal structures—*continued*
$OsH(CO)X(L)_3$, L = phosphine or arsine 148
palladium hydride 86
tr-$PtH(X)(L)_2$, X = Cl, Br; L = phosphine 148
ReH_9K_2 138
$RhH(CO)(PPh_3)_3$ 147–148
$RuH(CO)X(L)_3$, L = phosphine or arsine 148
TcH_9K_2 139
thorium hydride systems 67–68
titanium Group hydrides 72–74, 77
uranium trihydride 66
vanadium Group hydrides 81–83
ytterbium dihydride 36
zirconium, ternary systems 79–80
cyclopentadienyl metal hydrides 149

decaborane, alane and gallane products 115
deuterides, differences from hydrides 21, 24
see also under *neutron diffraction*
diborane, bonding 100–101
direct synthesis, of $LiAlH_4$ and related compounds 169–170
dissociation pressures of binary hydrides 21, 23, 25–26, 40, 59, 65

electrode, palladium-hydrogen and surface formation of hydride 88
electron deficient hydrides 100–102
electronic spectra,
K_2ReH_9 139
rhodium ammines 153
ruthenium complexes 152
place of H in spectrochemical series 152, 153, 155
entropy, configurational 54–55, 57
europium hydride,
EuH_2 35–37
EuH_3Li 36–37

gallium hydride,
GaH_3 and Ga_2H_6 112, 113, 182
adducts of gallane 113–115
halogallanes and adducts 114
$GaH_{16}B_{10}^-$ 115
GaH_4, compounds of 114, 168–169
germanium hydrides,
heats of formation and bond energies 129
spectroscopic properties 130–131
germanium chains 117
germanium-silicon, -phosphorus, and -arsenic hydrides 118–119
GeH_3X preparations and properties 121
Ge_2H_5X preparations and properties 123
Ge_3H_7I 124
$(GeH_3)_3P$, GeH_3NCO, GeH_3NCS, lack of π bonding 124, 181
$GeH_2\{Mn(CO)_5\}_2$ 126
GeH and GeH_2 125

H^- ion radius 21, 29, 36
hafnium hydride 71–79
hazards of hydrides 13
heats of formation of binary hydrides 5–6, 19, 22, 24, 40, 59, 65, 74, 78, 87, 129
holmium hydrides 55–59, 62
hydrides of the elements 4
hydrides of unstable metals 3, 5
hydride complexes of transition elements, preparation and properties 138–140, 141–145, 154–164
structural and spectroscopic properties 139, 146–153, 156–164, 182
hydride complexes with two metallic elements associated with hydrogen 150–151, 182
hydrogen, properties 2
hydrogen migration in transition metal hydrides 91
hydrogen solutions in sodium 35

indium hydride 116, 182
infra-red studies and vibrational properties of hydrides,
binary hydrides 25, 41, 60, 90, 105, 111–113, 115, 119–120, 130, 181
hydride complexes 139, 151–152, 156–164, 182
borohydrides 172–174, 177, 182
ionic nature of alkali hydrides 18–20, 29
iridium hydride complexes 142, 162–163
iron hydride,
non-existence of binary hydride 86
complexes 158–159, 182
isotopic differences, UH_3, UD_3 and UT_3 66
see also *deuterides*

lanthanon hydrides 35–38, 55–63, 181
lanthanum hydrides 56–59, 61–63
lattice energies 19, 23, 50–52
lattice vibrations in binary hydrides 90
lead hydrides 121, 129, 130
lithium hydride 18–24, 27, 29–32
  LiH-MH_2 systems 36–37
  LiH-lithium salt systems 33–34
lithium aluminium hydride 32, 168–172
lithium borohydride 168–172
lower hydrides 102, 125–126
lutetium hydride 55–63, 181

magnesium hydride and halohydrides 39–41
magnesium aluminium hydride and borohydride 175, 177
magnetic properties 37–38, 61–62, 67, 90–92
manganese hydride complexes 147–149, 157, 182
mercury hydride 108
metal hydride types 1–3, 11–13
metal-hydrogen distances, in transition metal binary hydrides 49
molybdenum hydride complexes 149–150, 156, 182

neptunium hydrides 69–70
neutron diffraction,
  $AlThD_2$ 69
  CaD_2, correction of x-ray structure 29
  CeD_2 and $CeD_{2\cdot7}$ 56
  copper hydride 90
  chromium hydride 85
  HoD_3 57
  LiD and NaD 29
  MgD_2 40
  ReH_9K_2 138
  $TaD_{0\cdot5}$ 83
  TbD_2 62
  UD_3 66
  $VD_{0\cdot5}$ 81
neutron scattering, and lattice vibrations of transition metal hydrides 90
nickel,
  hydride complexes 163
  hydride 84, 181
  NiZrH and related systems 79–80
niobium hydrides 80–84
non-metal hydrides, properties 5–10
nuclear magnetic resonance studies,
  alanes 112, 131
  gallanes 115, 131
  germanes 131
  plumbanes 131
  ReH_9K_2 139
  silanes 131
  stannanes 131
  and proton migration in binary hydrides 48
  transition metal binary hydrides 62, 90–92
  transition metal hydride complexes, high field signals (theories) 147
    structural applications 146
    data 156–164, 182

osmium, hydride complexes 148, 160–161, 182

palladium
  hydride 86–89, 182
  ternary hydride systems 89
  hydride complexes 163, 182
phase diagrams,
  lanthanide hydrides 58–59
  zirconium/hydrogen and related systems 72–77
  vanadium Group metal/hydrogen 81–83
π bonding in SiH_3 and GeH_3 compounds 119–120, 124–125
platinum,
  hydride complexes 142, 143, 148, 163–164, 182
  ternary hydride system with palladium 89
plumbanes, see *lead hydrides*
plutonium hydrides 64
polonium hydride 3
preparation of hydrides,
  general precautions 13
  alkali and alkaline earth hydrides 25–29
  lanthanide hydrides 60–61
  actinide hydrides 64, 66–68
  covalent hydrides 102–105
  hydride complexes 138, 141–142
  tetrahydro-boronates and -aluminates 168–170
protactinium hydride 64

reactivity,
  of MgH_2 and preparation method 39
  of alkali hydrides 30

rhenium,
hydride complexes 149–151, 157–158
enneahydride ion 138–141
rhodium,
hydride complexes 146, 147, 159, 161–162, 182
RhH_4Li 141
rubidium hydride 18–22, 24, 28
borohydride and aluminohydride 171, 172
ruthenium, hydride complexes 146, 148, 151–152, 159–160

scandium hydride 55, 61
silicon hydrides,
heats of formation and bond energies 129
spectroscopic properties 130–131
silicon-germanium, -phosphorus, and -arsenic hydrides 118–119
SiH_3X preparations and properties 120
Si_2H_5X preparations and properties 123
$(SiH_3)_3N$ 119–120
other silyl compounds showing π bonding 124
silicon chains in hydrides 117, 122–123
$SiH_3Co(CO)_4$ 126
silver, ternary hydride systems 79, 89
sodium hydride, thermodynamics of reduction by 18–22, 24–30, 32–33, 181
sodium borohydride and aluminohydride 169–173
spectrochemical series and H^-, see *electronic spectra*
strontium hydride,
SrH_2 20, 22–24, 29
SrH_3Li 37
SrHX (X = Cl, Br, I) 34–35
structures, relation of hydride and metal structures 46
see also *crystal structures*

tantalum hydride 80–84, 90
hydride complexes 149–150, 156
technetium, hydride complexes—see *rhenium*
thallium hydrides 116, 182
borohydride 172, 175
theoretical aspects,
bonding in transition metal hydrides 45–54
high field proton resonance spectra of transition element hydride complexes 147
structure of cyclopentadienyl hydrides 149
thorium hydrides 67–69
tin hydrides 117, 121, 129–131
borohydride and aluminohydride 175, 177
titanium hydrides 71–80, 90, 126–127
transition metals,
binary hydrides, properties and bonding 45–55, 90–93
supposed hydrides of later members 84–86
hydride complexes 138–164
borohydrides 175–176
tungsten, hydride complexes 149–150, 156–157, 182

uranium hydride 64–67
ternary system with zirconium 79–80
uses of metal hydrides 14–16, 29–33, 67, 79, 109, 110, 143, 181

vanadium hydrides 80–83, 90
hydride complexes 156

X-ray studies, see *crystal structures*

ytterbium hydrides 35–38, 61–62
yttrium hydrides 55–60, 90, 181

zinc hydride and borohydride 107–108, 175
zirconium hydride 71–78
ternary systems 79–80